The Researcher's Guide:
Film, Television, Radio and Related Documentation Collections in the UK

6th Edition

Editor: Jim Ballantyne

British Universities Film & Video Council

British Universities Film & Video Council
77 Wells Street, London W1T 3QJ
Tel: 020 7393 1500 Fax: 020 7393 1555
e-mail: ask@bufvc.ac.uk

First published 1981 as *The Researcher's Guide to British Film & Television Collections*
Second edition 1985
Third edition 1989
Fourth edition 1993
Fifth edition 1997
Sixth edition 2001 as *The Researcher's Guide: Film, Television, Radio and Related Documentation Collections in the UK*

ISBN 0 901299 71 5

Cover picture
Frame still from the only known film of the *Titanic*, in Belfast Docks, February 1912. Picture courtesy of British Pathe, New Pathe House, 57 Jamestown Road, Camden, London NW1 7DB

Typeset by Gem Graphics, Trenance, Nr. Newquay, Cornwall TR8 4BY.
Printed in Great Britain by Intype London Ltd, Units 3 & 4, Elm Grove Industrial Estate, Elm Grove, Wimbledon, London SW19 4HE.

Contents

Foreword

by Murray Weston

The publication of this book, and its accompanying web resource, sits firmly on a foundation of activity established by Elizabeth Oliver in 1981. During a period of expansion of the work of the British Universities Film & Video Council in the early 1980s the Council took the decision to compile the *Researcher's Guide* – partly to cope with the increasing numbers of film researchers using the Council's Information Service. During the intervening years the BUFVC has established a high reputation for its work in mapping and describing moving image archives in the UK and the rest of Europe. The Researcher's Guide has fallen naturally into a four-yearly updating and re-publishing cycle. The first edition appeared in 1981, with subsequent editions in 1985, 1989, 1993, 1997 and now 2001.

The latest development in our work is the addition of information on radio collections and on documentation collections relating to audio-visual works – scripts, scores, posters, still pictures and equipment. The extension into these fields was encouraged by a working group under the Research Support Libraries Programme (RSLP). RSLP grant support enabled us to re-engage Jim Ballantyne, retired Head of Information at the BUFVC, to undertake the new survey work and, with the collaboration of Luis Carrasqueiro, to move the resulting data into a structure capable of delivery online via the web (see www.bufvc.ac.uk/rgo). The web resource will be continuously updated and provide electronic links to other databases delivered by the listed archives and to new sites as they are launched.

Now that an online version of the *Researcher's Guide* is available there are many prospects for further development. The Guide fits neatly among the other online resources created and delivered by the BUFVC. These include: the Moving Image Gateway – a structured guide to some 350 reviewed internet resources; the Television and Radio Index for Learning and Teaching – offering access to information on programme content and transmission times (both pre- and post-transmission) for television and radio channels receivable in the UK; and the British Universities Newsreel Database – providing access to records of some 160,000 British cinema news stories (from 1911 until 1979) and copies of around 80,000 sheets of related script content.

The *Researcher's Guide* data available online conforms to the Research Collections Description Schema devised by the UK's Office for Library and Information Networking (UKOLN) to encourage inter-operability.

While so much work now focuses on the delivery of data designed to inter-operate with other electronic resources online, this does not in any way belittle the continuing importance of the printed work. Its portability, accessibility and relatively low cost remain virtues. The book also provides a temporal slice across an assemblage of data which in itself will have historical value.

The added value in the book version is the addition of important articles which provide further context to the listings section. We are grateful to the authors Professor Nicholas Cull, Alex Cowan, Tony Dalton, Emanuella Giavarra, Peter M Lewis, Barrie MacDonald and James Patterson for their contributions.

The reliably meticulous work of Jim Ballantyne in preparing the *Researcher's Guide* for publication and online delivery is self-evident. We are indebted to him for his expert assistance during the last twelve months. We are also indebted to three other people. Luis Carrasqueiro, BUFVC's Network Content Manager, constructed the underlying database which drives the online version and exported data for this print publication. Kush Varia assisted in gathering information on radio collections, and Marilyn Sarmiento provided proof-reading support to the team.

There can be little doubt that access to archive moving pictures and sound will continue to increase in importance for scholars. A publication such as the *Researcher's Guide* remains an essential tool and the online version, with its direct links to resources, will offer new access routes.

The last twenty years of the BUFVC's work in this field has been pioneering. With the assistance of our specialist team of staff, we intend to remain at the forefront of recent developments in data handling and delivery to support scholarly access to moving image and sound archives.

Murray Weston *is the Director of the British Universities Film and Video Council*

A Historian's Introduction to the Researcher's Guide

by Nicholas J. Cull

In 1888 a photographic pioneer named Louis Le Prince directed an experimental apparatus at traffic on a bridge in the centre of Leeds and, half a decade before Edison or the Lumière brothers, captured what were arguably the world's first moving pictures. He did not live long enough to market his system. In the one hundred and thirteen years since Le Prince, the moving image has become as ubiquitous as the printed text was to Victorians. Today, we know both our own times and the past principally through audio-visual images. Our lives are punctuated by common images of news and shared moments in popular culture. The space age has become both flickering images of astronauts on the moon and the Cadbury's Smash aliens; eighties' capitalism is both Mrs Thatcher quoting St Francis and the shooting of J. R. Ewing; the end of the Cold War is encapsulated by the dramatic images of the fall of the Berlin Wall. These images are consumed at the time and recalled as landmarks in forms as diverse as news broadcasts, feature films, documentaries, advertisements, nostalgia programmes, party political broadcasts and rock videos. More than this, media forms shape our self-perception. In the digital-age equivalent of Shakespeare's seven ages of man we all have our flashbacks and our Oscar clips. Life can sometimes seem just like soap opera (wasn't it supposed to be the other way round?) and strangely empty when it doesn't imitate art. I suspect that death will seem oddly unfulfilling if not accompanied by rolling credits before the eyes or perhaps an elegant 'fin'. The academic world has been slow to catch up, but today most historians accept that someone in their profession needs to consider audiovisual evidence in addition to the written word. Twenty years ago one still heard muttering against 'Mickey Mouse history'. Today the sceptical at least acknowledge that such a phrase underlines the importance of the mass media in contemporary life rather than minimizing it. This guide is the perfect starting point for the historian who wishes to begin exploring the way in which the mass media have shaped our world or using media archives as a window on it.

If you are reading this introduction you presumably do not need to be convinced about the importance of audio-visual evidence to an understanding of our times. You are either a hard-pressed commercial researcher, rushing to find the raw material for a documentary film or to illustrate a CD-ROM, or an equally hard-pressed academic, seeking to use film, television or radio evidence in your scholarship. This may be the first book that you open at the start of a research career, or a familiar companion in your day-to-day strivings. For twenty years successive editions of this guide have helped the media research community to get what its needs from film collections in the United Kingdom and the Republic of Ireland. Seasoned users will find new features and fresh entries, each arranged with essential access information and enough supporting text to afford a glimpse of exactly what the collection holds. This, the sixth edition, brings together new listings including, for the first time, radio archives and a new selection of perspectives on the use of film, television and radio as evidence. It is a treasure map for the rich and varied audio-visual heritage of these islands. Collections embrace everything from Le Prince's pioneering efforts (samples can be found at the Leeds Industrial Museum and Yorkshire Film Archive) to images that define our own times. The emerging patterns of life in the 21st century can be seen through sources such as the digital surveillance footage held by David Finch Distribution of Walton-on-Thames or the video-activism recorded by Undercurrents of Oxford as well as the obvious news libraries. All are listed here. Over the years the introduction to each edition of this guide has served as a place where archivists and academics have discussed issues of film preservation, access and the history of media archives. This time the introduction comes from perspective of a historian, who began his research career by scouring the dog-eared pages of an earlier edition of this book in a department library, and offers this introduction with those in a similar situation particularly in mind. Perhaps I will seem to be stating the obvious, but most of these points have been learned the hard way.

The ubiquity of film, radio and television in the modern world does not necessarily facilitate their use as evidence in historical or other research. The 21st-century eye tends take these media for granted. The first thing that a researcher needs is the imagination to consider the archive material in its own terms. Any piece of film will tell a story not only of the things placed in front of the camera but will also reflect on a web of social and industrial influences. Ask who paid for the film to be made and why; who censored or distributed it; who saw it; who put it in the archive. Each of these can be a rich and surprising seam for further research, and pursuing such questions cannot but enhance the value of your evidence. Conversely failure to ask such questions can lead to misunderstanding and misuse.

Remember the context in which the evidence you are using was originally exhibited. It takes an effort of imagination to recall what – for example – the images of the newly bombed ruins of Spanish Civil War must have looked like to a member of the British newsreel audience in 1937. One must factor in the intimate darkness of the cinema, the vast scale of the image on the screen (as opposed to the small picture in an archive viewer or video monitor) and the intensification of any reaction owing to the presence of several hundred anxious fellow human beings, who had not seen footage of Coventry in 1940 or Hiroshima in 1945.

Part of the context could be the other media to which an audience member was exposed. Look into the parallel presentation of an issue on the radio, in the press and in novels or feature films at that time. Many contemporary historians under-emphasise the importance of the radio, projecting back into the past a contemporary preference for the visual media. The time involved to produce a major feature film or documentary is such that the films are often more useful as a product of a time than a formative influence on it. In World War Two the British feature films planned during the Phoney War arrived in time for the Blitz, similarly MGM's classic Blitz film MRS MINIVER (1942), planned to woo America away from neutrality, did not actually reach the screens until well after US entry into the war.

Remember the physical process by which your film, television or radio clip came to be made. Consider the well-known case of Geoffrey Malin's 1916 film THE BATTLE OF THE SOMME. Key sequences of this film are transformed by the simple exercise of imagining the position of the cameraman. As many historians have pointed out, combat cameramen simply didn't stand in harm's way to film the first wave's advance. The film's most famous scene, in which soldiers charge 'over the top' and symbolically disappear into mist, is clearly staged. Yet, just because an image does not show exactly what is claimed does not mean that it is without value. As Roger Smither of the Imperial War Museum has argued, THE BATTLE OF THE SOMME considered as a whole has less staged footage than the average TV documentary (*see Historical Journal of Film, Radio and Television,* vol 13, no 2, 1993. 'A Wonderful Idea of the Fighting: the Question of Fakes in THE BATTLE OF THE SOMME', pp. 149-68). Researchers viewing this film may not be looking at images of the first wave of the Somme, but they are looking at a document that gives a unique insight into the manipulation of images of the Great War. Be open to the story that your evidence is telling: in this case it is an equally compelling story of the role of propaganda in modern war.

Parallel to the question of the authenticity of your source lies the question of your own use of the material. Historians have to guard against the tendency to over-emphasise the aspect of their evidence that most closely resembles a traditional historical document: the script. Even quite exper-ienced historians can shy away from elements in the evidence that stem from its nature as a piece of film, radio or television. If you are writing about radio – say Lord Haw-Haw's broadcasts to Britain in the World War Two – don't just repeat his words, consider that haughty, mocking tone of voice. If you are writing on the newsreel accounts of the London Blitz, don't just transcribe the booming commentary; consider the way in which the images interact with the text. It is never a bad idea to run a film without the sound as well as with to force yourself to engage with the images

Still from the first part of the 'over the top' sequence from The Battle of the Somme, *1916 (courtesy of the Imperial War Museum Film and Video Archive)*

and then observe what is added by the music and commentary.

Commercial researchers and producers face a parallel set of problems. As historians tune in to issues of authenticity in film they are quick to criticise contemporary representations of the past and slow to realise that most researchers have little control over the end use of the clips that they find. The following remarks are offered as an introduction to the debate among historians over the use of film, and as encouragement to those heroic souls working in media production who are keenly aware of the responsibility attending programme making – the power to generate what become the received images of the past for a new generation – and work to ensure that archive film is used with precision and care.

The key question is exactly how closely an image should match its implied (or explicit) description in the text of your film. Most historical documentaries minimise the danger of misrepresenting their content through deliberately vague

wording, but some cross the line. The film historian and producer, Jerry Kuehl, has traced the career of the Austrian battleship *Svent Istvan,* sunk in 1918 in view of a camera team and thus condemned to resurface like filmic equivalent of the *Flying Dutchman* in historical documentaries to illustrate sinkings of other ships in other wars. Sometimes a researcher can be caught between the historical specificity of an image and its accepted symbolic value. The image of a burned Vietnamese child running from her village now seems to sum up the entire Vietnam War in the collective memory, but it also has a geographical and specific temporal context: the village was Trang Bang; the girl was Phan Thi Kim Phuc; the date was 8 June 1972; the orders were American; the planes were South Vietnamese; the target was military enough to ensure that news crews had been invited to the scene to capture events for posterity. One or all of these details may be relevant to an understanding of the image. Is it legitimate to use this image, like the makers of the HBO film A BRIGHT SHINING LIE

(1998), to illustrate events in the year 1968? The American film historian, Peter Rollins, maintains that it is not.

The prize for the most outrageous abuse of archive footage recently must go to LOST FILM OF THE TITANIC a video, released in 1998, which purports to show film of the *Titanic* as found in a garden shed by an old lady. As the leading cultural historian of the sinking, Richard Howells, has pointed out, the old lady and the shed may be genuine but the ship depicted simply cannot be the *Titanic*, as it is clearly at anchor in New York harbour. Someone in 1912, wishing to pass off images of the *Titanic*'s sister ship, *Olympic*, as the ill-fated liner, made a rather crude attempt to hide his fact and frame-by-frame scratched the home-port designation from the stern of the tugboats seen in the foreground.

There is no easy way of avoiding the use of a film clip out of context; better labelling and indexing in archives would certainly help. More than this one needs to remain ever vigilant and sceptical. In the case of the *Titanic* clip, the scratched tug sterns should have been a tip-off. Other errors would be avoided by simply considering how a crew came to be available to film a particular event.

Despite the numerous tempting media archives listed in this volume, and the warning above against historians over-emphasis on text, it is necessary to add a word about written sources. Don't underestimate what a written archive can contribute to media research. Written archives can add new level of meaning to visual or audio evidence, directing attention to a scene cut from newsreel or a moment that was controversial in its time but today would escape comment. Written archives can also help to resolve one of the greatest problems facing a media researcher: evaluating the impact of a piece of film on its audience. It can be next to impossible to trace the impact of a piece of film located in the archive. It is substantially easier to read the written archive first, and allow that record to guide you to the film, radio or television that the people at the time – exhibitors, audiences, propagandists – believed to be powerful or significant. The BBC Written Archives at Caversham, for example, not only documents production of radio and television but also provides a wealth of material on audience reaction from the first days of radio right through to the mid-seventies (documents are open to research only after 25 years). The files cover everything from the reception of classics of broadcast history like Peter Watkins' CULLODEN (1964) to aghast reactions to the UK premiere of the frenetic American kids' programme THE BANANA SPLIT SHOW in March 1970. The latter provides a fascinating insight into attitudes in the face of on-rushing Americanisation. In my own work on film propaganda I've been able to use the Public Record Office, Kew and National Archives in Washington to establish exactly which films and broadcasts were recognised as effective by propagandists 'in the field'. I've then been able to hunt down the relevant film in the archives.

Similarly, don't underestimate the value of the perspective of the filmmakers themselves, either through memoirs or oral history projects such as the members' history compiled by BECTU (the Broadcasting Entertainment Cinematograph and Theatre Union), or the interviews and other resources collected as part of the BUFVC's own Newsreel Project, or through direct contact with surviving members of the profession. I've found newsreel cameramen, documentary producers and directors wholly delighted to speak about specific films, their careers, and a wonderful source on the filmmaking process. Interviews at their best can suggest connections one would never ordinarily have imagined, forcing the historian to consider the entire life experience of a filmmaker rather than just the portion of his life in which the film was made. In my own work on the documentaries of the 1960s, interviews have prompted me to consider filmmakers' formative experiences in the 1930s and 1940s. In some cases witnesses raise filmic experiences: a spell with the National Film Board of Canada or the Film and Photo League in New York. In other cases the evidence is more visceral, personal and wholly unexpected. Walter de Hoog, a Hearst cameraman who made the widely seen United States Information Agency short about the Berlin Wall: THE WALL (1963), had an astonishing earlier career in the wartime Italian resistance and escaped from a train bound for the Mathausen concentration camp. His personal experience of an early German totalitarianism inflected his depiction of the East German frontier guards twenty years later. Robert Drew, the pioneer producer of 'direct cinema' and grandfather of today's fly-on-the-wall documentary, interviewed in 1997, attributed his interest in realism not to exposure to the work of Pare Lorentz or John Grierson but to the print journalism of the 'GI's war correspondent', Ernie Pyle. Drew explained that in 1944, while a fighter pilot in Italy, he had met and become friends with Pyle. During a period of months when Drew was missing in action behind enemy lines, Pyle corresponded with his mother back home in the States. The two became close. In the event Drew escaped capture and returned unscathed, but Pyle died in combat. Drew recalled feeling that he had lost a second father, and sought to 'pick up the torch' first in his own journalism and later in film. It is a cross-media connection wholly absent from the documentary textbooks on non-fiction filmmaking.

Bias is, of course, never far from the surface in oral history. This is not so much a flaw, as part of the charm of the approach. Interviews emphasise the degree to which any historical view is subjective. Oral film history brings the historian face to face with the elements of contingency in filmmaking. Sequences that one assumed to be carefully set up can emerge as serendipitous or even wholly unintended, while moments one assumed to be spontaneous can emerge as products of a planning process equivalent to D-Day. It can also be a humbling experience for a researcher to pitch a complex reading of a sequence to its author and be told 'it just sort of happened that way'.

Finally, remember that as a researcher or historian of the audio-visual media you are not working alone. Pay attention to the folks who work in the archive, and take the time to chat to them about exactly what you are looking for. They know their collections. Some of the best finds come to

light when a friendly archivist suggests: 'why not also take a look at...' Take time to get to know your fellow researchers. Everyone's research is stronger for the tips, horror stories and hints that flow back and forth in archive tea breaks. Beyond this, take a look at the Research Services and Organisations section in the guide and visit the websites. Organisations such as the British Universities Film and Video Council, the Federation of Commercial Audio Visual Libraries and the International Association for Media and History regularly sponsor and/or organise conferences. For this historian the conferences are the highlight of any year: an opportunity to exchange ideas and view clips from films one simply hadn't considered. Recent conference 'show stoppers' have included an all-dog version of ALL QUIET ON THE WESTERN FRONT (the dachshunds played the Germans) and 'out-takes' of Mrs Thatcher bantering with Robin Day in the moments before a big interview. The IAMHIST conference in Leeds in June 1999 included a screening of a digital reconstruction of Louis Le Prince's 1888 footage. The researcher is cordially urged to use this book to enter the archives and find the material to wow the conferences of the next decade; to follow the trail of evidence and develop their own vision of the audio-visual heritage of these islands. If the breadth of entries in this guide is any indication, our understanding of the history of our own times and the craft of history itself should be in for quite a shake-up.

Nicholas J. Cull *is Professor of American Studies at the University of Leicester. He has written and researched widely on issue of media history and propaganda in Britain, the USA, and elsewhere. He is presently writing a history of the United States Information Agency, 1953–1999. He is Reviews Editor (Europe) for the* Historical Journal of Film, Radio and Television *and serves on the council of the International Association of Media History.*

Buried Treasure: the Case of Radio Archives[1]

by Peter M. Lewis

Introduction

A phone call from the office of *Analysis*, the prestigious Radio 4 current affairs programme. The year: 1998, a bad time for radio when restructuring and relocation seemed more important than programmes. The message was, in effect, a mayday call: 'We've been told to chuck all our tapes and transcripts. You've got till the end of the week to save them ...' At the other end was Sean Street, features producer as well as, now, Professor of Radio at Bournemouth University. With thirty years of archives at stake, he lost no time in organising a van to transport the tapes to safety. Subsequently the acquisition was regularised with the BBC and, with the aid of a grant from the Arts and Humanities Research Board (AHRB), the archive, safe now in Bournemouth University's School of Media Arts and Communication, has been put on to an electronic database, a unique record of the key political and social issues of the last three decades.

This dramatic episode illustrates one aspect of the case of radio archives – the need for a permanent system of emergency rescue. Another, more fundamental issue, underlies the incident. One can imagine the BBC dismissing the fuss because in any case the material was in its own archive, and perhaps also in the National Sound Archive (NSA). To this, a first reply would be that, notoriously in this area, to claim 'we never make mistakes' is unwise: there might have been gaps in the official archive. Secondly, and this is the main theme of this article, the vast majority of radio archives are virtually inaccessible to researchers and teachers of radio.

Radio archives represent a major part of this country's cultural and artistic heritage. Yet the situation with regard to their accessibility is a national disgrace. No single institution can take the blame for this: the problems involved are complex and their solution will require coordinated effort across a number of fields and organisations. A start has been made, and the initiative has come from Bournemouth University and the Radio Studies Network, working with the broadcasters, but the problem has yet to be recognised at the highest levels in the BBC and in government where alone can the resources to solve the problem can be authorised.

For the Radio Studies Network, archives are of crucial importance. British radio has a global reputation and radio has a major place in the nation's cultural heritage. Despite television's dominance, it plays a significant and intimate role in the everyday life of most people. With the arrival of digital radio and web broadcasting, supplemented by mobile telephony, the medium is entering a new and exciting phase, yet by comparison with film and television, it has until recently suffered from critical neglect. The relative absence of radio studies at university level has made itself felt throughout the education system and in the culture generally. The resulting lack of a critical discourse means that much good broadcasting goes unnoticed, and radio's lack of status impoverishes public debate, vocational provision and listeners' appreciation alike. It also has long-term negative effects on the radio industry itself. So our assumption is that the art of radio will benefit from increased attention being paid to it from the academic sector. The end result should be the development of a sustained, lively and critical discourse relating to sound and radio which will feed into practice and policy, and the perceptions of radio held by the rest of the media and the public.

To this end, the Radio Studies Network (see section 'Research Services and Organisations') has launched a programme of seven actions, one of which is dedicated to campaigning to make radio archives more accessible.

Archives as cultural memory

To put our campaign in context, it may help to look at archives as cultural memory. Raphael Samuel remarked that history is not the 'prerogative of historians'; it belongs to everyone. It is 'a social form of knowledge, the work, in any given instance of a thousand different hands'. (Samuel 1996:8). Samuel saw memory and history as having a dialectical relationship. Memory isn't some

1

'negative other' but an active shaping force. And like history, 'what it contrives symptomatically to forget is as important as what it remembers'. (Samuel 1996: x).

If we apply this notion specifically to sound and radio, and if we invoke that body of work (reception theory, or audience studies) that has discussed the viewer's (and not much the listener's) consumption of cultural products in social and domestic settings, we could say, following Samuel, that the history of radio is not the prerogative of the BBC, nor of its official historians, nor of a group of academics, but has a place in 'folk memory'. It's part of the people's heritage, of popular culture. When we consider the difference between sight and sound – sights are out there and can be inspected, sounds enter inside us – this difference may account for the possessive feeling of ownership that people have about radio – 'our tune', 'my station'. This feeling of possessiveness applies also to the programmes people remember from the past.

Turning specifically to radio archives, these exist in a number of different forms. First, there is a mass of material that exists informally due to people's habit of recording their favourite listening for repeated re-listening, or to catch what they were unable to hear off-air. Any re-use of this outside the home would be illegal, yet sometimes the existence of these private collections has come to the rescue of official archives when an official recording has gone missing.

At the other end of the spectrum are the official collections of recorded sound. A table in Silver (1988) lists collections of national importance (Imperial War Museum, National Sound Archive), network radio archives (BBC Sound Archive), regional centres (North West Sound Archive, Welsh Folk Life Museum, Ulster Folk Life Museum, School of Scottish Studies), local radio archives (BBC Bristol, Viking Radio in Hull), and local centres like Birmingham City Library where the Charles Parker archives are housed.

Silver's list includes recorded music and oral history collections, and it is over ten years out of date. It is high time that a mapping exercise is undertaken to determine what is the present state of *radio* archives.

If this were accompanied by an amnesty it would discover a number of 'private armies' operating in the field – collections midway in status between the public and the personal. Some of these would be the collections in university and college libraries, legally acquired through possession of an Educational Recording Agency (ERA) licence for purposes of teaching and research. Others would have been accumulated in ways that have less certain legality, e.g. the lodging by a producer, teaching at a university as a visiting lecturer, of a recording of a programme s/he had produced, or programmes obtained from abroad, or simply downloaded from the internet.

But for present purposes I want to concentrate on the national collections: the BBC and the National Sound Archive (NSA).

What radio do archives represent?

I want to ask the question what do these archives represent? Imagine a science fiction scenario where, in the distant future, Martians find radio archives among the remains of our civilisation. The totality of archives represents 'radio' – there is nothing else. We might recall the remarks of Scannell and Cardiff about what was broadcast before World War 2 on the BBC's one National Programme:

> The sum of the material transmitted on such a channel may be seen as amounting to a socio-cultural universe (a complete world) because the overall content or repertoire appears *exhaustive*; what lies outside the catchment of the channel (what is *not* broadcast) is not part of the 'normal' range of the social experience and needs of the audience… Programmes remain the final register and bearers of institutional intentions and assumptions about the scope and purposes of broadcasting and about the audiences to whom they speak.
>
> (Scannell & Cardiff 1982:168,170)

Applied to radio archives, we can say that the NSA/BBC collection in a certain sense *define radio* and what is *not* radio.

The Martians are closer than we think: they are the ones in first-year media studies courses who put up their hands when asked who listens to

Radio 4 or Radio 3. For them, as students of British media, it's not such a problem: all they have to do is tune to the channels and start listening. This is, in fact, what the BBC regards as the main recourse: 'as far as the BBC is concerned public access to the archives is on screen and on the airways every day of the week' (Fiander 1999).

However, for those of us in academia there's a twin paradox where radio is concerned: first, its abundant presence on the airwaves contrasts with (and to some extent contributes to) its comparative absence in media studies; second, its evanescence – daily, hourly – is in contradiction to the permanence archives bestow.

Radio texts for study

So we are concerned here with secondary use. The study of radio texts is central to the development of radio theory and the establishment of radio as an object of academic study. Access to archives would allow the evolution of genres to be traced and the development within and across genres of the significatory and narrative devices peculiar to radio. For lack of such texts, the development of such basic theoretical concepts, well understood in film and television study, has barely begun for sound and radio. The existence of radio archives is a pre-condition for such study. Teachers and students need to have access to legally recorded material which can be listened to and replayed and analysed.

If it's archives we are going to use, we are in a sense all Martians and the question of what the archives represent, and what they 'contrive to forget', becomes very important. Since, however, as I shall show shortly, archives are virtually inaccessible to most of us, and we could guess (though it would be interesting to test this empirically) that most of the general public don't even know of their existence, we must turn to another source – BBC Worldwide's Radio Collection, obtainable by mail order or at BBC Shops. Applying the Martian test, what does this say about radio?

1. Only the BBC exists
2. If a programme isn't going to sell 10,000 copies, it doesn't exist
3. Radio is comedy

4. Radio is sport
5. Radio is about personalities
6. Radio is dramatisation of literary classics

Clearly some questions need to be asked about both sources – the Radio Collection and the radio archives. For example,

- Who makes (and has made) the choices for inclusion?
- What have been the criteria for inclusion and exclusion?
- How have these criteria changed over the years?
- What notion of radio as a result has been bequeathed and is now represented by the totality of the archives?
- How do difficulties in using the material accord with current notions about access to museums and art heritage?

Limited access

I began by claiming that the majority of radio archives are virtually inaccessible. What is the position?

Radio programmes from the past can be heard in four ways: 1) by visiting the NSA's collection at the British Library at St Pancras, 2) by applying to BBC Information and Archives, 3) occasionally the BBC re-broadcasts programmes from its archives, 4) BBC Worldwide's Radio Collection.

1. The NSA collection. This includes (apart from the holdings of oral history and music) some 75,000 hours of radio programmes, mostly stored on shellac and vinyl disc, and on tape. The vast majority are BBC programmes going back to the early days of broadcasting and include all the programmes or extracts which the BBC pressed onto disc. The NSA also recorded selectively off the air *c.*1964–2000, and receives donations of privately recorded broadcasts. It therefore holds copies of some broadcasts which the BBC does not, particularly of music material from the 1950s to 1970s. The NSA no longer records off air because the BBC's current retention policies cover everything likely to be needed for use in the NSA Listening Service which provides public access to all programmes in the BBC Sound Archive.

(Ordering copies from the BBC usually takes three days.)

There are significant holdings of commercial radio (including the Capital Radio Archive) as well as of community, pirate and hospital radio, and of radio from overseas. All Sony Radio Award entries are held in the archive.

NSA collections are catalogued on the online CADENSA database (www.cadensa.bl.uk). BBC holdings are catalogued on the online INFAX system, to which the NSA expects access in March, though this may be confined to staff initially.

But what is *not* archived is significant: very little local radio, whether BBC or commercial is routinely sampled, nor does the NSA hold a representative collection of radio advertising. Moreover, the NSA criteria for archiving radio have to do with historical significance of content rather than radiophonic interest, e.g. examples of genre.

At present programmes may only be studied on the site and no copies can be ordered or taken away. The NSA is currently negotiating with the BBC to allow copies of programmes to be made for individuals for study and research use. Here, the main obstacle is not copyright but contracts with contributors. However, further copying or dissemination would not be allowed under such an arrangement.

2. **The BBC Sound Archive.** These archives are intended primarily for programme-makers. With the growth of independent production, the collection has been made available to outsiders for use in work commissioned by the BBC, but charges are high for academic budgets. Unless the researcher knows precisely what s/he wants, search fees can mount up, costing from £35 for 2 hours to £60 for a half day. Once the required programme has been identified, it is up to researchers to clear copyright, something that can take a long time and will not be done for them by the BBC. Fees for material that can be taken away, once copyright is cleared, make no concessions to academic researchers and are prohibitively high. What's more, the present agreement limits use to

within the researcher's own home, so strictly it could not be used in a lecture or lodged in a university library.

3. **BBC re-broadcasts.** BBC re-broadcasts of archival material are not regular or systematic, although they are a godsend for any educational institution holding a licence from the Educational Recording Agency (ERA).

4. **BBC Worldwide's Radio Collection.** As we have seen, this contains a number of classic comedy and light entertainment titles, and dramatisations of popular literary classics, but original plays and features are significantly absent from its catalogue because Worldwide's marketing policy is not oriented towards educational needs.

Overall, then, it is fair to say that most radio archives are effectively inaccessible for teaching purposes, and that for research purposes the barriers to access (geography, fees, rights clearance) are such as to deter all but the most persistent and well-resourced academic.

If we attempt to look at the question from the BBC's point of view, we can certainly accept that, though the NSA radio collection is public, 'back catalogue' represents a commercial opportunity for the broadcasters, especially now that there has been a significant increase in the number of channels to be filled. We can agree, too, with the Secretary of State, Chris Smith, that a balance must be struck between the public interest – 'things of quality must be available to all' as he has said – and the need, which he has also stressed (*Guardian* 12 January 1998), to attend to the economic health of the cultural industries.

It's also clear that the work of renegotiating the rights of material originally contracted for broadcasting and not for secondary use is a time-consuming and therefore costly business. On top of this there will be payments to the rights holders for the new use, although it is gradually becoming practice in the BBC to allow for additional non-broadcast use in the original broadcasting contract. It's not at all obvious that the licence fee should pay for this. A common BBC position is that any development of this kind must be on a cost-covering basis. But this still leaves start-up or development costs to be found.

A distinction also needs to be made between the needs of individual researchers, the opportunities for wider public enjoyment and education of a range of archival material, and universal access. The last is perhaps an ideal too expensive to contemplate. A modest goal would be to try to reach agreement among the parties concerned to clear rights on a limited selection of programmes and make them available for wider use, at first in cassette or CD format, and subsequently online.

The Archive Working Group

In fact, as I began by saying, such a start has already been made. The Archive Working Group of the Radio Studies Network, at a colloquium held at Bournemouth University last year, agreed a plan of action to which a range of interests committed themselves. Present were representatives of the NSA, the BBC Sound Archive, the Radio Authority, the British Universities Film & Video Council and the Radio Studies Network. Among the ideas discussed were:

- a mapping exercise for all UK radio archives
- setting up an emergency alert system to facilitate rescue of endangered archives
- training courses and an accreditation system to allow more efficient use of archives
- the need for a curator at the NSA with specific responsibility for radio
- consultation with the NSA on ways to improve acquisition, archiving, cataloguing and access
- encouraging and coordinating university-based recording
- finding ways to audit BBC and commercial local radio archives
- explore with the BBC Sound Archive the possibility of concessionary rates for accredited researchers

Meanwhile, for the first time the BUFVC's Researcher's Guide Online has included radio in its survey. Of 110 returns, 105 came from radio stations, both BBC and commercial, which hold programme archives. The entries can be found in the directory. Most stations are under a legal obligation to keep recordings of all output for 42 days, but a surprising number keep output for much longer.

Bournemouth University has had further success in an application to the AHRB for a project which will digitise the archive of the Independent Local Radio (ILR) Programme Sharing Scheme. This was a scheme dating from the pre-1990 Broadcasting Act period of commercial radio when a combination of the 'secondary rental' system operated by the Independent Broadcasting Authority (IBA). The IBA's mandated requirements for 'meaningful speech' encouraged the production of quality programmes of a kind not heard since the lighter regulation after 1990. The Programme Sharing Scheme enabled features, drama, music and news producers to offer material – including a significant body of speech-based material produced locally – to other stations at no charge. The archive consists of 1,570 quarter-inch analogue audiotapes, a unique record of a key period in the history of British commercial radio, one which has been largely forgotten and was in danger of being lost forever as the oxide on the original tapes progressively degenerated.

Another project, for which funding is currently being sought, would transfer a much larger collection to digital format and create a searchable database. This is the archive of Independent Radio News and LBC (IRN/LBC)[2] and includes such programmes as *Hayes on Sundays, Decision Makers, Arts Week*, one-off documentaries and the end-of-year news and sports reviews from 1973 to 1995.

Conclusion

Underlying these initiatives is the perception that research and cataloguing, for which otherwise time and finding might not be available, if undertaken by academic researchers, enhances the useability (hence value) of the archives and feeds back into the radio culture generally making for a more appreciative and informed listenership. It is a sad state of affairs when the record of a rich cultural heritage lies inaccessible to listeners and scholars, unknown for the most part even to the best of present-day radio producers. It is as if a contemporary generation of writers and readers lived in ignorance of Chaucer, Shakespeare, Austen, Dickens. A remark of Milan Kundera's is pertinent: 'the struggle...against power is the struggle of memory against forgetting' (Kundera 1983:3). Men and women, old and young, we have our memories intimately intertwined with this medium. What is needed is a shift of power from 'them' to us. In our case, in the case of radio, the power we have to struggle against is that of inertia and complexity.

Over two years ago *A Netful of Jewels* proclaimed: 'Learning through digital networks... is central to the Government's vision of the learning society. As individuals take greater responsibility for their own learning, organisations will need to respond by creating new opportunities for this' (National Museum Directors' Conference 1999). Museums are beginning to use the new technologies to improve access; it is time to rescue radio archives from obscurity. May we expect the BBC's still new Director-General to apply to this problem the vision he spoke of before taking office: [a vision of] 'harnessing the power of new technology to offer everyone the opportunity to flourish through learning, at every stage of life' (BBC 1999).

References

BBC (1999). 'Greg Dyke offers to fire the popular imagination and bring learning to all', BBC Press Office summary of The Spectator/Zurich Financial Services lecture, 18 November 1999.

Fiander, P (1999). unpublished notes accompanying BBC Radio 4 *The Message*, 11 June 1999

Kundera, M. (1983). *The Book of Laughter and Forgetting*, London: Penguin.

National Museum Directors' Conference (1999). *A Netful of Jewels: New Museums in the Learning Age* NMDC.

Samuel, R. (1996). *Theatres of Memory Vol 1: Past and Present in Contemporary Culture*, London: Verso

Scannell, P. & Cardiff, D. (1982). 'Serving the Nation: Public Service Broadcasting before the War'. In Waites, B., Bennett, T. & Martin G. (eds) *Popular Culture: Past and Present*, London: Croom Helm/Open University Press, pp.161–188.

Silver, J. (1988). 'Astonished and somewhat terrified: the preservation and development of aural culture'. In Lumley, R. (ed) *The Museum Time-Machine: putting cultures on display*, London: Comedia/Routledge, pp.170–195.

Peter Lewis *is Visiting Research Fellow in the Department of Sociology at the London School of Economics, funded by the Economic and Social Research Council to work on the Radio Research Project. The Radio Studies Network, of which he is Development Director, is one of the main outcomes of the project so far. After a period working in educational and community broadcasting, he taught media and cultural studies at Middlesex and City Universities and at Goldsmiths College. He has published widely on community media and is the author, with Jerry Booth, of* The Invisible Medium: Public, Commercial and Community Radio *(Macmillan, 1989).*

[1] This article draws on a paper delivered at the Radio History Symposium, Bournemouth University School of Media Arts and Communications, 24–25 June 1999.
[2] LBC has held the London area news licence from 1973 to the present date. IRN, housed within LBC, acted as a news agency for the commercial radio system as it developed.

UK Copyright: the Path to the Future

by Emanuella Giavarra

Introduction

After three years of negotiations within the Council of Ministers and the European Parliament, the draft EU Directive on the harmonisation of certain aspects of Copyright and Related Rights in the Information Society was finally adopted by the European Parliament[1] on 14 February 2001. The European Parliament claims that this Directive has been the most lobbied Directive in its history. The discussions were held up due to major differences amongst the representatives of the fifteen Member States on the scope of the exceptions to copyright and the scope of the legal protection of technical measures.

At stake for the UK HE and FE community was the possible loss of existing copyright exceptions for print, a limitation to digital copying by libraries to conservation and archiving, fair compensation as a pre-condition for each and every exception and far-reaching new exclusive rights for rights owners.

In the next few months, the Directive will be formally adopted by the Council of Ministers. The Directive allows the UK government to implement the Directive into the national copyright law within a period of 18 months. Once implemented, the Directive will be enforceable within the UK.

Whilst it does not happen very often, the implementation of this Directive will bring the law ahead of the digital market developments. As a safeguard, the Directive includes an obligation on the European Commission to monitor the application of the Directive in relation to developments of the digital market and consumer rights. By 2005, the European Commission has to submit a report to the European Parliament and the Council of Ministers that examines in particular the application of Articles 5 (exceptions), 6 (technical measures) and 8 (sanctions and remedies) of the Directive.

Isues covered by the Directive

According to the European Commission, this Directive adjusts and complements the existing legal framework, with particular emphasis to new products and services containing intellectual property (both on-line and on physical carriers such as CDs, CD-ROMs and Digital Video Discs). The Directive also implements the main obligations of the WIPO Copyright Treaty 1996 and the WIPO Performances and Phonograms Treaty 1996.

The issues covered by the Directive are:
- Right of Reproduction
- Right of Communication to the Public
- Legal Protection of Technical Measures and Rights-Management Information
- Distribution Right

The Right of Communication to the Public and the Legal Protection of Technical Measures and Rights-Management Information are new features, once implemented, in UK copyright legislation.

Right of reproduction

The Directive contains a very broad definition of the right of reproduction. It reads as follows:

'Member States shall provide for the exclusive right to authorise or prohibit direct or indirect, temporary or permanent reproduction by any means and in any form, in whole or in part:
a) for authors, of their works;
b) for performers, of fixations of their performances;
c) for phonogram producers, of their phonograms;
d) for the producers of their first fixations of films, in respect of the original and copies of their films;
e) for broadcasting organisations, of fixations of their broadcasts, whether those broadcasts are transmitted by wire or over the air, including by cable or satellite.'

The definitions of the various terms can be found in Article. 2 of the WIPO Performances and Phonograms Treaty 1996:

'fixation'   means the embodiment of sounds, or of the representations thereof, from which they can be perceived, reproduced or communicated through a device;

'performers' are actors, singers, musicians, dancers, and other persons who act, sing, deliver, declaim, play in, interpret, or otherwise perform literary or artistic works of expressions of folklore.

Right of communication to the public

This new exclusive right was introduced by the WIPO Copyright Treaty 1996 and the WIPO Performances and Phonograms Treaty 1996. There is still a lot of confusion about the extent and application of this right, especially over the definition of 'public' The Explanatory Memorandum to the draft EU Copyright Directive states that the communication to the public' (the 'making available to the public') precedes the stage of its actual transmission.

In other words, the storage of material with the (future) aim of offering it on a publicly accessible site may amount to a 'communication to the public'.

The Directive grants the exclusive right to authorise or prohibit any communication or making available to the public, by wire or wireless means (in such a way that members of the public may access them from a place and at a time individually chosen by them) to:
a) authors, of their works;
b) performers, of fixations of their performances;
c) phonogram producers, of their phonograms
d) producers of their first fixations of films, in respect of the original and copies of their films;
e) broadcasting organisations, of fixations of their broadcasts, whether those broadcasts are transmitted by wire or over the air, including by cable or satellite.'

Exceptions

The exceptions to the right of reproduction and the right of communication to the public are listed in Article 5 of the draft Directive. The Commentary on Article 5, states that 'Member States will **not be allowed** to provide for **any exceptions other** than

those enumerated in Article 5'. Article 5 only lists one mandatory exception (Art. 5.1) and all other exceptions are optional for the national governments. The allowed exceptions are as follows:

Exceptions to the right of reproduction:

5.1 transient and incidental acts of reproduction, such as caching and browsing (mandatory)

5.2.a reproductions on paper (except sheet music), fair compensation (optional)

5.2.b analogue and digital reproductions on any medium by a natural person for private use for ends which are neither directly or indirectly commercial, fair compensation (optional)

5.2.c specific acts of reproduction by publicly accessible libraries, educational establishments, museums or archives, which are not for direct or indirect economic or commercial advantage (optional)

5.2.d ephemeral recordings of works made by broadcasting organisations and preservation of these recordings in official archives (optional)

5.2.e reproductions of broadcasts by social institutions, fair compensation (optional)

Exceptions to the right of reproduction and the right to communicate to the public:

5.3.a illustration for teaching or scientific research, for non-commercial purposes, fair compensation (optional)

5.3.b uses for the benefit of people with a disability (optional)

5.3.c reproduction by the press, communication to the public of published articles on current economic and political topics, broadcasts of works or use in connection with the reporting of current events (optional)

5.3.d quotations for purposes such as criticism or review (optional)

5.3.e use for purposes of public security or reporting of an administrative, parliamentary or judicial procedure (optional)

5.3.f   use of political speeches, extracts of public lectures or similar works (optional)

5.3.g   use during religious or official celebrations (optional)

5.3.h   use of works, such as works of architecture or sculpture located in public places (optional)

5.3.i   incidental inclusion of a work or other subject matter (optional)

5.3.j   use for purpose of advertising public exhibitions or sale of artistic works (optional)

5.3.k   use for the purpose of caricature, parody or pastiche (optional)

5.3.l   use in connection with demonstration or repair of equipment (optional)

5.3.m   use of drawings or plans of a building (optional)

5.3.n   use by communication or making available for the purpose of research or private study, to individual members of the public by dedicated terminals on the premises in respect of reproductions made by establishments referred to in para 5.2.c of works and other subject matter not subject to purchase or licensing terms which are contained in their collections (optional)

5.3.o   use in certain other cases of minor importance where exceptions already exist under national law, provided that they only concern analogue uses and do not affect the free circulation of goods and services within the Community, without prejudice to the other exceptions and limitations contained in this Article (optional)

All these exceptions are subject to the 'three step test' of Article 5.5. This means that the exceptions can only apply in 1) certain special cases, 2) as long as they do not conflict with the normal exploitation of the work or other subject matter 3) and as long as they do not unreasonably prejudice the legitimate interests of the right holder.

Fair compensation

Several exceptions require the payment of a fair compensation. The Council of Ministers agreed after extensive discussions on the words 'fair compensation' instead of 'equitable remuneration', which is the basis for many existing remuneration schemes in the EU. 'Equitable remuneration' implies that in return for the exception there must be a payment. 'Fair compensation' not only requires that the compensation must be 'fair' but must compensate for real loss. Indeed, compensation need not be financial. These concepts are reflected in Recital 35, which makes the following important statements:

1. that where rights holders have already received payment in some other form, such as part of a licence fee, no specific or separate payment may be due.
2. that the level of fair compensation should take full account of the degree of use of technological protection measures.
3. that in certain situations where the prejudice to the right holder would be minimal, no obligation for payment may arise.

The last of these statements is very important as it creates an opportunity to challenge future levy or other remuneration legislation. The UK government delegation could certainly use this to curb requests from the industry for the introduction of levies in relation to time-shifting.

Less positive is Recital 36 which gives the UK government the free hand to extend the provisions for fair compensation for rights holders to the exceptions in the Directive which at the moment do not require such compensation.

Licensing

The legal solution for activities other than the ones listed as an exception can be found in the Explanatory Memorandum to the Directive. The Memorandum states 'with respect to the use of digitised material by libraries, on-line as well as off-line, initiatives are on-going in a number of Member States, notably the UK, where library privileges are most developed, to arrive at more flexible contractual solutions'.

This shift in focus of attention from a bundle of exceptions which has developed over many years in the print-on-paper environment towards contractual licensing solutions, especially accompanied with a broad protection of (new) rights of the rights holders is one that should make HE and FE institutions wary.

Contract law is dominated by the concept of freedom of contract – that is to say the parties to a contract are free to negotiate the terms of use of copyrighted materials. Negotiations with a holder of an exclusive right could turn out to have a harsh result for the information purchaser. Especially for these cases, the copyright exceptions (statutory rights) provide an essential tool to guarantee access to information and library services. In order to safeguard these rights, the following clause should be included in a licence:

'This Licence shall be deemed to complement and extent the rights of the Licensee under the Copyright Designs and Patents Act 1988 and nothing in this Licence shall constitute a waiver of any statutory rights held by the Licensee from time to time under that Act or any amending legislation.'

Legal protection of technical measures and rights-management information

This kind of protection was discussed for the first time in the framework of the WIPO negotiations on certain questions on copyright and related rights. The WIPO Performances and Phonograms Treaty 1996 (WPPT) and the WIPO Copyright Treaty 1996 (WCT) contain parallel provisions on 'technological measures' and on 'obligations concerning rights management information'. The first prohibits the circumvention of technical measures that are used by holders of copyright or related rights in connection with the exercise of their rights, the latter prohibits the removal and altering of certain electronic rights management information attached to a work or other subject matter.

These obligations have been implemented and subsequently extended in Article 6 of the Directive. This article entitles rights holders to protect their works against the circumvention of any effective technological measures. However, where rights holders have not taken voluntary measures to give the beneficiaries of certain exceptions access to their protected works, the UK government can take appropriate measures to enable users to benefit from the exceptions concerned.

The expression 'technological measures' is broadly defined in Article 6 of the Directive and refers to any technology, device or component that, in the normal course of its operation, is designed to prevent or restrict acts, in respect of works or other subject matter, which are not authorised by the rights holder. Technological measures shall be deemed 'effective' where the use of a protected work is controlled by the rights holders through application of an access control or protection process, such as encryption, scrambling or other transformation of the work or other subject matter or a copy control mechanism, which achieves the protection objective.

Article 6.4 of the Directive is very important to the HE and FE community as it balances the potential technical monopoly of information by rights holders. Several doubts have been raised concerning the effectiveness of this article as Article 6.4 does not provide an outright permission to circumvent a technical block for lawful uses by a lawful user (a user exercising an exception). The provision puts the obligation on the right holder to make available the means of benefiting from that exception through the use of voluntary measures or agreements which accommodate such exceptions. If they fail to do so, the UK government is entitled to step in and take 'appropriate measures'.

This protection mechanism only applies to the exceptions provided for in Article 5.2a. 2c. 2d. 2e. 3a. 3b or 3e. It is worrying that they have not been extended to the exceptions in 5.3.f, 3i and 3j. The legal protection of technical measures is retrospective, but only for the Directive on the legal protection of databases which was implemented in the UK copyright legislation in 1998.

According to Article 6.4, fourth paragraph, the circumvention by lawful users will not be allowed if the work was made available on demand on agreed contractual terms. In other words, where content is delivered online subject to contractual terms rights holders will be permitted to block technically any copying of such content, irrespective of whether such copying is allowed by law or not. Recital 52a tries to clarify that this provision only applies to interactive on-demand services, in such a way that members of the public may access works or other subject-matter from a place and at a time individually chosen by them.

Besides the protection of technical measures in Article 6, Article 7 requests Member States to provide adequate legal protection against any person who, without authority, removes or alters electronic rights management information or distributes, imports, communicates with the public or makes available copies to the public or other subject matter from which electronic rights management information has been removed or altered without authority.

Distribution right

The distribution right refers exclusively to fixed copies that can be put into circulation as tangible objects. The European Commission already harmonised the distribution right for certain categories of works such as computer programs and databases.

During the preparations and adaptation of the WIPO Copyright Treaty 1996 and the WIPO Performances and Phonograms Treaty 1996 all potential Contracting Parties to the Treaties agreed to establish a distribution right for tangible objects in order to provide for a coherent level playing field for the distribution of protected material and for the need to draw a clear line between electronic (communication to the public right) and tangible distribution (distribution right) of protected material. The provision can be found in Article 6 of the WIPO Copyright Treaty 1996 and Article 8 and 12 of the WIPO Performances and Phonograms Treaty 1996. The Articles only establish the right, but do not provide for a national or international exhaustion of the distribution right, but leaves it to the Contracting Parties to determine the conditions under which the exhaustion of this right applies.

Pursuant to the WIPO Copyright Treaty 1996, the Directive provides in Article 4 for a nearly identical worded exclusive distribution right. For the smooth functioning of the Internal Market, the European Commission included in Article 4 of the Directive a provision that the distribution right should be exhausted within the Community only when the first sale or other transfer of ownership of the object is made by the right holder or with his consent in the Community. According to Article 5.4, Member States are allowed to provide for an exception to the right of distribution to the extend justified by the purpose of the authorised act of reproduction.

Further thoughts

The implementation of this Directive will change the copyright environment as we know it. How the implementation in the UK will work out is far from certain. Only through a continuous dialogue with the Patent Office in the coming months, will the HE and FE community be able to influence the future of copyright and the impact of it upon its services.

Emanuella Giavarra *is a specialist international contract and copyright lawyer. From December 1990, she dedicated herself to the protection of the copyright interests of the library world with the European institutions. From June 1992 until January 1996, she was Director of the European Bureau of Library, Information and Documentation Associations (EBLIDA). From January 1996 until January 1999, she was Project Director of the European Copyright User Platform (ECUP+ Concerted Action). At present, she is a partner in the Chambers of Mark Watson-Gandy in Amsterdam and London and a member of the Legal Advisory Board of the European Commission (DG-XIII).*

[1] The amendments of the European Parliament and the Common Position of the Council of Ministers can be found at http://www.eblida.org/ecup/lex under DGXV- draft Directives. The final text of the Directive will be added to the website in due course.

Clearance of Feature Film Clips

by Tony Dalton

As anyone will know who has tried to clear feature films, especially Hollywood features, the process can be gruelling and sometimes even painful. But it need not be as daunting as one might think. The purpose of this article is to help the researcher plan and then negotiate the easiest route through the labyrinth of do's and don'ts. However I should make it clear from the start that there are no quick or easy answers. The knowledge that one particularly expensive film can be replaced by another much cheaper title is acquired by years of experience. Some of the steps detailed here may seem obvious and would apply to most film research but they are never the less important, especially in the research for features. I should also point out that most of the information is really aimed at UK researchers. The reason for this is the difference in copyright laws in the US and Europe and if I went into detailed analysis of these then I would have to write a world guide, which would perhaps take up all the pages of this volume.

The first and most crucial point to remember is that each feature is different and that contrary criteria can apply from one title to another. Therefore, the golden rule is that few titles are the same and each must be treated individually. Also, it should never be assumed that because you have cleared a film with a copyright holder once that the same conditions will apply to the next title you request from them. Clauses in the licence agreement, fees or credits can alter from one day to the next and between one title and the next.

The first part of the process is to make sure the producer, director and production manager are aware that the cost of feature clips can be, but are not necessarily, excessive in comparison with other footage. In my experience the director has the great idea to feature movies in his masterpiece, often in the hope that they will enliven his otherwise dull programme. What is not considered is either the copyright cost or indeed the time it can take to secure feature clips. Some US companies can reply to a request with a few days or even overnight but others can take months.

Always assume the costs will be high and that the process can take the maximum.

The next stage is to research the title or titles to ensure that you have the correct copyright holder. This can be complicated, especially with new independent features that have more than one production company and also with some old titles that have been bought and sold as assets. For example the old MGM library (GONE WITH THE WIND, SINGIN' IN THE RAIN, etc.) was bought by Turner Entertainment and is now held by Warner Bros. However, there is also the newer MGM company that handles current MGM product plus a library of classic United Artist titles, some of the old Polygram titles and a number of other companies features. Another example is the pre-1945 Paramount feature library. These are not owned by Paramount Pictures (which incidentally is now controlled by Viacom), but by Universal Pictures.

If you think this is a phenomenon of US libraries, then think again. The old EMI library has over the years been bought by three or more companies and now resides, along with the Ealing comedies and others, with Canal+ Image UK Ltd at Pinewood Studios. The same applies to the Rank, Korda, Romulus and ITC collections, which are now held by Carlton International. It's all very confusing and I am certain that by the time this article is published the game of musical assets will again be in session and that another classic collection will be changing hands. Making sure you have the correct company is important as some of them, especially the Hollywood libraries, become very irritated with requests that do not relate to them. So much so, that they will not bother to reply to your request and you are left high and dry waiting for an answer that never comes. There are many approaches to checking copyright. The easiest is to refer to a film guide that includes production company references. Personally, I have always used *Halliwell's Film & Video Guide* because I have found it the most complete. Other alternatives are to contact the information depart at the British Film Institute or the Library of Congress in Washington, DC.

Once you think you have located the copyright source, then the next step is to fax (most companies prefer faxes) details of the titles and the clips you require. This initial request should include as much information as possible; otherwise you could waste weeks whilst the request is processed through the bureaucracy and then sent back to you to fill in the blanks. You should detail the title or titles (with a date of production in case there is more than one version), the exact clip or clips the production wants to use and how they want to use them. You should of course, also include details of kind of production it is and advise them of clearances required, namely whether you require one territory or world, type of media, number of transmissions and duration of clearance. Most of the companies will not consider a request until they have all this information. Occasionally, if there is concern about how the clips are to be used, they will ask for script pages.

If you require clearance for world then you must (and this will apply to any copyright holder) establish that they have whatever rights you are after for all world territories. I recently requested the use of SHANE (1953) and was initially advised in writing that my request was approved for world all-media, but when I subsequently asked for a licence agreement I was told that they didn't own that title in Japan. By the same token it is vital to establish that you will be able to clear the film for the number of years you require. Again I was recently advised in writing by a company that the number of years I needed to clear a particular title was approved. However, when I asked for the licence agreement it came to light that the details hadn't been checked and they only had the film rights for half the number of years I had requested. In both cases there was little I could do except to try and find the other copyright holders or find alternatives. It is therefore wise to double-check that the copyright holder has what you want and confirms it all in writing. However, even this (as proven in the above examples) will not help if they have made a mistake, but at least the paperwork will illustrate to the production that you have endeavoured to clarified the situation to the best of your ability.

If securing approval is tortuous, then locating masters is perhaps the second most difficult task in feature film clearance. Before you ask for a licence agreement, you must be confident that you will be able to secure a master of the title or titles. With very few exceptions, most US copyright holders will not supply masters of the clips you require. They will grant approval and take the money but will not help with physically obtaining a master. There is no easy answer with respect to Hollywood titles; you just have to search until someone is willing to let you use their master. However, most of the classic UK titles are much more straightforward as they are owned by Canal+ Image UK Ltd and Carlton who are usually more than willing to supply masters for transfer.

The final stage is to then ask for a licence agreement, which must be checked by the film researcher and then signed by the production. It must not be signed by the film researcher. There are several reasons for this. The first is that it must always be the responsibility of the production to comply with the clauses of the agreement. The second is that in my experience the film researcher is often not privileged to see the completed programme until it is too late to object to how clips are being used. If the production has used that clip or clips in a manner that is contrary to the licence agreement then the onus must be with the production. For this reason, before the use or inclusion of clips in any edit, the production should be made aware a number of key points that might be contained in the agreement:

1. No feature film companies will grant usage approval for any subject that is considered to be derogatory to either the film it is extracted from or to the film copyright holder or the film industry in general.

2. Most copyright holders will only grant approval for per clip per minute. This means that you will have to pay each time the clip is cut no matter for what reason.

3. Few, if any, US companies will grant permission for the use of the clip in any advertising or publicity for the programme.

4. Few if any of the companies will supply feature clips in perpetuity for television use.

5. Only a handful of copyright holders will grant

use for Internet use as either part of the standard agreement or independently. At the time of writing, most will not even consider the Internet.

6. All music contained within the clip or clips must be cleared separately and is the responsibility of the production. This is a very specialised area and my advice to anyone is to ensure that the production obtains the services of a qualified music clearance researcher.

7. The standard licence agreement will contain a clause similar to 'the Licensee will obtain all other authorisation, consents, and releases and will pay all re-use fees and other compensation.' This means in short that it is up to the production to clear what is known as all third parties which might include artists and even stuntmen if they appear in the clip, as well as the director, producer and the scriptwriter of the film whether dead or alive. In some cases this may not be necessary even if it states in the licence agreement but once again it depends on the film and the date of production. Some companies will advise you that in certain cases an individual's approval is required in writing before a licence agreement can be issued. If this is the case then you will be required to clear approval.

8. An end credit must be given to the copyright holder. The wording for this will be included on the licence agreement.

9. Once the licence agreement has been signed it is usually required that the fee is paid, whether or not the footage is used. An alternative used by some US companies is a kill fee, which may not be the full licence fee but is a percentage, which is again payable whether or not the clip is used.

These are by no means all of the clauses or conditions you may be faced with. Once again it depends on the title, the date of the film, the company, and exactly what clearances you are asking for. Read the licence agreement carefully and point out any clauses that might cause concern to the production and most important of all, make sure the production reads the agreement themselves.

So far I have concentrated mainly on US and UK titles, but there is the tricky area of Continental titles. Some are relatively straightforward but in my experience most are complicated. There are a number of reasons for this. Sometimes it can be because of their co-production status, or that more than one producer needs to approve the use, or that they have sold the rights to different distribution companies in separate world territories. This last problem is acceptable if you only require one country or even two but if you are after world clearance then to achieve this aim can involve three, four or even up to six different distribution companies, which of course would prove prohibitively expensive. There is also another possible problem if there is no obvious distributor or copyright holder. European copyright law basically says that the copyright is held for 70 years after the death of the 'author'. For example the films of the pioneer Georges Méliès are in fact in copyright until 2008 because he died in 1938. It is not the date of the titles, as applies to many US titles; it is the death of the author. Establishing the 'author' can be the problem.

If, as is the case with almost all productions these days, the budget for archive is, shall we say, underachieved, then there are a few alternatives if feature film enhancement is still wanted by the director. One way is to use stills and posters. These are generally available through specialist libraries (contact BAPLA) who will usually advise about copyright clearances. Still images do not necessarily need to be static and boring and if rostrumed imaginatively can often make a more direct point about a subject.

The other alternative is trailers. Trailers are a wonderful source of enabling a programme to look more expensive than it really is. They can also encapsulate the essence of a film within their two or three minute duration and as an added bonus they can often reflect an era that says more about a subject that any clip can. However, like all good things, there are limitations. They must be trailers based on US features (European feature trailers are owned by the film's copyright holder); they must have a production date prior to 1962 (before that date US trailers are mostly considered to be in the public domain) and finally they must be shown as a trailer. This final point means that you cannot take a clean clip (without titling or trailer narration) and claim it as a clip from the complete feature. *It must be obvious it is a trailer* and therefore you must ensure that either the trailer titles are shown ('a cast of thousands' etc), and/or the narration is heard, and/or a caption is shown over the clip saying it is a trailer.

As I have already mentioned, the reason that these trailers are so readily available is that pre-1964 titles are *generally* considered to have fallen into the public domain. However this doesn't mean you can just pick them off the shelf at the Library of Congress, they all have to be bought through libraries in the US and the UK. As you can imagine this is a grey area and some companies will encourage you to purchase post-1964 titles. There are occasions when post-1964 titles are legitimately available but you must ensure that the company has researched that all titles they offer are public domain and ask them to verify this in writing. Even so, always remember that not all pre-1964 trailers are in the public domain and you should carefully research them yourself if possible, to establish if there are any hidden problems like literary rights etc. Also please remember that all music still has to be cleared.

I realise that I may have encouraged more questions than I have answered, but as you will now appreciate this is a very complex and involved area of research that must be carefully trodden. To treat features as easy would most definitely be a mistake. I hope that this has been of some use to the reader and will enable him or her to find their way through the often-daunting task of feature film clearances. Having said that, I should say that the process need not be difficult. As I always say to a producer, 'you can have any film you like, any film in the history of movies, as long as you have enough time and money in the budget'.

Tony Dalton *is an archive consultant and film researcher. He is also a writer, director and producer.*

Researching Film and Video on the Internet

by Alex Cowan

Introduction

In 1992 when I started out as a film researcher I had to go through the archive records for a major historical series from the 1980s. As I flicked through the typewritten logs (and accompanying carbon copies) noting down 1″ spool numbers and (in some cases) duped film items, the production notes often seemed to date from another era.

Eight years later, many of the libraries I previously had to fax or physically visit to conduct research have a presence on the Internet. Like writing and submitting this article, browsing and searching collections can be done electronically, without having to leave my home. Researching and assembling data on disparate subjects at the same time has become much easier – I can't imagine modern freelance work without the development of new IT systems, especially the Internet. The future appears even brighter, with the promise of remote viewing and acquisition of moving images.

However, I can't imagine these new systems without the skills, knowledge and 'content' of the pre-Internet world. A good website shows the future and reflects the past in equal measure. If it does not, its utility will always be limited. It should be a gateway to a variety of possibilities other than those exclusive to the Internet, including access to biological members of staff.

General research – is there anybody out there?

On the most basic level the Internet offers a way to shorten radically and economise the research process. While personal contacts and insights still count for a lot, the information on screen also makes where you've searched as important as who you know. Virtually any library, professional organisation and individual can afford to have a presence on the Internet. For the more obscure or distant sources, even simple contact details can invaluable. E-mail is often be more reliable than phone or fax and removes the tiring aspect of coping with international time differences.

In the past, finding local television news in the USA has caused me a great deal of frustration, but it gets simpler year on year, as does locating obscure sources in former Communist countries where simple economics, out-dated technology and a service ethic 'nurtured' by years of Communism can often frustrate the most dedicated researcher and supplier. Finding the right person or library is often half the battle and the web makes it simpler, as well as providing a pleasant alternative to the world of commercial libraries, an increasing number of which are losing the 'personal touch' as they are absorbed by huge international corporations like Microsoft and News International.

There is also a wealth of supporting information to be utilised by the researcher before any commercial online catalogue needs to be visited. This ranges from sites run by academic institutions to those created as a labour of love by members of the public. Television companies may come and go and editorial policies change over time, but the sort of media monitoring conducted by some academic institutions can remain reassuringly constant – it has been a constant source of enjoyment over the years to hear the baffled responses from US TV companies when confronted with thoroughly specific details of their own broadcasts from websites like those run by Vanderbilt University at http://www.tvnews.vanderbilt.edu

The Internet Movie Database (http://imdb.com), a brilliant site devoted to all the minutiae of feature film, is a classic example of the Internet at its best. Its records and reviews are the result of compiling information from thousands of online contributors, its pages open to perpetual updating by movie obsessives. Individuals on the web can create a space to pursue their own obsessions – if you are looking for a filmography for Richard Kiel ('Jaws' in THE SPY WHO LOVED ME) or want to know how BBC testcards and their inimitable backing music changed over the years then the World Wide Web is the place.

Hitherto elusive groups like film collectors use the Internet as a forum to swap advice and news. Searching in this way I was able to find home movie and old government films from the time of UDI in Rhodesia (adding greatly to sources in the UK and those of the Zimbabwe National Archives), as well as intimate details of the past exploits of Bagpuss and the Clangers. Freed from the expenses of regular publishing, the vagaries of academic fashion or commercial pressures, the Internet is the place to find all kinds of extras on obscure topics, to a level that can often shame the original producer – both the National Film and Television Archive and the BBC have benefited from the apparently obsessive world forum made possible by the Internet.

However, some sites run by individuals or special interest groups do raise a major issue for Internet users and one which may prevent Internet resources from eclipsing more conventional sources – that of attribution and accuracy. Internet articles rarely have any footnotes or bibliography and the copyright status of included images is often open to question. If the site is written to eulogise a particular individual or to maintain a certain view of historical events, the information may not be reliable. Personal opinion can form the bulk of many sites and they can sometimes be depressingly biased towards the popular and current at the expense of anything else. Anyone intending to use the Internet for a large proportion of their research needs to accept the fact that due to its unregulated nature, it is as open to hidden agendas and fads as any mainstream source, if not more so.

Newsgroups

One of the oldest functions of the Internet is to provide a forum for group discussion, either via e-mail or in real time. Newsgroups exist for virtually every research discipline where news and information can be exchanged, as well as heated debate! This totally removes all restrictions of distance and time and can often lead to the most fruitful discoveries including copies of long sought after films or programmes. Subscribing to some newsgroups has the added bonus of a delivering regular digests of useful material via e-mail. It can also be an inexpensive path to locating potential interviewees, home movies or never-published

work as, any queries posted will reach a large audience.

Catalogues – the world at your fingertips

For archive researchers, probably the most important development of the last few years in is the increasing availability of online catalogues. This has paralleled the gradual globalisation of the media through co-production and cross-ownership which has irreversibly changed the world of footage research. Where previously archive research was conducted on-site by researchers or on their behalf by an allotted member of staff, this can increasingly be done remotely. Since travel and staff availability are less of an issue, research can be conducted with less expense and much faster. In the case of collections held in other countries, the online catalogue has proved vital – few people, professional or academic, can afford foreign travel for every project. However, given the accompanying reduction in budgets for many television and film projects, which are often justified by assuming that the researcher can rely on the Internet as his or her only source, it remains to be seen whether money 'saved,' will ever trickle down to other areas of the research process that demand equal attention, like proper use of foreign sources and the extra costs this can sometimes entail.

Successfully locating a catalogue site is not always the start of a satisfying research relationship. A good site should allow the user to search an organisation's collections in a variety of ways. The search options should allow for combinations of word or phrases and, most importantly, search tools and advice to refine any search results. When researching on the Internet with search engines of limited flexibility, it is important to think carefully before and during searches – a carelessly chosen search word such as 'film' can lead to literally millions of hits, including multiple links to the Internet's seedier side. A site that is poorly designed or that downloads slowly can make phone or fax enquires seem like the sensible option every time. Though it is understandable if the catalogue is for a visual collection, the inclusion of too many images on a website can often contribute to slow site operation. Browser software often comes with options to avoid downloading images from sites when researching. This can often be a big time-saver.

Personally I've been convinced that the presence of one function is vital on any search facility – the ability to search within a date range. In addition, online catalogues can only really replace an actual visit if details of the whole collection are online. Limited catalogues or those that aspire to offer a collection of images or information advertised as the 'best of,' or 'most popular' might be useful for those in search of images for advertisements or unoriginal research and creative work, but they're probably best described simply as a way to remove the common everyday enquiries from the library's daily workload. Still, older card indexes are virus-proof, and they cost no money to access, once you arrive at their point of storage. In addition, they can have the added back-up of staff who really know their collections. Ironically, since the web often groans under the weight of its many users, staff and these older indexes can sometimes provide faster access, often with cross-referencing capabilities that put many search engines to shame. As I gain more online research experience I'm increasingly struck by the fact that what a really useful site should offer me, other than convenience, is everything that the old system of access used to offer and more.

One of the most exciting developments in the field of online catalogues is the way that access to individual sites can be coordinated through one site, instead of by locating them one by one, which can be frustratingly long-winded. Probably the best example of this is FOOTAGE.net (http://www.footage.net) This site is the gateway to a number of online catalogues and also features contact details and news. Its most interesting function is probably the Zap request which distributes your e-mail request for footage or information to around 200 collections, all of whom are possible respondents. While not appropriate for ever subject, I still wonder at how many potential phone calls, assuming I knew whom to call, that it replaces.

Many sites allow you to collate all the items you are interested in into a virtual 'shopping basket' or 'research folder' which you can return to when your search is done. Some even allow you to order

viewing tapes of this material online, though online payment and delivery, the final piece in this commercial puzzle, are still some way off. However, many collections of still images already offer this service, offering browsing, purchase and acquisition online. An increasing number of labs can produce digital photographic quality prints of such material.

Apart from the possible savings in printing and paper, information from the Internet, either as saved pages or text cut and pasted from the screen into a simple piece of software like the virtually ubiquitous WordPad™ can be compiled on a PC before collation of reports or publication. This can lead to greater accuracy or better presentation, though my notebook still seems to be just as full of important-looking scrawlings. Since text can be transferred to other applications, it is even possible to add information to databases for personal research projects, although you must remember to examine the copyright implications thoroughly first.

A catalogue or website's utility can also be graded by the amount of secondary information it offers in the form of access to camera dope sheets, programme documentation and other information. The researcher who requires access to this material is still probably best served by an actual visit to the library in question. To a company with a large collection about to spend £40,000 or more presenting its entire catalogue on the web, the inclusion of any material such as this, with low commercial value, is still unlikely. However, it can already be found on some intranet networks – online services available internally within companies like the BBC.

Should these kind of cross-departmental services ever be widely available to outside users, the world of online research will take a vast leap forward as library catalogues, copyright information, news clipping services and other sources become cross-referable. Current newspaper and magazine sites offering a selection of past articles and searchable indexes give an indication of how much impact the arrival of this 'secondary' printed information will have on academic study when archives and libraries start to offer it freely on their websites. Though the British Library and BFI collections will still be visited physically, more and more research is and will be taking place via the Internet. However, I suspect that the pleasure of handling a book will never be eliminated.

Libraries whose resources have no commercial value will probably take longer to reach the Internet as a resource because of costs and the difficulties of scanning thousands of print documents and uploading them to web pages. The same is true of the smaller film libraries representing more specialist material. Sometimes their appearance on the Internet is simply the signal that they have been absorbed by a larger, less specialised collection.

Basically, online sites can be divided into two categories: those that offer a service and those that are simply established to be provide a presence for a collection. While the former might offer an online catalogue and other services, the latter simply offers a gateway to more conventional research services. The important thing to bear in mind is that some resources will never be displayed on the Internet – researching online will never fully replace more traditional research avenues.

Conclusion – looking to the future

Commercial forces will directly effect the development of online research resources. Information and services that have commercial value may never be available for free, and users can be kept at arms length by the lack of adequate human staff or an unfriendly web presence. However, as the Internet Movie Database and the development of the British Universities Newsreel Project Database

(http://www.bufvc.ac.uk/newsreels) have shown, adequate provision for user feedback can provide important added value to a site or multimedia catalogue. The great strength of researching on the World Wide Web is that it truly helps to bring people and information together free from so many of the restrictions of past technologies and business practices.

Ironically, in what can appear to be an impersonal electronic future, e-mail has probably had the greatest effect on researchers to date, for the very reason that it facilitates person-to-person communication at lower charges and virtually free of the imperfections in world telecommunications. However, knowing that some of my business relationships will only ever be through e-mail is even stranger than the realisation that some of them would only ever be disembodied voices on the phone. This is the dichotomy involved in using information technology – it has developed both the personal and impersonal aspects of research.

As online catalogues and web services increase in number and complexity, they become as invaluable a resource as old card indexes and experienced and long-serving library staff. However, like my laptop, database software and mobile phone, while they ease the archive researcher's task, they can never be more than another tool, albeit one that provides the freedom to explore subjects and material in ever increasing depth. If you want the proof – visit my website.

Alex Cowan *is a freelance archive researcher, working mainly in television.*

ABC Television Ltd
Midlands
Saturdays and Sundays
North of England
Saturdays and Sundays

Anglia Television Ltd
East of England
Whole week

Associated Television Ltd
London
Saturdays and Sundays
Midlands
Mondays to Fridays

Border Television Ltd
The Borders
Whole week

Channel Television
Channel Islands
Whole week

Grampian Television Ltd
North-east Scotland
Whole week

Granada Television Ltd
North of England
Mondays to Fridays

Rediffusion Television Ltd
London
Mondays to Fridays

Scottish Television Ltd
Central Scotland
Whole week

Southern Television Ltd
Central Southern and
South-east England
Whole week

TWW Ltd
Wales and the West
of England
Whole week

Tyne Tees Television Ltd
North-east England
Whole week

Ulster Television
Northern Ireland
Whole week

Westward Television Ltd
South-west England
Whole week

**Independent Television
News Ltd**
Provides the main news
bulletins for all
Independent Television
areas

**Independent Television
Companies Association**
The Association acts on
behalf of all the programme
companies on certain matters
of common interest

Logos of the original ITV companies, 1955–1964
(photo courtesy of the Independent Television Commission)

Independent Television from ITV to Channel 3: Franchises, Licences and Programmes, 1955–2000

by Barrie MacDonald

In the maelstrom of market activity in the television industry over the past few years one development stands out – the consolidation of ITV – changing it from a federation of fourteen separately owned and independent regional television companies to a virtual duopoly of two major media groups, Carlton Communications and Granada. The long prophesied single ownership of ITV is now almost within sight with forthcoming legislation following soon on the heels of the Government White Paper, *A New Future for Communications*, which recognised that further moves towards greater consolidation of the network were inevitable, and would have the benefit of streamlining ITV and promoting its international standing. So at this crucial point for ITV, it seems appropriate to reflect on its origins, development and programme achievements, and look at the implications for television research.

Basic principles

Sir Robert Fraser, the first Director General of the Independent Television Authority firmly believed in 'people's television', and was certain that Independent Television (ITV), competing with the BBC could be a popular service for a mass audience but still produce varied and stimulating programmes. And, indeed, since its inception in 1955 ITV has consistently been the most popular channel, but has none the less provided a range and diversity of good quality programming.

ITV, or Channel 3 as it is now known, was designed to be a national television channel provided by a network of regional television companies. Unlike the BBC, it has always been independent of public funds, being financed through income from advertising (and latterly sponsorship), with no funding from the licence fee or government. Each company has been licenced to provide the Channel 3 service in its area, giving the channel a strong regional character as well a national brand identity.

Laying the foundations

On 30th July 1954 the *Television Act 1954*, which established commercial television in Britain, received the Royal Assent. It broke the monopoly on broadcasting held by the BBC for over thirty years, surprisingly causing more fierce debate and controversy than ever had the earlier government decision in 1926 to effectively nationalize a whole means of communication by creating a public monopoly of broadcasting. Five days after the legislation reached the Statute Book, on 4 August 1954, the Members of the Independent Television Authority (ITA) were appointed, with Sir Kenneth Clark as their first Chairman. Fifty-nine weeks later, on Thursday 22 September 1955, Independent Television began. Between those dates the foundations of policies for setting up and regulating ITV were laid, the extensive transmitter building programme begun, and the first programme companies formed and awarded contracts.

The Act had provided a framework, not a blueprint for commercial television in Britain, delegating to the ITA the responsibility for creating the policies and procedures necessary to establish the new system. Sir Kenneth Clark and Sir Robert Fraser set about designing the structure and institutions of ITV with the aim of creating a free television system to stand beside a free press. A federal structure was chosen of independently owned and separate local television stations (based on an American model) linked together for the supply of programmes, and the result was the distinctive ITV system of a national television channel with strong regional base and character. Under this system a benevolent form of cross-subsidy, whereby the larger (and richer) companies produced most of the peak-time programming for the whole network, enabled the smaller stations to provide the same high-quality and popular programming as the larger ones. Each ITV company supplied its own regional news and local interest programmes suitable for viewers within their area.

The *Television Act* had implied not only competition between commercial television and the BBC, but also within ITV, by laying on the ITA the duty 'to secure that there was adequate competition to supply programmes between a number of programme contractors' by appointing from the start two or more competing stations in each franchise area. However, this was not possible because the necessary frequencies were not available. So the Authority devised a system whereby the first three (and largest) franchise areas – London, Midlands, and the North of England – would be shared on a 5:2 division between contractors for the weekdays (Monday to Friday) and weekends (Saturday to Sunday). This would ensure a degree of competition whereby companies would be competing with each other to get their programmes on the network. So, though not as envisaged by the *Television Act*, there was competition between the weekday and weekend companies for reputation and sale of advertising time, as well as the supply of programming through the 'competitive optional network'.

Contracts 1955–64

The process of allocating the television franchises, described by *The Spectator* (4 July 1958) as 'an unprecedented exercise in state patronage', was begun on 25 August 1954 with the advertisement by the ITA of the first programme contracts. The Authority received twenty-five applications, and interviewed applicant groups between 28 September and 20 October 1954. For these first ITV franchise awards the ITA made a mosaic of appointments: Associated-Rediffusion to the London weekday contract; Associated Television (ATV) to London weekends and the Midlands weekdays; Granada Television to weekdays in the North of England; and ABC Television to the weekend service in the Midlands and North. This original weekday/weekend split now only remains in the London area, still (so far) thought too financially dominant for ownership by one company. Apart from those three, the remaining regional franchises were appointed for seven-day services, and were awarded as the transmitting stations were built and became operational. Between 1955 and 1962 further programme contractors were

appointed for Central Scotland (Scottish Television), Wales and West of England (TWW), South of England (Southern Television), North-East England (Tyne Tees Television), East of England (Anglia Television), Northern Ireland (Ulster Television), South-West England (Westward Television), The Borders (Border Television) North-East Scotland (Grampian Television), Channel Islands (Channel Television), and the last to go on air on 14 September 1962, Wales (West & North) (WWN). It had taken seven years for the ITA transmitter network to be complete and ITV to be available nation-wide.

ITV began transmission on 22 September 1955, when Associated-Rediffusion and Associated Television jointly opened the London area service with television coverage of an inaugural banquet from the Guildhall in the City of London. The new service not only introduced advertising to British television, but also brought fresh look to programmes. The first ITV companies jointly established in 1955 Independent Television News (ITN) to provide their national news service. ITN was not a contractor of the ITA, though the Authority had a duty under the *Television Act* to ensure that news was 'presented with due accuracy and impartiality'. ITN revolutionised television news, introducing personality newsreaders, usually working journalists such as Robin Day and Christopher Chataway, and plentiful actuality coverage and visuals. Current-affairs programmes flourished with *This Week* and, later on, *World in Action*. ITV introduced exciting new drama as well, whether home-produced, original plays in the *Armchair Theatre* series or drama serials such as the perennially popular *Coronation Street*, or imported American series such as *Dragnet*, *Gunsmoke* and *I Love Lucy*. More lively light entertainment was brought to viewers – live variety with celebrity performers (*Sunday Night at the London Palladium*), and American-style games and talent shows (*Take Your Pick*, *Double Your Money*, and *Opportunity Knocks*). During this period ITV also pioneered other types of programmes, including the first schools television programmes (starting with *Looking and Seeing* in 1957), and election coverage with the 1958 *Rochdale By-Election*. Despite success with audiences and critics, the *Report of the Committee on Broadcasting* (Chairman: Sir Harry Pilkington) was highly critical of the ITA and ITV, and as a result adjustments were made to the regulation of ITV by the subsequent *Television Act 1963*.

These first ITV programme contracts, whether entered into in 1955 or as late as 1962, all ended simultaneously on 29 July 1964.

Contract period 1964–68

The contracts for the second period were drafted to comply with the new legislation, consolidated into the *Television Act 1964*, which gave the ITA increased powers of programme and advertising control. Despite applications from eight new groups, all fourteen original, surviving ITV companies were re-appointed with contracts coming into force on 30 July 1964 and to end in July 1967, with a possible extension to a maximum of six years (unless an expected second ITA service had begun which would have resulted in changes to the current contracts). In fact ambitions for a second commercial channel were not to be realised for many years, until the start of Channel 4 in 1982, and even then not as envisaged by the companies.

During this period ITV continued to produce good quality popular drama (*The Power Game, The Stories of D. H. Lawrence* and *The Prisoner*), documentaries, situation comedies, and trend-setting and innovative programme formats such as *The Frost Programme* and *Ready Steady Go*. ITN's acclaimed and popular *News at Ten* bulletin began in 1967.

All ITV contracts were later extended by one year until the end of July 1968.

Contract period 1968–81

Advertisements inviting applications for fifteen regional franchises for the third contract period beginning in July 1968 (initially for a six-year period until 1974) had appeared in the press on 28 February 1967. There was one more franchise area than in the previous period, due to the Authority's decision to divide the former North of England ITV region into two separate seven-day contracts for Lancashire and Yorkshire. The ITA

also decided to extend the London weekend contract (now from Friday evening to Sunday), and make the Midlands a seven-day contract (as well as the two covering the North). London therefore remained the only station served by two companies. By the closing day of 15 April 1967, thirty-six different applications had been received from the fourteen then-existing companies and a further sixteen new companies, and with particular interest in the new Yorkshire franchise (ten applications). All applicants were interviewed, even in cases where the incumbent company was the only applicant, because it provided opportunity for the appraisal of their past performance as well as future intentions. Decisions were based on written applications and the interviews. The original companies for the North of Scotland, Central Scotland, the Borders, North-East England, Northern Ireland, South of England, South-West England, and the Channel Islands were re-appointed with new contracts. Changes were made in Wales with Harlech Television (HTV) replacing TWW, and in London with the appointment of London Weekend Television for the weekends and Thames Television (a merger enforced by the ITA of Rediffusion and ABC Television) for weekdays. The Midlands seven-day service went to ATV, and in the two halves of the former North of England, Granada was awarded Lancashire and the neighbouring franchise area to a new company, Yorkshire Television. TWW assigned the last months of their contract to HTV, who took over the Wales service early from 4 March, otherwise all contracts began in July 1968.

Colour came to ITV in 1969, and it was used increasingly effectively in a succession of fine drama series throughout this period, in particular with *Upstairs Downstairs, The Brontes of Haworth, Edward the Seventh, Jesus of Nazareth, Edward and Mrs Simpson*, and *Brideshead Revisited*. There were also strong documentaries and factual series: *The Life and Times of Lord Mountbatten, The World at War, Disappearing World, Johnny Go Home* and *Kitty – Return from Auschwitz*.

During this period the ITA was renamed the Independent Broadcasting Authority (IBA) to reflect new responsibilities for establishing and regulating commercial radio laid on it by the *Sound*

Broadcasting Act 1972. The 1968 contracts, originally intended to last six years, were extended by stages to 31 December 1981.

Contract period 1982–92

The award of the ITV contracts due to start on 1 January 1982 was the culmination of a two-year process by the IBA, which included a national research survey on attitudes to ITV, widespread consultation with over 250 public meetings, and the screening of promotional films inviting written comments from the viewers. On 24 January 1980 the IBA announced the particulars of the new contracts, which included of two more dual regions (in the Midlands and the South of England) along the lines of the Wales and West of England region. Also, for the first time there was the possibility of a national breakfast-time service (previously the morning schedules were kept for trade transmissions and schools programmes). By the closing date of 9 May, 43 applications had been received for the 16 franchises (though one was withdrawn later), including eight for the breakfast contract. Throughout the summer, the final public meetings were held across the country to gauge public opinion on both the existing companies' past performance and the rival groups' applications. The interviews of the 42 applicant groups were held between 22 October and 11 December, followed by intensive discussions by the Members of the Authority of each group's company structure, management, programme plans, financial and technical arrangements and industrial relations policy. The decisions reached, announced by IBA Chairman, Lady Plowden, on Sunday 28 December 1980, included offering contracts to two new companies: the South and South East of England to TVS (Television South) replacing Southern Television; and South-West England to TSW (Television South West) supplanting the troubled Westward Television. The contracts for the East and West Midlands dual region (ATV), Yorkshire (Yorkshire Television), and North-East England (Tyne Tees Television) were offered to the incumbents subject to conditions regarding their future structure and ownership. Subsequently, ATV restructured and relocated its studios entirely within the region and renamed the

company Central Independent Television. All the others were re-appointed.

The Authority also awarded the first national breakfast-time television contract to TV-am. A dazzling group of well-known and experienced broadcasters, headed by Peter Jay and David Frost, persuaded the IBA of the viability of breakfast television with their impressive 'mission to explain' philosophy. However, a troubled lead-up to their on-air date of 1 February 1983 was followed by an even more troubles and crises before a change of style, presenters and management eventually brought audience popularity, financial success though not always critical approval.

ITV continued in the 1980s to produce quality drama, notably such ambitious literary adaptations as Paul Scott's *The Jewel in the Crown* and J. B. Priestley's *Lost Empires*, as well as original drama series developed for television – *Minder*, *Rumpole of the Bailey*, *Reilly – Ace of Spies*, and *Widows*, amongst others. A few investigative current affairs or documentary programmes such as *Death of a Princess* and, most notably *Death on the Rock* (*This Week*) brought the IBA and the ITV companies into conflict with the Government. The final years of the contract period brought to the screen the enormously successful drama series of *Inspector Morse*, *Poirot*, *The Ruth Rendell Mysteries* and *The Darling Buds of May*.

The contracts, due originally to end on 31 December 1989, were extended under the terms of the *Broadcasting Act 1987* to 31 December 1992, to allow time for the introduction of radical changes to the system by new legislation.

Licence period 1993–2002

The *Broadcasting Act 1990* changed the structure of broadcasting in Britain, in particular by introducing a new licensing and regulatory regime for commercial television and radio services. The IBA, which had established, transmitted and regulated ITV, Channel 4, Independent Local Radio and the satellite services, was (together with the Cable Authority) abolished and replaced by three successor bodies: the Independent Television Commission (ITC) to licence and regulate all commercial television whether terrestrial, cable or satellite; the Radio Authority for all commercial radio; and National Transcommunications Ltd (*NTL*) to provide transmission services.

One of the first tasks of the ITC on assuming its full statutory powers on 1 January 1991 was to begin the process of allocating the new licences for the ITV service on Channel 3 to begin in 1993. The Act replaced the previous contract-based system with a new licensing system for certain television and radio licences, whereby licences are awarded by competitive tender to the applicant who submits the highest bid after quality threshold and sustainability tests had been passed. Most importantly licensees have to comply with the positive programme requirements for original material, European origin programmes, independent productions, and diversity through mandatory programme strands. On 15 February 1991 the ITC published the terms and conditions for the breakfast-time and regional television licences. By the closing date of 15th May, three months later, the ITC had received 40 qualifying applications in all, 37 for the 15 regional licences and three for the breakfast-time service. The ITC's assessment of the applications covered their proposals, as well as the summarised comments sent in by over 2,200 members of the public and external companies and organisations. The Commission's decisions, announced on 16 October 1991, included the replacement of four ITV companies by new groups: Thames Television in London by Carlton Television; TSW by Westcountry Television in South-West England; TVS by Meridian Broadcasting in the South of England; and TV-am by Sunrise Television (later renamed GMTV) for the breakfast-time service. All ITV contractors in the other regions were re-appointed and awarded Channel 3 licences. The licences took effect from 1 January 1993, and were to last for a ten-year period (until 31 December 2002) in the first instance though renewal for a further ten years was possible after six years from 1 January 1999. By then eight ITV companies had agreed to new terms set by the ITC and renewed their licences, with the remaining licensees making formal expression of interest by the end of 2000.

By the mid-nineties the digital revolution was upon us. The *Broadcasting Act 1996* provided a legislative framework for allocating use of the spectrum, as well as the licensing and regulation of the transmission and broadcasting of digital terrestrial television (DTT) by the ITC (and digital radio by the Radio Authority). DTT is licenced

TABLE 1:   TAKEOVERS IN ITV, 1992–2000

Year	Original licensee	Region	*New parent company
1992	Tyne Tees Television	North-East England	Yorkshire Television
1994	Central Television	East & West Midlands	Carlton
	Anglia Television	East of England	MAI (*later* United News & Media)
	London Weekend Television	London (Weekends)	Granada
1996	Westcountry Television	South-West England	Carlton
1997	Grampian Television	North of Scotland	Scottish Television
	Yorkshire Tyne Tees	Yorkshire	Granada
	HTV	Wales & West of England	United News & Media
2000	Border Television	Borders	Capital Radio
	Anglia Television	East of England	Granada
	Meridian Broadcasting	South/ South East England	Granada
	HTV	Wales & West of England	Carlton

Note: * Parent or holding company as at 31st December 2000

under a two-tier structure whereby the carriage and delivery system – the multiplex – is licenced separately from the programme services it carries. Two of the six multiplexes were reserved by the Government for the existing broadcasters (ITV, BBC, Channel 4, public teletext, etc.). The four remaining were awarded by the ITC in 1997 – Multiplexes B, C and D to British Digital Broadcasting (BDB) (jointly owned by Carlton and Granada) and Multiplex A to S4C Digital Networks. BDB changed name to ONdigital and launched its DTT service on 15 November 1998.

Pressure from the media industry in the nineties resulted in a gradual relaxation of the ownership rules, eventually empowered by the *Broadcasting Act 1996*. ITV consolidation began with the agreed takeover of Tyne Tees Television by its larger ITV neighbour Yorkshire Television in 1992, and ended the decade as a virtual duopoly of ownership by Carlton and Granada. Currently Carlton Communications owns Carlton Television, Central Television, Westcountry Television, HTV, 50% of ONdigital, 25% GMTV and 20% ITN. Granada owns Granada Television, LWT, Yorkshire-Tyne Tees Television, Anglia Television, Meridian Broadcasting, 50% of ONdigital, 20% GMTV, and 20% ITN (See Table 1 on page 25).

Competition for viewers in the new multi-channel environment and a declining audience share led ITV (in common with other terrestrial channels) to seek popular and proven programmes. Strong, good-quality drama, such as *Prime Suspect*, *A Touch of Frost* and *Cracker,* as well as the documentaries *Hillsborough* and *The Murder of Stephen Lawrence,* succeeded with audiences and critics. The television phenomenon at the end of the decade, however, has to be *Who Wants to Be a Millionaire?*

Film libraries and archives – where are they now?

As can be seen from this article ITV has changed considerably over the past forty-five years. Though in nine of the fifteen ITV/Channel 3 areas the original contractor is still the current licensee, many of them now have been acquired by the major players – Carlton and Granada. Two of the companies have shown remarkable longevity and continuity: Granada Television (the longest extant ITV company) and Scottish Television, on air respectively since 1956 and 1957. However, in other areas there has been a succession of programme companies, with some a new appointment in each of the main contract rounds. A point of concern is those companies not re-appointed and the fate of their valuable film libraries and archives.

It is only possible to discuss the fate of the outgoing companies in general terms. Most straightforwardly the newly appointed company will negotiate with its predecessor to take over its studios and assets, also effecting a transfer of some of the staff, thereby ensuring a continuity of service while still introducing new ideas and programmes. Broadly speaking this is what happened when HTV was awarded the contract for Wales and West of England in 1968 and bought the Cardiff and Bristol studios of its predecessor TWW (then a condition of the contract), TSW acquired the Plymouth studios of Westward Television in 1981, and TVS bought the Southern Television studios in Southampton 1981 (later to sell them on to its successor in 1992, Meridian Broadcasting). Thames Television, formed from a merger of Rediffusion and ABC Television had inherited its parent companies' studios in London and Teddington in 1968. However, this has not always the case as in the example of Westcountry Television in 1992, which developed new premises rather than take the Plymouth city centre studios at Derry's Cross of its predecessor TSW.

So much for bricks and mortar, but what of the film/videotape libraries and archives representing the programme output of these companies. Again, most simply the new company acquires the film/videotape library and rights to the programmes of its predecessor. However, because of the residual value of peak-time television programmes for repeat or resale for years to come (long after original transmission and after the company ceased to be an ITV contractor) it is quite often only the local news and magazine output. HTV, in Wales, took on the local newsfilm and programme recordings, with the scripts and programme documentation of its predecessor TWW. TSW acquired the local programme output of Westward Television. Central Television held on to the local newsfilm and some other programme material of ATV, but the valuable drama and light entertainment programmes were retained for resale by ITC Entertainment (the former production company for ATV and subsidiary of its parent company ACC), and later sold to Polygram and then on to Carlton International. To continue to market its valuable network programmes after the contract has ended until they have no further sales potential the outgoing ITV contractor will form a sales company. This was the case with Southern Television selling its programmes through Southern Pictures and Associated Rediffusion programmes through Global Television. Programme libraries are now very sought after because of the demand from a huge number of channels and outlets in the UK and abroad requiring television repeats, so they are valuable assets to be sold or acquired. The considerable film libraries of ABC Television and ITC Entertainment have been sold on several times, and are now contained (and exploited) within large commercial film and television libraries – Canal+ UK and Carlton International respectively.

Regrettably, the written archives often become separated from the film/vt library. In the case of TV-am, the national breakfast-time television contractor from 1983 to 1992, the film/vt material was acquired by a commercial film library (now Moving Image) but the written archives remained with the company that acquired TV-am's company registration (Capital Corporation). Following the changes in the ITV licences in 1993 there was a dispersal of film/vt libraries, often to commercial film libraries. The consolidation in ITV of major media groups acquiring the smaller regional companies is also posing a challenge to the preservation of television output. However, it may also be an opportunity for the large players such as Granada to co-ordinate archive policies and standardise procedures across their licensees.

The commercial value of some of the output of ITV over the past forty years, and the frenzied activity to acquire and commercially exploit this material, has often obscured the tremendous cultural and social value of this inheritance. Thankfully, much of ITV output over the years has been preserved by the British Film Institute's National Film and Television Archive at Berkhamsted, either through the acquisition of selected programmes, funded by the companies through the ITV Association, or since 1985 through an off-air recording arrangement. Also many of the regional ITV companies enter into arrangements for the preservation of local news material by the regional film archive within their area. An example of this is Granada Television local news material being deposited with the North West Film Archive. Similar arrangements for the preservation of television material exist with the Wales Film & Television Archive, the Scottish Film Archive, and the Northern Film & Television Archive. However, there is no doubt that some valuable and unique material, whether programmes or their documentation, has been lost. An attempt to remedy this was made by the IBA in 1981, through introducing an archive clause into the 1982–92 ITV contracts, requiring the companies to accumulate and preserve recordings of their programmes and the associated documentation, and make suitable arrangements for their future retention at the end the contract period. This provision for company archives was regrettably not retained in the Channel 3 licences for 1993–2002. However, the *Broadcasting Act 1990* did make it a statutory requirement for the Channel 3 and Channel 5 licensees to contribute to the costs of a national television archive, and laid responsibility for nominating the body for maintaining a national television archive on the Independent Television Commission. The ITC nominated the National Film and Television Archive, and a monitoring group representing the ITV companies supervises the operation of the arrangements.

The preservation of television output and its archives is of crucial importance. It is to be hoped that the realisation of the commercial value of programme libraries, as well as the recognition of the contribution of television to the social, political and cultural life of the country, will ensure the preservation of the best of British television for future generations.

TABLE 2:   CHRONOLOGY OF ITV COMPANIES, 1955–2000

On-air	Off-air	Company	Region and contract
Contract periods, 1955–64, and 1964–8			
22.9.55	29.7.68	Associated-Rediffusion	London (Weekday)
24.9.55	28.7.68	Associated Television (ATV)	London (Weekend)
17.2.56	31.12.81	# Associated Television (ATV)	Midlands (Weekday)
18.2.56	28.7.68	ABC Television	Midlands (Weekend)
3.5.56		# Granada Television	North of England (Weekday)
5.5.56	28.7.68	ABC Television	North of England (Weekend)
31.8.57		Scottish Television	Central Scotland
14.1.58	3.3.68	TWW	South Wales and West of England
30.8.58	31.12.81	Southern Television	South of England
15.1.59		Tyne Tees Television	North East England
27.10.59		Anglia Television	East of England
31.10.59		Ulster Television	Northern Ireland
29.4.61	11.8.81	Westward Television	South-West England
1.9.61		Border Television	The Borders
30.9.61		Grampian Television	North of Scotland
1.9.62		Channel Television	Channel Islands
14.9.62	26.1.64	* Wales (West & North) Television	West & North Wales
Contract period, 1968–81: new ITV contractors appointed			
4.3.68		HTV	Wales & West of England
29.7.68		Yorkshire Television	Yorkshire
30.7.68	31.12.92	Thames Television	London (Weekday)
2.8.68		London Weekend Television	London (Weekend)
Contract period, 1981–92: new ITV contractors appointed			
12.8.81	31.12.92	TSW – Television South West	South-West England
1.1.82	31.12.92	TVS – Television South	South & South-East England
1.1.82		+ Central Television	East & West Midlands
1.2.83	31.12.92	TV-am	National Breakfast-time
Contract period, 1993–2002: new Channel 3 licencees appointed			
1.1.93		Carlton Television	London (Weekday)
1.1.93		GMTV	National Breakfast-time
1.1.93		Meridian Broadcasting	South & South-East England
1.1.93		Westcountry Television	South-West England

Note: # ATV and Granada became seven-day contractors in 1968.
         * Wales (West & North) Television and its franchise area became absorbed by TWW
         + ATV restructured as Central Independent Television

TABLE 3: ITV/CHANNEL 3 REGIONS

ITV/C3 Region	Company	On-air	Off-air
Channel Islands	Channel Television	1.9.62	
England			
The Borders	Border Television	1.9.61	
East of England	Anglia Television	27.10.59	
London (Weekday)	Associated Rediffusion	22.9.59	29.7.68
	Thames Television	30.7.68	31.12.92
	Carlton Television	1.1.93	
London (Weekend)	Associated Television (ATV)	24.9.55	28.7.68
	London Weekend Television	2.8.68	
Midlands	Associated Television (ATV)		
(later East & West	(Weekdays)	17.2.56	29.7.68
Midlands)	ABC Television (Weekends)	18.2.56	28.7.68
	Associated Television (ATV)	30.7.68	31.12.81
	Central Television	1.1.82	
North-East England	Tyne Tees Television	15.1.59	
North of England	Granada Television (Weekdays)	3.5.56	29.7.68
	ABC Television (Weekends)	5.5.56	28.7.68
North-West England	Granada Television	30.7.68	
South of England	Southern Television	30.8.58	31.12.81
(later South & South-	TVS – Television South	1.1.82	31.12.92
East England	Meridian Broadcasting	1.1.93	
South-West England	Westward Television	29.4.61	11.8.81
	TSW – Television South West	12.8.81	31.12.92
	Westcountry Television	1.1.93	
Yorkshire	Yorkshire Television	29.7.68	
Northern Ireland	Ulster Television	13.10.59	
Scotland			
Central Scotland	Scottish Television	31.8.57	
North of Scotland	Grampian Television	30.9.61	
Wales			
Wales & West of England	TWW	14.1.58	3.3.68
	HTV	4.3.68	
West & North Wales	Wales (West & North) Television	14.9.62	26.1.64

TABLE 4:   FILM LIBRARIES AND ARCHIVES OF ITV

List of the current holders of the film/vt and written archives of the ITV companies.

For companies still in existence the actual programmes (on film or videotape) are generally held by the film/tape Library of the company. The programme documentation is normally held by the archives (if they have them), otherwise the Film/Tape Library, Business Affairs or Company Secretary may be able to give advice on the location of the programme records. Programme Sales and Extract (Clip) Sales are often not handled by the Film/Tape Library itself, but by a separate sales function.

ITV REGULATOR		WRITTEN ARCHIVES
ITA/IBA/ITC (1954–)		I.T.C. Tel: 020 7306 7766 Contact: Records Manager

ITV COMPANY	FILM/VT ARCHIVES	WRITTEN ARCHIVES
ABC Television (1956–68)	Canal+ Image UK, Tel: 01753 631111 Contact: John Herron	Pearson Television Tel: 020 7691 6000 Contact: The Archivist
ATV (Associated Television) (1955–68)	Carlton Broadcasting - Central Region, Tel: 01159 863322 Contact: Film Library Note: ATV regional programmes only Carlton International, Tel: 020 7612 7353 Contact: Sales Division Note: ATV network and ITC Entertainment	Carlton Broadcasting – Central Region, Tel: 01159 863322 Contact: Film Library
Associated Rediffusion Television (1955–68)	Archbuild Ltd Tel: 020 7424 0450 Contact: David Osterley Note: Rediffusion programmes are preserved in the NFTVA	I.T.C. Tel: 020 7306 7763 Contact: The Library
Anglia Television (1959–)	Anglia Television, Tel: 01603 752282 Contact: Film Library/Clip Sales	Anglia Television Tel: 01603 756850 Contact: Business Affairs

TABLE 4:   FILM LIBRARIES AND ARCHIVES OF ITV (Continued)

ITV COMPANY	FILM/VT ARCHIVES	WRITTEN ARCHIVES
Border Television (1961–)	Border Television, Tel: 01228 525101 Contact: News and Archive Library Note: 2' VT transferred to the NFTVA/BFI; local programmes also in Northern Film & Television Archive	Border Television Tel: 01228 525101 Contact: News and Archive Library Note: Written records scarce for older programmes
Carlton Television (1992–)	*see* Carlton Broadcasting – Central Region	*see* Carlton Broadcasting Central Region
Central Television (1982–)	Carlton Broadcasting - Central Region, Tel: 01159 863322 Contact: Film Library Note: Central programmes since 1982, and ATV local programmes 1955–81	Carlton Broadcasting - Central Region, Tel: 01159 863322 Contact: Film Library
Channel Television (1962–)	Channel Television, Tel: 01534 816816	Channel Television, Tel: 01534 816816
GMTV (1992–)	GMTV Ltd, Tel: 020 7827 7361/2/3 Contact: Library Sales	GMTV Ltd, Tel: 020 7827 7361/2/3 Contact: Library Sales
Grampian Television (1961–)	Grampian Television, Tel: 01224 846846 Contact: TV Library	Grampian Television, Tel: 01224 846846
Granada Television (1956–).	Granada Television, Tel: 0161 827 2309 Contact: Library Services Manager, Manchester Granada Television, Tel: 0161 827 2332 Contact: Clip Sales	Granada Television, Tel: 0161 827 2981 Contact: Archivist

TABLE 4:   FILM LIBRARIES AND ARCHIVES OF ITV (Continued)

ITV COMPANY	FILM/VT ARCHIVES	WRITTEN ARCHIVES
HTV (1968–)	HTV Wales, Tel: 029 2059 0177/731 Contact: Film Library Note: HTV also holds material for the previous ITV companies for Wales: TWW; Wales (West & North) Television	HTV Wales, Tel: 029 2059 0177/731 Note: Programme records held in relevant department
ITC Entertainment	*see* ATV	*see* ATV
ITN (1955–)	ITN, Television News Archive, Tel: 020 7430 4480 Contact: Archive Manager	ITN, Television News Archive, Tel: 020 7430 4480 Contact: Archive Manager
LWT (1968–)	London Weekend Television Tel: 020 7578 4420 Contact: Film/VT Archivist London Weekend Television, Tel: 020 7261 3309 Contact: Manager, Clip Sales	London Weekend Television Tel: 0161 827 2044 Contact: Head of Library Service, Granada Media
Meridian Broadcasting (1993–)	Meridian Broadcasting Tel: 023 8071 2052 Contact: News Librarian	Meridian Broadcasting Tel: 023 8022 2555 Contact: News Librarian
Scottish Television (1957–)	Scottish Media Group plc, Tel: 0141 300 3000 Contact: Film & VT Library Note: Grampian news now held, some earlier STV material deposited with the Scottish Film Archive	Scottish Media Group plc, Tel: 0141 300 3000 Note: No central written archive (records held departmentally) but some available through the the Film & VT Library
Southern Television (1958–1981)	Meridian Broadcasting, Tel: 023 8071 2052 Contact: News Librarian Note: Holds Southern news/ regional magazine programmes 1970–1981.	British Film Institute, Tel: 020 7255 1444 Contact: Manager, Special Materials Note: Southern archives deposited with BFI.

TABLE 4:   FILM LIBRARIES AND ARCHIVES OF ITV (Continued)

ITV COMPANY	FILM/VT ARCHIVES	WRITTEN ARCHIVES
TSW – Television South West (1981–1992)	TSW Film & Television Archive for the South West, Tel: 01752 202650 Contact: Archive Manager	TSW Film & Television Archive for the South West Tel: 01752 202650 Contact: Archive Manager
TV-am (1983–1992)	Moving Image, Tel: 020 7580 3300 Note: Moving Image acquired TV-am film/vt material and some records	Capital Corporation, Tel: 020 7317 6889 Contact: Company Secretary Note: Capital acquired the TV-am company.
TVS – Television South (1982–92)	Meridian Broadcasting Tel: 023 8071 2052 Contact: News Librarian Note: Meridian holds some TVS regional programmes 1982–1992: rights for others belong to Fox Family Channel who own TVS Network shows	Meridian Broadcasting Tel: 02380 712052 Contact: News Librarian
TWW (1958–68)	*see* HTV	*see* HTV
Thames Television (1968–92)	Pearson Television, Tel: 020 7691 6732 Contact: PTI Film Library Sales	Pearson Television, Tel: 020 7691 6838 Contact: The Archivist
Tyne Tees Television (1959–)	Tyne Tees Television Tel: 0191 261 0181 Contact: Film/Tape Library & Clip Sales	Tyne Tees Television Tel: 0191 261 0181 Contact: Film/Tape Library & Clip Sales
Ulster Television (1959–)	Ulster Television Tel: 028 9032 8122 Contact: Archives Supervisor	Ulster Television Tel: 028 9032 8122
Wales (West & North) (1962–1964)	*see* HTV	*see* HTV
Westcountry Television (1992–)	Carlton Broadcasting Tel: 01752 333333 Contact: Lydia North	Carlton Broadcasting Tel: 01752 333333 Contact: Lydia North

TABLE 4:   FILM LIBRARIES AND ARCHIVES OF ITV (Continued)

ITV COMPANY	FILM/VT ARCHIVES	WRITTEN ARCHIVES
Westward Television (1961–1981)	*see* TSW Archive	*see* TSW Archive
Yorkshire Television (1968–)	Yorkshire Television Tel: 0113 243 8283 Contact: Library Services Manager, Leeds Tel: 0113 243 8052 Contact: Manager, Clip Sales	Yorkshire Television Tel: 0113 243 8283 Contact: Library Services Manager, Leeds

Further reading

Briggs, Asa, and Spicer, Joanna. *The Franchise Affair: Creating Fortunes and Failures in Independent Television.* London: Century Hutchinson, 1986.

Davidson, Andrew. *Under the Hammer: the Inside Story of the ITV Franchise Battle.* London: Heinemann, 1992.

Independent Television in Britain. London: Macmillan, 1982–98. 5 vols. Vol 1: *Origin and Foundation*, 1946–62, by Bernard Sendall; Vol 2: *Expansion and Change*, 1958–68, by Bernard Sendall; Vol 3: *Politics and Control*, 1968–80, by Jeremy Potter; Vol 4: *Companies and Programmes*, 1968–82, by Jeremy Potter; Vol 5: *ITV and IBA, 1981–92, the Old Relationship Changes*, by Paul Bonner with Lesley Aston.

Barrie MacDonald *has been the Librarian of the Independent Television Commission, and its predecessor the Independent Broadcasting Authority, since 1979. He is the co-author of* Keyguide to Information Sources in Media Ethics *(London: Mansell, 1998), author of* Broadcasting in the United Kingdom: a Guide to Information Sources *(London: Mansell, revised 2nd edition, 1994), and various articles and bibliographies on the literature of broadcasting.*

Establishing a Regional Media Archive:
the Media Archive for Central England (MACE)

by James Patterson

This is a story without a happy ending. In fact this is a story without an ending at all yet, because as I write it we are still only half way through....

Before we start I ought to make it clear that the observations that follow are personal. They do not represent the official position of the MACE, its Board of Trustees or anyone else. They are my version of the history of the project to date and my comments on its progress. And they are not a prescription for establishing a regional film/media archive. Indeed, given that the Media Archive for Central England, once established, completes the network of public sector regional moving image archives in England, there should be no need for anyone to go through the process again.

Process implies a series of steps that, if taken, will give the desired end result. As things stand at the time of writing, MACE is in the middle of a series of steps which we hope will end in the establishment of a permanent moving image archive for the Midlands. But these steps are less a process than an unsteady progress along the road to our final destination.

The journey for MACE has been a long one. But before we begin to look back, we should first look forward. What is a public sector regional moving image archive? What are we trying to achieve here?

In 1999 the Film Archive Forum, the body which represents the public sector moving image archives in the UK, published 'Moving History', a statement of principles. In it the Forum defines these archives as 'repositories for the custody and preservation of, and access to, the history of our times as recorded on film, videotape and other moving image formats. Such archives contain works made by amateur and professional producers for cinema, television and other purposes. These archives encompass the history and culture of the moving image media and respect the integrity of the works above any commercial or short-term exploitation. These institutions operate for the public good on a 'not for profit' basis.'

The fundamental responsibility of a public sector archive therefore, is to select, collect, preserve and document our moving image culture in order to make it publicly accessible. Underpinning this work is a set of archival ethics which ensure the professionalism of the archivists and safeguard the material itself. So within a public sector archive the material is protected both in terms of its physical well-being and in terms of the integrity of the work and the rights of its author.

These tenets translate into particular ways of working which mean that the master physical copy will not be exposed to the possibility of damage through use but will be copied in order to make it accessible. Neither will ownership or rights be abused in pursuit of short-term commercial gain.

It comes as no surprise therefore to find that MACE's mission statement reads 'to enrich the life and experience of the Midlands by collecting and preserving its moving image culture and making it widely accessible'.

But to be able to undertake this work MACE needs staff, facilities and revenue. MACE is fortunate in that there are a variety of models within the existing English regional public-sector moving image archives which can be emulated to achieve an appropriate balance for the two regions it has to serve.

Most, though not all, of the English regional moving image archives are supported by a mixed basket of funding and 'in kind' support which comes from the national centre (BFI via Regional Arts Board – from this year Film Council via regional film agency), from local Authorities and from higher education.

MACE's task has been, and continues to be, to put together such a basket of support in order to realise the establishment of the archive.

The regional moving image archives in England, though sharing the same basic principles and ethical position, are differently constituted and funded, and have a wide variety of development histories. There is no single pattern to the way they deliver benefit to their regions. Each must respond to regional priorities and imperatives, and each region is different.

MACE aims to develop a single centre for the storage and conservation of its archival collections and from this centre develop services across the East and West Midlands through a series of partnerships.

The location of the main archival facility is more a political than a practical issue. MACE is being established to provide moving image archive services to both the East Midlands and to the West Midlands. Apart from the challenges of serving such a geographically large area it is made up of two distinct political regions. Each region has a set of structures which mirror each other but which tend to compete rather than to work together. After a considerable time it is now accepted that what is important is the service that is provided for each region rather than the location from which the main archival work is carried out.

Ideally MACE seeks to establish its main facility in a location which is easily accessible to users and staff by both road and public transport. Equally there are certain benefits which would accrue from being close to other established media organisations. For these reasons Nottingham of all the places in the East and West Midlands seems to hold the most obvious advantages at present. The city already has a well-established media cluster as well as being home to both the BBC and Carlton.

In such a large region MACE cannot hope to develop its services without engaging in a variety of partnerships. MACE has ambition to develop access points to its catalogues, its collections and to its expertise through local archives, museums and libraries. By so doing we hope that the ability to engage with moving image culture and history will become as straightforward as accessing other forms of culture and history through libraries, museums and archives.

Similarly MACE will seek to develop relationships with the education community at all levels to explore the research use of the collections and to ensure that they are used in innovative ways within the curriculum across the whole spectrum of subjects.

Beyond the purely traditional archive role of developing its own collections, MACE also perceives its role as acting as a source of advice and advocacy in the regions and acting as an access conduit to other collections.

Even at this development stage MACE is already engaged with the Black and Ethnic Minority Experience in Wolverhampton and has contributed to educational events with schools in Nottingham using archival football film as a way into the history curriculum.

Though clearly our core function and responsibility is to concern ourselves with the moving image culture and history of the East and West Midlands, there is a secondary role in working with other collections national, regional and within the region to increase their accessibility across the region.

Beyond the core activity of archiving, therefore, MACE aspires to be a proactive force for moving image activity in the East and West Midlands.

So much for our aspirations. How have we reached the level we are at now? Where are we now? And where next in the development plan?

Over the years there have been a number projects which have done much to further the cause of film preservation within the Midlands. The Lincolnshire and Humberside Film Archive, the Staffordshire Film Archive and the Northamptonshire Film Archive Trust and the Leicester Film Archive have been established for a number of years and have made a huge contribution to the survival of regional film materials.

None of these, or other collections, however, has the strategic aim of developing into a public sector regional moving image archive to cover the whole of the East and West Midlands.

Regional film archives in England had developed independently in East Anglia, the North West and Wessex (based in the Hampshire Record Office) during the 1970s and 1980s. Recognising their value, the British Film Institute developed a policy that encouraged the development of further independent regional film archives. The hope was that ultimately a complete network would develop to provide regional film archive services across the entire UK.

In 1993, the Film Archive Forum, working with the BFI, arranged a series of three public meetings in areas still without regional film archives and invited significant players in each region to come together to discuss the possibility of developing such an archive. From these initial discussions there emerged the impetus to create the TSW Film and Television Archive for the South West, and the Yorkshire Film Archive, both now established and full members of the Film Archive Forum.

The geographical area stretching from the Welsh border in the west to the Lincolnshire coast in the east remained one of the most significant areas of the UK without an organisation dedicated to the collection, preservation, documentation and accessibility of its moving image culture.

The Midlands meeting, held that year in Wolverhampton, led to a number of follow-up meetings hosted by Central Television at which the Midlands Film Archive project began to take some shape.

Perhaps inevitably, the initial thrust was Birmingham-led and Birmingham-focussed. Moves were being made within the city in the early 1990s to establish a media centre encompassing all the elements of film activity, production, exhibition, archive and education. The fledgling Midlands film archive project was written into this development. However, though considerable development work was undertaken leading to a major bid to the Arts Council Lottery, this ambitious plan never reached fruition and the archive was left once again trying to develop on its own.

The move of Central Television from its large premises on Broad Street in Birmingham to smaller, more modern premises round the corner in Gas Street gave the archive project its next developmental push.

The Gas Street premises were not sufficiently large to house the library and archives of ATV and Central TV and options were being considered for their future.

An ambitious plan was conceived to run the library alongside a Midlands Film Archive with a level of cross-subsidisation. A listed industrial structure, the Retort Building, next door to Central Television's new offices in Gas Street, was identified as a potential home for the archive and library and considerable work was undertaken by Central TV to incorporate what at this time became the Media Archive for Central England Trust. Consultants were engaged by Central to draw up a bid to the Heritage Lottery for funds to convert the Retort Building into suitable premises for the Library and Archive. In this form the bid was submitted to the Heritage Lottery.

Central Television's own commercial imperatives finally overtook this bid during the period in which the Heritage Lottery was making its assessment. The broadcast libraries were moved by new owners, Carlton TV, to Nottingham. The bid to the Heritage Lottery Fund was withdrawn for the time being. HLF was appraised of the probability of a bid from MACE at a later stage. Though there had been misgivings in some quarters about how MACE would have operated as an independent preservation archive so closely related to the commercial activity of the Carlton libraries, there was considerable disappointment at the loss of this opportunity to establish the archive. However, MACE was now formally constituted, had a board of trustees and the development activity that had been undertaken gave the project a new impetus.

As an aside it is interesting to note that in my first round of meetings across the region after taking up the post of MACE director there was still considerable suspicion about the project which stemmed from its very close association with Carlton at that time. The county archive sector especially had developed the perception that MACE would be a commercial film library associated with the broadcasters.

The choice of the title Media Archive rather than film archive also stems from this time. It was born out of a proposal that the archive should also house a considerable collection of still photographs offered to the organisation by a large Midlands based newspaper group.

After discussion it was felt that, whereas there was no professional provision for film archiving in the region, there were existing photographic archives and that the establishment of another might undermine the development of the film archive. The proposal to incorporate the still photographs was shelved at this time but the name remained. Though 'Film and Video Archive', or 'Film and Television Archive' would convey an easier understanding of our primary purpose, Media Archive is a title which will give us considerable flexibility to respond as we move into the 21st Century and as moving image technologies move on and the boundaries between one form and another become increasingly blurred.

But back to the history...

After the collapse of the Retort Building bid development funding from the BFI and the Regional Arts Boards was provided for the project and the board decided that the best use of these limited funds was to pay consultants to explore the potential in the regions East and West for a new supporting partnership for the Archive.

Discussions were held with potential consortia in cities across the East and West Midlands and an open day held for potential partners at the Carlton Studios in Nottingham.

From this process, two serious expressions of interest emerged. One involved the Central Library in Birmingham in partnership with the University of Birmingham and the University of Central England. The other came from a consortium made up of Leicester City Library, Leicestershire Archives, De Montfort University and the Phoenix Arts Centre in Leicester.

In each case their interest was limited to working in their own region, East or West.

The board felt at the time, and still do, that there needed to be a single consolidated archival facility to provide the expertise and facilities for both regions and to co-ordinate the development of services across the region as described earlier.

In response to the presentations made by the two consortia, therefore, the Trust developed a model whereby the archive facility could be developed wherever the best opportunity for support could be established. In conjunction with each of the main bidding consortia, MACE would additionally develop principal access points in Leicester and Birmingham.

With this model as a guide to the way forward, and with further development support from the

BFI and the regional arts boards, the Trust moved to appoint a full-time director to develop the project further. A period of nearly a year elapsed from the time the policy was developed to my arrival in post as Director of the MACE project. During that time changes both in personnel and in broader plans within the cities of Birmingham and Leicester had taken place. This required that I begin again the development of relationships between the MACE project and potential partners.

Our attempts to establish a regional moving image archive for the Midlands have coincided with a number of political developments that have had a considerable bearing on strategy in these early months.

The establishment of regional government offices, regional development agencies and their associated cultural consortia, has given rise to each region developing a cultural strategy. Ensuring that the development of a moving image archive was written into the cultural strategies became a priority. At a national level, the establishment of the Film Council as the new body responsible for film culture and education was changing the landscape of inter- and intra-regional media relationships. The development of an awareness and understanding of the MACE project within the regional media sectors also became a priority.

The publication, in November 2000, of the Film Council's regional strategy document 'Film in England' marked a major step forward for the regional moving image archives in England, with a written recognition of the need to support the development of these bodies and a commitment to increase the level of funding to them.

Hand in hand with this change came the requirement for each region to develop a business plan and strategy for film and moving image media activity across all sectors (Production, Exhibition, Archive, Education and Training and the Screen Commission). This process in the East Midlands has been inclusive and has allowed MACE to develop a series of relationships across the sectors as well as help media colleagues to understand the role that the Archive can play within the region. A similar process is about to be undertaken in the West Midlands.

Simultaneously with the development of the Film Council, the Government was bringing together of the library, museum and archive communities under one body, Resource. The importance of using this moment to establish the film archive community as part of the national archive provision as well as part of the film and media sector was not lost on Film Archive Forum members.

At national level the Film Archive Forum was invited to take a seat at the National Council on Archives and each of the English regional moving image archives has been invited to become members of the regional archive councils which have been established.

In the East and West Midlands, the strategy documents being prepared by the RACs recognise the gap in provision left by not having an established regional film archive and prioritise its establishment.

And at the turn of the year 2000 this is where we are, recognised, prioritised, written into strategies at regional and national level. The challenge of 2001 is to turn this groundswell of support into a concrete development plan. It is my hope that before the next edition of this invaluable guide is published the Media Archive for Central England will be a valuable and valued and accessible addition to the research resources for film and television in the UK.

James Patterson, *formerly of the National Film and Television Archive, is Director of the Media Archive for Central England (MACE).*

Generic shot of airliner in flight (photo courtesy of Index Stock Shots)

Film, Television, Radio and Related Documentation Collections – United Kingdom

104.7 ISLAND FM

12 Westerbrook Street
Sampsons
GUERNSEY
GY2 4QQ
Tel: 01481 242000
Web: http://www.islandfm.Guernsey-net

Contact: Mr Carl Ward, Programme Controller.

E-mail: kevin@islandfm.Guernsey-net

Radio station. Holds 42 days' output. Also keeps Christmas days and some special local and extended programmes.

106 CTFM RADIO

16 Lower Bridge Street
CANTERBURY
Kent
CT1 2HQ
Tel: 01227 789106
Fax: 01227 785106
Web: http://www.ctfm.co.uk

Contact: Mr John Maxfield, Programme Controller.

E-mail: info@ctfm.co.uk

Radio station. Holds material to meet legal requirement. Some unlogged news material is kept for in-house use only.

107 OAK FM

7 Waldron Court
Prince William Road
LOUGHBOROUGH
Leicestershire
LE11 5GD
Tel: 01509 211711
Fax: 01509 246107
Web: http://www.oakfm.com.uk

Contact: Mr Sheldon James, Station Director.

E-mail: info@oakfm.com

Radio station. Holds 42 days' output only.

107.8 SOUTHCITY FM

City Studios
Marsh Lane
SOUTHAMPTON
SO14 3ST
Tel: 023 8022 0020
Fax: 023 8022 0060
Web: http://www.southcityfm.co.uk

Contact: Mr Jon Earley, Programme Controller.

E-mail: info@southcityfm.co.uk

Radio station. Holds output to meet legal requirement only. Keeps news scripts for 2 years. Music library of about 2,500 items is held on hard disc.

107.9 FUSION RADIO

PO Box 107
OXFORD
OX1 1FL
Tel: 01865 724442
Fax: 01865 726161
Web: http://www.fusion1079.co.uk

Contact: Mr Tony Dibbins, Programme Controller.

E-mail: tony@dibbzy.co.uk

Holdings: Three months' output. Also keeps topical news stories, large news stories (audio + script), a large private music collection, and commercials. Holds minidisc copies of film clips. A new large Internet music service is also being provided covering different genres of music, and there are services for students on a 24-hour basis. The radio station aims to expand its archive.

Note: *Formerly Oxygen 107.9 FM.*

2CR FM

5 Southcote Road
BOURNEMOUTH
Dorset
BH1 3LR
Tel: 01202 259259
Fax: 01202 255244
Web: http://www.2crfm.co.uk

Contact: Mr Craig Morris, Programme Controller. Rosemary Mundy.

E-mail: sales@2crfm.musicradio.com

Holdings: 2CR FM – key clips of its *Breakfast Show* (weekdays 06.00–09.00) and all logger tapes of output for up to 60 days.

95.8 CAPITAL FM

30 Leicester Square
LONDON
WC2H 7LA
Tel: 020 7766 6000
Fax: 020 7766 6100
Web: http://www.capitalfm.com

Contact: Mr Jeff Smith, Programme Controller.

E-mail: info@capitalradio.co.uk

The radio station holds 3 months' output to meet legal requirement. Other programmes have gone to the National Sound Archive, including early programmes from the start of Capital FM. The Capital Group's central library is based in London. A music library is maintained.

Access: No public access.

96 TRENT FM

29–31 Castle Gate
NOTTINGHAM
NG1 7AP
Tel: 0115 952 7000
Fax: 0115 912 9302

Contact: Mr Dick Stone, Programme Controller.

E-mail: admin@trentfm.musicradio.com

Radio station. General local interest and news items kept.

96.3 QFM

26 Lady Lane
PAISLEY
Renfrewshire, Scotland
PA1 2LG
Tel: 0141 887 9630
Fax: 0141 887 0963

Contact: Mr Dougie Jackson, Programme Controller. Mr Colin Kelly, Head of News.

E-mail: dougie.jackson@Q-FM.com

Radio station. Local Paisley/local Glasgow news collection held.

97.4 VALE FM

Longmead
SHAFTESBURY
Dorset
SP7 8QQ
Tel: 01747 855711
Fax: 01747 855722
Web: http://www.valefm.co.uk

Contact: Mr Martin Lee, Programme Controller.

E-mail: studio@valefm.co.uk

Radio station. Local news kept for one year only.

ABERDEEN UNIVERSITY LIBRARY

Queen Mother Library
Meston Walk
Old Aberdeen
ABERDEEN
Grampian
AB24 3UE

Tel: 01224 272590
Fax: 01224 487048

Contact: Ms Jennifer Beavan, Site Services Manager, Arts & Divinity Section. Ms Jennifer Beavan, Library.

E-mail: j.a.beavan@abdn.ac.uk

The collection of films on video reflects the interests of a number of departments within the University's Faculty of Arts & Divinity; Film Studies (within English), Hispanic Studies (Spanish and Latin American), French and German. In particular Film Studies focuses on American, European and Irish-Scottish films. We also buy documentary videos to support teaching in Philosophy, History, Women's Studies and Medicine.

Video and film holdings: c.1,000 videos – commercially produced.

Music holdings: c.500 CD-ROMs of classical music.

Books holdings: 1,300.

Datasets holdings: AVANCE.

Journals holdings: 11 titles currently taken.

Access: Available for loan.

Access to researchers from outside: Yes.

Viewing and listening facilities: 10 video machines, 6 of which are triple standard.

Charges: None except for external users who wish to have borrowing facilities.

Copyright: None.

The AFRICAN VIDEO CENTRE LTD

7 Balls Pond Road
LONDON
N1 4AX
Tel: 020 7923 4224
Fax: 020 7249 6886

Contact: Mr Magnus Macauley.

A small family run business, specialising in sale/hire of video cassettes by, for or about black persons. Only items released on video format available.

Video and film holdings: Video: 15,000 reels/cassettes. Documentary, feature films, news and current affairs, music and dancing.
Video components: VHS Video.

Cataloguing: Lists of topics available for sale only. Rental availability by phone or fax.

Access: Access available. Mon-Sat 10.30–21.30.

Viewing and listening facilities: Viewing off premises. Sales.

Copyright: Copyright not held.

ALAN PATEMAN FILM ARCHIVE COLLECTION ▣

6 Brookfield Gardens
CARLISLE
Cumbria
CA1 2PJ
Tel: 01228 527141

Contact: Mr Alan Pateman.

E-mail: alanpateman@freenetname.co.uk

The collection includes film archive material dating from 1900 onwards. Material on the following countries and regions is held: Australia, France, India, Egypt, USA, Germany, China, Soviet Union, England, Scotland, Ireland, Hague, Sweden, Isle of Man, South Africa, Rhodesia, Bermuda, Corsica, Bavaria, Switzerland, Italy, Mexico, Borneo, Costa Rica and other countries. Subjects include politics, geography, newsreels, comedians, animation and trick photography, westerns, Mack Sennet, custard pies, lace making, French Riviera, sports, River Thames, motor car manufacturers, boats, ships, sampans, railways, aircraft, music hall, royalty, farming, milking, traditional ceremonies, beaches, piers, world wars, film stars, firefighting, London, mining, propaganda, Nazis, speed attempts, dancing, holiday camps, advertising, fashion, animals, earthquakes, ENSA, oil, glaciers, mechanical toys, Gretna Green, marriage, horse-racing, Ayr, Edinburgh, glamour-adult nude from 1915.

Storage: Reasonable uniform temperature.

Cataloguing: Information available on request.

Access: No access. By arrangement only.

Viewing and listening facilities: Viewing off premises. Duplicating. Sales. Viewing on VHS copies can be arranged.

Charges: Charges for facilities and handling. A price list is available upon request.

Copyright: Copyright held. Copyright advice available. Copyright adviser: Alan Pateman.

ALEXANDER KEILLER MUSEUM ▣

Avebury
MARLBOROUGH
Wiltshire
SN8 1RF
Tel: 01672 539250

Material from archaeological excavations carried out at Windmill Hill, Avebury, in 1925, directed by Alexander Keiller (1889–1955).

Video and film holdings: Video: One tape.
Film: Small collection. About 10 minutes of film, black and white, 16mm. (Copy of 1920s' film made on 35mm and transferred to video in 1995). Archaeological excavation on Windmill Hill, Avebury, 1925.
Film components: 16mm, positive film.

Storage: Stored in controlled environment.

Access: Access available. Free access for researchers.

Viewing and listening facilities: Limited viewing facilities at the museum.

Copyright: Copyright is held by the Department of National Heritage.

ALPHA 103.2 ◖◗

Radio House
11 Woodland Road
DARLINGTON
Co Durham
DL3 7BJ
Tel: 01325 255552
Fax: 01325 255551

Contact: Mr Dave Lee, Programme Manager.

E-mail: admin@alpharadio.demon.co.uk

Radio station. Holds 42 days' output – local *Darlington Line* weekly programme.

ANGLESEY COUNTY RECORD OFFICE ▣

Swyddfa'r Sir
Glanhwfa Road
LLANGEFNI
Isle of Anglesey
LL77 7TW
Tel: 01248 752080

Contact: Ms Anne Venables, Archivist.

Very small collection consisting of items of local history interest.

Video and film holdings: Video: 8 reels/cassettes. Advertising, amateur.
Video components: VHS Video.
Film: 16 cans. 100% black and white film. Amateur.
Film components: 8mm.

Storage: Storage in strongroom; no temperature and humidity control.

Printed catalogue: Available, indexed.

Conservation policy: Films all copied by Archif Ffilm.

Access: Access available. Mon-Fri 09.00–13.00 and 14.00–17.00, by arrangement only.

Viewing and listening facilities: Viewing on premises.

Charges: Charges for research for broadcast productions. Charges for research for academic purposes. A price list is available upon request.

Copyright: Some unknown.

ANGLIA POLYTECHNIC UNIVERSITY

East Road
CAMBRIDGE
CB1 1PT
Tel: 01223 363 271 ext 2206
Fax: 01223 352 900

Contact: Mr Roderick M Macdonald, Head of Media Production. Jane McCarren.

E-mail: r.m.macdonald@anglia.ac.uk

The Library collection at Cambridge holds approximately 4,000 tapes – off-air recordings on all subjects, plus British and European films. It also houses a specialist collection of documents and facsimile documents, as well as audio-visual materials, on the history of the French Resistance in World War 2.

Books holdings: Books purchased to support APU learning and teaching – approx. 1,500 volumes.

Journals holdings: Approx. 10 non-specialist journal subscriptions.

Library OPACs with major holdings on moving image and radio: Yes.

Catalogue(s) available via the Internet: Yes.

Access: Access to general public for reference use only.

Access to researchers from outside: As above.

Viewing and listening facilities: 8 individual and 4 small group rooms equipped with monitor. VTR.

ANGLIA TV

Anglia Television Ltd
Anglia House
NORWICH
NR1 3JG
Tel: 01603 615151
Fax: 01603 768350

Contact: Ms Anne Edmonds, Librarian.

All material is of Anglia TV news stories, features and documentaries. Selected black and white film retained between 1959 and 1969. Thereafter all transmitted material retained. The source of news material is mainly Anglia TV Region (East Anglia). Documentaries and features of wider interest. Over 7,500 transmitted film items are taken in each year. News, current affairs, magazine items, local interest, farming and local crafts. Multi-subject features and documentaries.

Video and film holdings: Video: Documentaries, news and current affairs, science and education. Subjects include arts and crafts, leisure pursuits and country pursuits, and cooking.
Video components: VHS Video, hi-band U-matic, Beta/Beta-SP, 1-inch Video, DigiBeta.
Film: Documentaries, news and current affairs, science and education. Subjects include archaeology, St Helena, Falklands and Antarctica. 70% colour film, 30% black and white film.
Film components: 16mm, positive film, negative film, final mix.

Storage: Movable and stationary racking systems in the basement.

Card catalogue: Available. Indexed.

Computerised database: Current computer database is on Idealist. To date (November 2000) this includes most of the contents of the card index.

Catalogue(s) available via the Internet: There are no immediate plans to go online.

Conservation policy: All transmitted programmes retained.

Access: Limited access. 09.00–17.30. Research undertaken by library staff only. Telephone and written requests.

Viewing and listening facilities: Duplicating. Sales. VHS viewing copies can be provided.

Charges: Charges for research for broadcast productions.

Copyright: Copyright held. Some documentaries contain archive material from other sources. Copyright advice available. Copyright adviser: Paddy Burns.

ARCHIFDY CEREDIGION ARCHIVES

County Office
Marine Terrace
ABERYSTWYTH
Wales
SY23 2DE
Tel: 01970 633697

Contact: Ms Helen Palmer, County Archivist.

E-mail: archives@ceredigion.gov.uk

Video and film holdings: Video: Advertising.
Film: Two rolls of advertising film, normal cinema programme c.1970. Deposited December 1977. One-off collection. Advertising.
Film components: 35mm, positive film.

Storage: Normal archival paper storage – temperature and humidity controls.

Access: Not available without consent of the owner.

ARCHIVE FILM AGENCY

21 Lidgett Park Avenue
Roundhay
LEEDS
LS8 1EU
Tel: 0113 266 2454
Fax: 0113 266 2454

Contact: Ms Agnese Geoghegan, Director.

The collection has been put together over the past 30 years, with material ranging from the first film experiments to the early 1960s and with a world stock shot library covering the last 30 years.

Video and film holdings: Video: 200 hours. Most of the video material held is documentary and is stored on Beta/Beta-SP. Advertising, amateur, documentary, feature films, news and current affairs.
Video components: Beta/Beta-SP.
Film: Current footage is well over 2 million feet. A good percentage is documentary and newsfilm of the 1920s and 1930s, mostly British and American. The archive also holds material from Birmingham and Yorkshire. The remainder comprises feature films and shorts of the 1920s and 1930s, mainly British and American, with a small percentage of foreign film. Negatives and master positives are on 35mm and 16mm, and viewing material is mainly 16mm. 10% colour film, 90% black and white film, 10% nitrate film. Advertising, amateur, documentary, feature films, news and current affairs, science and education, short films.
Film components: 16mm, 35mm, positive film, negative film.

Storage: Special vault storage areas, temperature controlled.

Card catalogue: Available, indexed.

Computerised database: Available.

Cataloguing: Some printed catalogues for news and documentary are available.

Documentation: A small amount of cuttings and press clippings available. 50,000 stills from British feature films of the 1930s.

Conservation policy: No film or tape is discarded.

Access: Access available. By arrangement only.

Viewing and listening facilities: Viewing off premises.

Charges: Charges for research for broadcast productions. Charges for facilities and handling. A price list is available upon request. There is a charge for viewing.

Copyright: Copyright for stock shot material held. Copyright advice available. Copyright adviser: Bob Geoghegan.

ARCHIVE FILMS

Note: *Library has been re-named. See Film Images (London) Ltd.*

ARCHIVE IRELAND

3 Demesne Gardens
DERRY
Northern Ireland
BT48 9NA
Tel: 028 7137 2432
Fax: 028 7137 7132
Web: http://www.northlandbroadcast.com

Contact: Mr Vinny Cunningham, Director.

E-mail: northlan@iol.ie

Archive Ireland is a new library which has been set up by a lighting cameraman who has a great interest in archive and contemporary material. The library at the moment is made up of material shot by himself all over Ireland and is being added to on a daily basis. Subjects include everyday life, sports, hobbies, pastimes, news and current affairs, etc. The library also provides access to other collections. Amateur and professional material on tape and film are being acquired continuously and the material currently held dates back to the 1950s. The library aims to provide a source of material on Ireland for film and television producers, broadcasters, educational establishments, archive researchers, independent companies and others.

Video and film holdings: Video: 2,000 hours. Advertising, amateur, documentary, news and current affairs, science and education, sports.
Video components: VHS Video, hi-8, lo-band U-matic, Beta/Beta-SP, MiniDV, DVC Pro, DigiBeta.
Film: 133 hours. The library is continuously being added to. 60% colour film, 40% black and white film. Amateur, documentary, feature films, news and current affairs, science and education.
Film components: 8mm, Super 8mm, 16mm.

Storage: At the moment all holdings are being kept in a purpose-built strong room in a temperature and humidity controlled environment. New facilities providing mobile shelving, etc. will be built in 2001.

Card catalogue: Available.

Cataloguing: A computerised database is currently

being developed. For the majority of the holdings there are logsheets for contents. Copies are available on request.

Documentation: Cameraman's logsheets exist for majority of the material. All typed on word-processor. Handwritten lists also exist for other material. Copies of this are available.

Conservation policy: No material is discarded.

Access: Access available. By arrangement. Access for disabled.

Viewing and listening facilities: Viewing on premises. Viewing off premises. Duplicating. Duplicating facilities for U-matic, VHS and Beta. Telecine work would be sub-contracted.

Charges: Charges for research for broadcast productions. Charges for research for academic purposes. Charges for facilities and handling. A price list is available upon request.

Copyright: Copyright held for the majority of the material. Copyright advice available. Copyright adviser: RTE, Dublin and UTV, Belfast.

ARKive

The Wildscreen Trust
PO Box 366
Deanery Road, College Green
BRISTOL
BS99 2HD
Tel: 0117 909 6303
Fax: 0117 909 5000
Web: http://www.arkive.org.uk

Contact: Ms Harriet Nimmo, ARKive Development Officer.

E-mail: harriet.nimmo@wildscreen.org.uk

ARKive will be a centralised specialist digital library of wildlife and environmental images and recordings. It will bring together films, photographs and sound recordings currently held in a wide variety of private, commercial and specialist collections – many of which are at risk of loss or dispersal, and much is inaccessible for public access. ARKive will hold digitised copies of the films and photographs – copyright will remain with the image owners. Its components will include: 1) complete productions of scientific and historical importance; these will include the top wildlife programmes from around the world, as well as a large collection of historical films documenting the changing genre of wildlife filmmaking; 2) Species holdings – a representative selection of moving images, stills and sound recordings of the world's endangered species, as

well as a comprehensive 'British' chapter documenting this country's natural history; 3) Collection of filmed interviews with pioneering wildlife filmmakers and others associated with the industry; 4) Library of books and journals associated with the history and techniques of wildlife filmmaking and photography; 5) database of the location and copyright details of all known collections of wildlife and environmental images and recordings. ARKive is being created by The Wildscreen Trust, organisers of the internationally renowned Wildscreen festival of moving images from the natural world. There will be public access to the entire collection at the project's headquarters in Bristol and key images and accompanying educational resources will be openly available on the Internet.

Video and film holdings: Initially approx. 1,500 hours of videos of wildlife productions; CD-ROM library of interviews with wildlife filmmakers.

Stills holdings: Digitised still images of endangered species.

Books holdings: Library of books about history of wildlife filmmaking and books associated with wildlife films.

Catalogue(s) available via the Internet: Probably. Controlled access.

Websites relating to radio and moving images: Yes.

Digitised collection: It will be, according to funding.

Access: Normal working hours, plus evenings. The film library will be open for public access in autumn 2000.

Access to researchers from outside: Yes. All open.

Viewing and listening facilities: In Bristol; video theatre, classroom, arkive research room with 2 viewing terminals.

Charges: To be announced.

ARROW FM

Priory Meadow Centre
HASTINGS
East Sussex
TN34 1PJ
Tel: 01424 461177
Fax: 01424 422662
Web: http://www.arrowfm.co.uk

Contact: Mr Peter Quinn, Programme Director. Mr Andy Knight.

E-mail: info@arrowfm.co.uk

Holdings: Normal 42 days' output. Very small collection of material of local interest and news collections is kept by the radio station.

ASTON UNIVERSITY LIBRARY & INFORMATION SERVICES

Aston University
Aston Triangle
BIRMINGHAM
B4 7ET
Tel: 0121 359 3611 ext 4398
Fax: 0121 359 7358

Contact: Dr N R Smith, Director. Mrs Anne Perkins, Counter Services Coordinator Library & Information Services.

Video and film holdings: Small collection of commercial videos, mainly Management and Health & Safety; also collection of MBA lectures on video.

Masters holdings: None.

Library OPACs with major holdings on moving image and radio: Yes, but no major holdings.

Catalogue(s) available via the Internet: Yes.

Websites relating to radio and moving images: No.

Digitised collection: No. No plans to do so.

Access: Reference use only.

Access to researchers from outside: Small collection of videos in Short Loan Collection.

Viewing and listening facilities: Four videotape players in Short Loan Collection in Library.

Copyright: ERA licence held.

AUSTIN SEVEN FILM LIBRARY

9 Arden Road
LONDON
N3 3AB
Tel: 020 8349 0770
Fax: 020 8346 2998

Contact: Mr Joseph Henri Spalter.

Most of the films are 16mm copies of films made by Austin Car Ltd in the 1930s for showing in the cinema and car show-rooms. They were presented to the Austin Seven Club Association when the 16mm library was closed. In addition there are films made in the 1920s and 1930s on 16mm, 8mm and Super-8mm, and film shot in the 1950s–1980s of Austin Seven Club events. Most of the collection is also on Video VHS, U-matic lo-band and some on Hi-8 video.

Video and film holdings: Video: 5 hours. Copies of film.
Video components: VHS Video, hi-8, lo-band U-matic.
Film: 25 cans, 6 hours. 25% colour film, 75% black and white film. Amateur, documentary.

Film components: 8mm, Super 8mm, 16mm, positive film.

Cataloguing: A list of some films on video is available.

Documentation: Catalogue of Austin Film Library.

Access: Access available. By arrangement.

Charges: Charges for research for broadcast productions.

Copyright: Copyright held for most of the material. Copyright advice available. Copyright adviser: Joseph Henri Spalter.

The BALINESE TELEVISION PROJECT ARCHIVE

c/o Dr Mark Hobart
Department of Anthropology and Sociology, SOAS, University of London
Thornhaugh Street
LONDON
WC1H 0XG
Tel: 020 7898 4415
Fax: 020 7898 4439

Contact: Dr Mark Hobart. Secretary.

This video collection is a comprehensive archive of programmes on Balinese culture, broadcast on Indonesian state television (TVRI) since September 1990. The project is a collaborative venture between STSI (the Indonesian Academy of Performing Arts) and SOAS (the School of Oriental and African Studies). The project has some 750 hours of theatre and dance as well as 300 hours on general culture and ethnographic topics among other subjects. Sales: 155 hours is available with transcriptions on CD-ROM in MPEG1 for purchase as three sets. Price on application. Set 1: *Classical Balinese Theatre and Dance* (49 hours). Set 2: *Modern Balinese/Indonesian Theatre and Culture* (62 hours). Set 3: *Modern Indonesian Society, Culture and Economy* (43 hours). Sale is subject to copyright restrictions. The materials are strictly for research and teaching purposes only.

Video and film holdings: Video: Some 1,500 hours. Advertising, documentary, feature films, theatre and dance, general cultural materials.
Video components: S-VHS Video.

Storage: 155 hours have been copied to MPEG1. A major project is under discussion with the School of Communication Studies, Nanyang Technological University, Singapore, to remaster the entire collection in MPEG2. The originals will then be deposited in the National Film and Television Archive; a viewing copy will be held in the library of SOAS.

Printed catalogue: Available, indexed.

Cataloguing: Computerised database with a comprehensive subject index and brief resumes of each programme is currently being organised. This will be available on a website. About two-thirds of the collection has been transcribed to computer disc.

Documentation: A booklet of the project's holdings.

Conservation policy: Remastering to MPEG2.

Access: Limited access. Copies of the 155 hours in MPEG1 with transcriptions are available for research use via the SOAS Library.

Viewing and listening facilities: Viewing on premises. Those who wish to view should apply for membership of the Library. Reference membership carries no charge for University staff and students. Details: http://www.soas.ac.uk/Library/Guides/membership.html

Charges: Charges for research for academic purposes. A price list is available on request.

Copyright: Copyright of video not held as it remains exclusively with the Indonesian television companies and/or the original producers. Copyright of the transcriptions belongs to the Project. Copyright adviser: Alan Bicker.

BARBICAN LIBRARY

Barbican Centre
Silk Street
LONDON
EC2Y 8DS
Tel: 020 7638 0569
Fax: 020 7638 2249

Contact: Mr John Lake, Librarian. Libraries & Guildhall Art Library.

E-mail: barbicanlib@corpoflondon.gov.uk

Video and film holdings: 4,400 VHS video cassettes.

Masters holdings: None.

Music holdings: 650 CDs, 25 books on film music, 25 scores of music.

Books holdings: 2,000.

Datasets holdings: *International Film Index on CD-ROM.*

Journals holdings: 6 journals.

Library OPACs with major holdings on moving image and radio: Library OPAC – minor holdings.

Catalogue(s) available via the Internet: No.

Digitised collection: No.

Viewing and listening facilities: Video facilities for access to Music Performance Research Centre material.

Charges: Hire charges for loan of videos, £1.70 per week. Fines, 65p per day overdue.

Copyright: None.

BARNARDO'S FILM & PHOTOGRAPHIC ARCHIVE

Barnardo's
Tanners Lane
Barkingside
ILFORD
Essex
IG6 1QG
Tel: 0181 550 8822
Fax: 0181 550 0429

Contact: Mr John Kirkham, Photographic Resources Officer.

150 films dating back to 1905 regarding the social history of the 20th century, focussing on children, child care and education. The collection includes material relating to emigration and the war years.

Video and film holdings: Video: 300 reels/cassettes, 200 hours. Documentary.
Video components: VHS Video, hi-band U-matic, lo-band U-matic, Beta/Beta-SP, 1-inch Video.
Film: 300 cans, 36 hours. 50% colour film, 50% black and white film, 50% nitrate film. Documentary.
Film components: 16mm, positive film, negative film, final mix, master sound tracks.

Storage: Archive vault, temperature and humidity controlled, fireproof.

Stills holdings: Barnardo's Photographic Archive of 500,000 images spans 125 years of voluntary child care.

Printed catalogue: *Film Archive Catalogue* (2000, 46 pages).

(photo courtesy of Barnardo's Photographic Archive)

Computerised database: Available.

Documentation: Mailshot and poster.

Conservation policy: Material is never discarded.

Access: Access available. Mon-Fri 09.30–16.30. Staff are available to assist. Access for disabled. Film catalogue and seven-minute show reel available.

Viewing and listening facilities: Viewing on premises. Viewing off premises. Duplicating. Sales. Viewing by appointment only. Duplicating facilities for VHS on site.

Charges: Charges for research for broadcast productions. Charges for facilities and handling. Charges for other services. A price list is available upon request. There is a charge for duplicating and for viewing off premises.

Copyright: Copyright held.

BATH SPA UNIVERSITY COLLEGE

Sion Hill Library
8 Somerset Place
BATH
BA1 5HB
Tel: 01225 875648
Fax: 01225 427080
Web: http://www.bathspa.ac.uk

Contact: Ms Helen Rayner, Campus Librarian. as above. Note: Ms Rayner job-shares with Claire Tylee.

The Library and Information Services are housed on two sites: Newon Park Campus and Sion Hill Campus. Both libraries include a video collection of roughly the same size, but numbering over 500 videos in all. A small percentage of these are off-air recordings. Sion Hill Library's book collection relates to film, video, television and radio, mostly at undergraduate level.

Video and film holdings: 512 videotapes comprised of feature films, off-air recordings and video periodicals.

Music holdings: 32 items.

Sound holdings: 249 Audio Arts audio cassettes; 36 radio recordings.

Books holdings: 630 volumes on film, video, television and radio.

Theses holdings: 10 BSUC theses.

Journals holdings: 5 titles.

Printed catalogue: Printed list, alphabetical by title.

Library OPACs with major holdings on moving image and radio: Yes – OLIB WebView.

Catalogue(s) available via the Internet: Yes – OLIB WebView, Z39.50.

Digitised collection: No. No plans to do so.

Access: Non-members of the College must make an appointment.

Access to researchers from outside: Reference only.

Viewing and listening facilities: 3 video viewers.

Charges: None.

Copyright: ERA.

BBC ASIAN NETWORK

Epic House
Charles Street
LEICESTER
LE1 3SH
Tel: 0116 251 6688
Fax: 0116 253 2004
Web: http://www.bbc.co.uk/asiannetwork

Contact: Mr Mike Curtis.

The radio station is working on its archive at the moment. Holdings: a limited news archive for the last two years, and 16 half-hour programmes based on immigrant experiences in the UK from *The Century Speaks* series (copies of these are held in the National Sound Archive.)

BBC BRISTOL NEWS LIBRARY

Broadcasting House
Whiteladies Road
BRISTOL
BS8 2LR
Tel: 0272 732211
Fax: 0272 744114

Contact: Mrs Jan Abbott, News Librarian. Malcolm Rigby.

E-mail: bristol.news.library@bbc.co.uk

Regional television began in the late fifties and the Library was set up in 1979 to cope with the vast backlog. Newsfilm is available from 1957 when the area covered by Bristol was England south west of a line from Gloucester to Brighton. later, smaller sites at Southampton and Plymouth reduced the regional area.

Video and film holdings: The Library stores all transmitted reports from the regional news programme. These are held on film from 1957 to 1983; on a mixture of film and High-band U-matic cassette (ENG) from 1984 to 1986; on U-matic from 1986 and Beta from 1991. VHS copies of *News West* are held for one year for viewing purposes. The Library also has a collection of over 2,000 stockshot cassettes of regional interest. Regionally produced and transmitted documentaries are stored on film and videotape in Bristol.

Manuscripts holdings: The Library holds Programme as Broadcast ('P as B') sheets, running orders and shotlists for each evening news, *News West,* up to 1998. The Library also holds P as Bs for the regional documentaries.

Card catalogue: For items transmitted before 1994 a card catalogue is used giving name/subject access to news reports.

Computerised database: Since 1994 the Library has used the STRIX system which employs free text plus keywords for retrieval.

Archiving: All transmitted news reports and documentaries are kept although coverage of earlier years (1960–1966) is not complete.

Access: The Library's first responsibility is to the regional production teams. All enquiries from outside of the BBC should be directed to BBC Worldwide, 80 Wood Lane, London W12 0TT. Tel: 020 8576 2000.

BBC EAST RECORDED MATERIALS LIBRARY

BBC East
All Saints Green
NORWICH
NR1 3ND
Tel: 01603 619331. Direct line: 01603 284358
Fax: 01603 764303

Contact: Ms Nora Wilson, Recorded Materials Librarian.

E-mail: nora.wilson@bbc.co.uk

Although BBC East started transmitting in 1959 a librarian was not appointed until 1979. Very little material exists from before 1976. BBC East produces news bulletins throughout the day, a daily regional news programme, one thirty-minute programme on various subjects each week and a weekly parliamentary programme. News and features material exists on film (negative and colour master), and 1-inch, 3/4-inch and 1/2-inch videotape. The Library also has a collection of Beta stock shots.

Video and film holdings: Video: *c.*5,600 reels/cassettes. Documentary, news and current affairs.
Video components: VHS Video, hi-band U-matic, Beta/Beta-SP, 1-inch Video.
Film: 10,000 cans. Documentary, news and current affairs.
Film components: 16mm.

Storage: Film and 1-inch videotapes are stored at the East Anglian Film Archive at the University of East Anglia in an air-conditioned and humidity controlled area.

Computerised database: Yes. BBC INFAX database became operational in June 1998.

Conservation policy: All transmission material is kept indefinitely.

Access: No access.

Viewing and listening facilities: Viewing on premises.

Charges: Charges for research for broadcast productions. Charges for research for academic purposes. Charges for facilities and handling.

Copyright: Copyright held. Copyright advice available. Copyright adviser: Nora Wilson.

BBC GMR

PO Box 951
Oxford Road
MANCHESTER
M60 1SD
Tel: 0161 200 2000
Fax: 0161 236 5804

Contact: Ms Karen Hannah, Editor.

Very small private and in-house radio collection of major Manchester News. Coverage of forthcoming 2002 Games will be archived. Other material is deposited with the North West Sound Archive, q.v.

BBC INFORMATION & ARCHIVES

Television Centre
Wood Lane
LONDON
W12 7RJ
Tel: 020 8225 9952
Fax: 020 8740 8755

Contact: Ms Sue Malden, Corporate Affairs Manager. Mr Chris Wilkie.

BBC Information & Archives comprises the BBC's libraries, programme archives and information centres. It is one of the largest such services in the UK. The programme archives and collections of recorded and printed music are regarded as the most extensive in the world. There are libraries in each of the BBC sites across England, Scotland, Northern Ireland and Wales. External access to the BBC libraries is available at a charge, subject to copyright or contractual restrictions. Such enquiries should be directed to the specific library or to BBC Information & Archives, BBC White City, Wood Lane, London W12 7TS. Tel: 020 8752 5824. Fax: 020 8752 5585. E-mail: infoarch@bbc.co.uk. Licensing of the use of any BBC material is handled by BBC Worldwide.

BBC Information & Archives is a whole media research service. Holdings are BBC television and Radio programmes and News in broadcast master format with film or VHS cassette access copies for television and DAT or cassette copies of radio programmes. The BBC Photograph Archive contains over 3 million stills. The Gramophone Collection is one of the largest in the UK and there is a considerable Sheet Music Collection. BBC Written Archives Centre (q.v.) is part of this archive grouping. A commercial research and access service is offered in conjunction with Worldwide Library Sales which licenses the use of the BBC content. The Programme Collections date from 1936 for television and from 1922 for Radio.

Video and film holdings: 300,000 VHS cassettes.

Masters holdings: 1.5 million items of film and television.

Music holdings: 1.2 million records and CDs. 4.5 million items of sheet music.

Sound holdings: 750,000 radio recordings.

Stills holdings: 3 million; BBC publicity pictures and actualities collection.

Manuscripts holdings: 550,000 document files. *See BBC Written Archives entry.*

Datasets holdings: INFAX (television and radio); ELVIS (pictures); NEON (press cuttings).

Computerised database: INFAX for television and radio holdings; ELVIS for photographs.

Library OPACs with major holdings on moving image and radio: In-house designed databases.

Digitised collection: As part of a preservation programme.

Access: Weekdays, 09.30–17.30 for external enquiries.

Access to researchers from outside: Yes, at commercial rates.

Copyright: All archive material is subject to licensing by BBC Worldwide; much of the content also contains third-party rights.

The collection comprises local material from 1962 to date plus local feature/documentary programmes from the same period. Not all material was kept in the early years. The South West region covers Devon, Cornwall and the Channel Islands and some bordering areas.

Video and film holdings: Film holdings: 4,330 cans. 90% colour, 10% black and white. Documentary, news and current affairs.
Video holdings: 1,258 1-inch VT spools. 506 U-matic tapes. 1,742 Beta SP tapes. 290 DigiBeta tapes. Complete programmes/transmitted news items plus 5,000 rushes/stockshot tapes.

Masters holdings: Film components: 16mm positive, negative and final mix masters.

Video components: 1-inch VT, U-matic, Beta/Beta SP, DigiBeta, VHS. Just starting to acquire DVcam and Mini DV.

Storage: Film stored with *TSW Film and Video Archive* (q.v.) due to lack of space. Video stored in three store rooms with mobile racking.

Conservation policy: All transmitted material kept permanently. Non-transmitted material regularly reviewed and selected rushes retained.

Manuscripts holdings: P as B's kept for feature/documentary programmes.

Card catalogue: Card catalogue, indexed but not fully shotlisted until 1985.

Computerised database: Computer database since November 1993, fully indexed and shotlisted.

Access: Access for BBC production staff only. External requests redirected to BBC Worldwide Library Sales.

Charges: Charges for research for broadcast and academic purposes. Charges made for facilities, handling and transfers. External requests redirected to BBC Worldwide will be charged through them.

Copyright: Copyright held unless bought in archive material. Copyright clearance through BBC Worldwide Library Sales. Copyright advice available.

BBC INFORMATION & ARCHIVES:
BBC SOUTH WEST PLYMOUTH TELEVISION
NEWS LIBRARY

Seymour Road
PLYMOUTH
Devon
PL3 5BD
Tel: 01752 234559
Fax: 01752 234596
Contact: Ms Paula Griffiths, Senior Librarian. Ione Lee.
E-mail: plymouth.library@bbc.co.uk

BBC INFORMATION & ARCHIVES:
BELFAST RESEARCH CENTRE

Ormeau Avenue
BELFAST
Northern Ireland
BT2 8HQ
Tel: 028 9033 8323
Fax: 028 9033 8329

Contact: Ms Fiona Johnston, Library Services Co-ordinator.

E-mail: fiona.johnston@bbc.co.uk

The Research Centre provides a multi-media research service to BBC NI programmes and network productions.

Video and film holdings: Television/film holdings on film – (colour and black and white 16mm) and video – U-matic, VHS, 1-inch VT, 2-inch VT, Beta, D3, DigiBeta.

Sound holdings: Radio holdings on 1/4-inch audio reels, DAT. minidisc, CD.

Manuscripts holdings: Scripts. P as C's, Contracts, Programme files.

Newspapers holdings: News cuttings from 1968–2000.

Computerised database: News material all catalogued. Selected programmes catalogued. Online access to several BBC databases.

Conservation policy: All transmission tapes are retained. All news cut stories retained and selected rushes stockshots also retained.

Access: Restricted access now provided for external production company researchers. Anyone wishing to purchase BBC NI footage can contact BBC NI directly. Contact: Paul McKevitt on Tel: 028 9033 8046.

Copyright: BBC copyright held.

BBC INFORMATION & ARCHIVES: BIRMINGHAM BROADCASTING CENTRE

Pebble Mill Road
BIRMINGHAM
B5 7QQ
Tel: 0121 432 8922
Fax: 0121 432 8736

Contact: Mr Garry Campbell, Information and Archives Manager.

E-mail: garry.campbell@bbc.co.uk

Information and Archives provides a service primarily to BBC Regional and Network programme-making departments covering both radio and television that are based in Birmingham. This includes *Midlands Today,* the daily local news programme, and the weekly *Midlands Report* and *Midlands at Westminster.* Network programme departments located in Birmingham include: Television: Lifestyle and features (*Top Gear, Countryfile*) and television drama (*Doctors, Dalziel and Pascoe*). Radio: A range of programmes including *The Archers, Costing the Earth, Music Restored* and *Best of Jazz.*

Video and film holdings: Film holdings: Approx. 1,700 cans. Mainly local news and regional programmes.
Video holdings: Approx. 42,000 reels/cassettes. Regional news items and rushes. Selective duplicates, studio recordings, edited inserts and rushes of network programmes.
Film components: 16mm.
Video components: VT 2-inch, VT 1-inch, U-matic, Beta SP, DigiBeta, D3, DV.

Computerised database: A combination of a central BBC Information and Archives database, local databases and the card catalogue for older material.

Documentation: Programmes-as-Completed and production files are retained in the BBC's central document archive.

Conservation policy: All local news items and regional programmes are retained permanently. Rushes are retained depending on their reuse value. Masters of programmes made for network transmission are stored in the BBC's central archive.

Access: Limited access. The service exists primarily for BBC staff. Members of the public and independent companies wishing to view or purchase material should go through the BBC Public Enquiry Unit or BBC Worldwide.

Charges: There are research charges for broadcast and academic purposes. A price list is available on request.

Copyright: Copyright held, apart from purchased sequences contained within production.

BBC INFORMATION & ARCHIVES: BRISTOL RESEARCH CENTRE

BBC Broadcasting House
Whiteladies Road
BRISTOL
BS8 2LR
Tel: 0117 973 2211
Fax: 0117 923 8879

Contact: Ms Jaqui Gupta, Manager – Information and Archives.

The Research Centre provides a multimedia research service to network documentary and feature programmes, the Natural History Unit, regional television and network radio productions. The collection (1960 to present) comprises viewing, safety, archive/insert and rushes material for network television features and regional news on a variety of formats – 16mm, 1-inch, Beta-SP, U-matic, D3 and VHS. All BBC Network transmission material is archived at BBC Information & Archives – Television Archive, Windmill Road, London. Access to information/material is via the online BBC Information & Archives computer system. All regional news archived on site.

Video and film holdings: Video: 25,000 reels/cassettes. Documentary/features.

Video components: VHS Video, hi-band U-matic, lo-band U-matic, Beta/Beta-SP, 1-inch Video, digital – D3, DigiBeta.

Film: 3,000 cans. 95% colour film, 5% black and white film. Documentary.

Film components: 16mm, 35mm, positive film, negative film, effects mix, final mix.

Storage: Purpose-built vaults, temperature and humidity controlled.

Card catalogue: Available.

Computerised database: Available.

Cataloguing: BBC INFAX System – stock control and information retrieval system by subject, title of programme, contributors, reporters, presenter, programme number and transmission date – for all BBC network programmes. BBC adaptation of UDC. All programmes indexed.

Documentation: 'P as Cs' – Programme as Completed sheets for all Bristol Network and regional programmes – BBC Bristol holdings to date held at RAPIC – BBC London.

Conservation policy: In line with BBC archival policy all transmission/safety material on film and videotape archived in London. VHS, Beta, DigiBeta and film negative trims/inset material retained for at least two years in Bristol.

Access: Access for BBC production staff only. Access for disabled. External researchers directed to BBC Information & Archives, London.

Copyright: Copyright held. Copyright advice available. Copyright adviser: BBC Worldwide.

BBC INFORMATION & ARCHIVES: BRISTOL RESEARCH CENTRE: RADIO COLLECTION

BBC Broadcasting House
Whiteladies Road
BRISTOL
BS8 2LR
Tel: 0117 973 2211
Fax: 0117 923 8879

The Research Centre provides a multi-media research service to network documentary and feature programmes, the Natural History Unit, regional television and network radio productions. The collection (1960 to present) comprises viewing, safety, archive/insert and rushes material for network television features and regional news on a variety of formats – 16mm, 1-inch, Beta-SP, U-matic, D3 and VHS. All BBC Network transmission material is archived at BBC Information &

Archives – Television Archive, Windmill Road, London. Access to information/material is via the online BBC Information & Archives computer system. All regional news archived on site. Radio holdings are listed below.

Sound holdings: Sound Radio holdings: 1/4-inch reels + DAT tapes – 10,000 – for Network Radio and Radio 2 programmes produced in Bristol (All TX material).

Computerised database: BBC INFAX System – stock control and information retrieval system by subject, title of programme, contributors, reporters, presenters, programme number and transmission date – for all BBC Network programmes. Selection of archive holdings indexed.

Documentation: 'P as C's' – Programme as Completed sheets for all Bristol Network programmes to date held at RAPIC – BBC London.

Conservation: As with television, video and film – in line with BBC archival policy.

Storage: Purpose-built vaults.

Access: For BBC production staff only. Access for disabled. External researchers are directed to BBC Information and Archives.

Copyright: Copyright held. Copyright advice available. Copyright adviser: BBC Worldwide Television.

BBC INFORMATION & ARCHIVES: LEEDS NEWS LIBRARY

BBC TV
Broadcasting Centre
Woodhouse Lane
LEEDS
LS2 9PX
Tel: 0113 244 7218
Fax: 0113 243 9390

Contact: Ms Jane Sheehan, Research Librarian. Richard Walsh, Research Librarian.

E-mail: leeds.library@bbc.co.uk

Collection based on regional magazine programmes from its commencement in 1968, regional feature and documentary programmes and supporting material. The region includes Yorkshire and parts of Nottinghamshire, Derbyshire and Lincolnshire.

Video and film holdings: Video: 10,000 reels/cassettes. Documentary, news and current affairs.

Video components: VHS Video, hi-band U-matic, Beta/Beta-SP, 1-inch Video.

Film: 8,000 cans. 75% colour film, 25% black and white film. Documentary, news and current affairs.

Film components: 16mm, positive film, negative film, effects mix, final mix, Ekta masters.

Storage: Four rooms with adjustable mobile racking.

Card catalogue: Available, indexed.

Printed catalogue: Available, indexed.

Computerised database: Available.

Documentation: Programmes-as-Broadcast and programme files.

Conservation policy: All transmitted material kept permanently. Non-transmitted material are regularly reviewed.

Access: Limited access. Access for disabled. Ground floor location; ramp and WC.

Viewing and listening facilities: Viewing on premises. Duplicating. Sales.

Charges: Charges for research for broadcast productions. Charges for research for academic purposes. Charges for facilities and handling. Charges for other services. A price list is available upon request.

Copyright: Copyright held. All BBC copyright material. Copyright advice available. Copyright adviser: Jane Sheehan.

BBC INFORMATION & ARCHIVES: MANCHESTER RESEARCH CENTRE

New Broadcasting House
Oxford Road
MANCHESTER
M60 1SJ
Tel: 0161 244 4391
Fax: 0161 244 4376

Contact: Ms Heather Powell, Manager Information And Archives, North.

E-mail: heather.powell@bbc.co.uk

The Library primarily provides a service to BBC Region and Network programme-making departments – both Radio and television – based in Manchester. This includes the daily local news magazine *Northwest Tonight* and the weekly *Close Up North* and *North Westminster*. Network programme made in Manchester for television include *Everyman, Songs of Praise, Heaven & Earth, Question of Sport, I Love the 80s* and *Crime Squad*.

Radio output includes *Radio 4 Archive Hour*, drama plays, and *The Sunday Programme*.

Regional programmes: All transmitted news items, programmes and rushes produced on tape have been retained since 1984. Selected earlier newsfilm has been deposited at the North West Film Archive (q.v.) based at Manchester Metropolitan University.

Network programmes: Master film and tape programmes are stored at the BBC's Information & Archives premises in London. Some duplicates are held on site in Manchester together with rushes material.

Video and film holdings: Video: 12,000 reels/cassettes. Regional news items and rushes. Selective duplicates of network programmes and rushes.
Video components: VHS Video, U-matic, Beta SP, VT 1-inch, D3, DigiBeta and DV.
Film: 2,000 cans. Mainly regional programmes.
Film components: 16mm, Super 16, 35mm. Print, magnetic track, effects mix and final mix.
Storage: Vault on site. Mobile racking.

Storage: Two temperature controlled vaults on-site for the storage of all components. Mobile racking.

Sound holdings: 4,000 1/4-inch tapes, 1,000 DAT tapes.

Manuscripts holdings: Programme-as-Completed sheets and scripts are retained. Production files are retained in the Document Archives in Manchester or London.

Card catalogue: For older news items.

Computerised database: For post-1996 news and all network programmes. The Library is linked online to the BBC Information & Archives system in London and other BBC regions. Regional programmes are catalogued and indexed on to the system locally.

Cataloguing: The Library is linked by computer to the BBC Information & Archives in London. Regional news is catalogued and indexed on to the system locally. The computer terminals also provide access to information relating to other BBC Libraries.

Documentation: Programmes-as-Completed sheets and scripts are retained. Production files are retained in the document archives in Manchester or in London.

Conservation policy: All regional transmitted news items and programmes are permanently retained. Rushes are kept according to their reuse value. Masters of programmes made for network transmission are stored in London.

Access: Limited access. Easy access – no special facilities. The Library exists primarily to serve BBC staff. However, members of the public and independent companies wishing to view and/or purchase material can get in touch with the Library direct or can go through BBC Worldwide.

Charges: Charges for research for broadcast productions. Charges for research for academic purposes. Charges for facilities and handling. Charges for other services. A price list is available upon request. There is a charge for viewing and listening.

Copyright: Copyright held. Apart from purchased sequences contained within productions.

BBC INFORMATION & ARCHIVES: NEWCASTLE NEWS LIBRARY

Broadcasting Centre
Barrack Road
NEWCASTLE UPON TYNE
NE99 2NE
Tel: 0191 244 1217
Fax: 0191 221 0796

Contact: Ms Deborah Greaves, Research Librarian. Lesley Gildersleeve, Research Librarian.

E-mail: look.north.northeast.cumbria@bbc.co.uk

The Library was formed in 1973 to serve regional news and magazine programmes, but was not properly organised until 1977 when more news stories were retained. It covers North East England (from North Yorkshire to Berwick) and northern Cumbria.

Video and film holdings: Video: 3,000 hours. Hi-band U-matic was introduced in 1984 for *Look North* news items, and approximately 7,000 rushes cassettes have been retained from these. From 1991 *Look North* has been shot on Beta-SP, and a rushes stock shot collection is growing weekly from this. News and current affairs.

Video components: VHS Video, hi-band U-matic, Beta/Beta-SP, 1-inch Videotape, rushes on DVC from August 2000.

Film: 6,760 cans. Over 6,760 cans of *Look North* stock shots and news stories (all Ektachrome reversal). 300 cans of archive film from older *Look North* stories. 95% colour film, 5% black and white film. Documentary, news and current affairs.

Film components: 16mm, positive film, negative film, final mix.

Storage: One air-conditioned room; space is limited. Most newsfilm is now stored at the University of Teesside.

Card catalogue: Up to 1989.

Computerised database: From 1989 onwards.

Cataloguing: The Library is linked by computer to the BBC Information & Archives in London.

Documentation: Programme-as-Broadcast sheets are retained for both *Look North* and regional documentaries.

Conservation policy: All completed documentaries and Look North items are retained; selected rushes are retained for important stories and for use as stock shots.

Access: No access to public.

Charges: Charges for research for broadcast productions. Charges for research for academic purposes.

Charges for facilities and handling. Price list available via BBC Worldwide.

Copyright: Copyright held. All BBC copyright material, apart from purchased sequences contained within programmes.

BBC NATURAL HISTORY UNIT FILM AND SOUND LIBRARY

Broadcasting House
Whiteladies Road
BRISTOL
BS8 2LR
Tel: 0117 974 2416 (Film)
0117 974 2415 (Sound)
Fax: 0117 970 6124

Contact: Mr Alan Baker, Senior Librarian NHU Libraries.

E-mail: alan.baker@bbc.co.uk

The Library has been an integral part and growth area of the Natural History Unit since its formation in 1957. It is a production media library servicing the entire Corporation for data and materials in the field of wildlife, ecological and environmental subjects. There is also an associated Sound Library covering wildlife atmospheres and specific sounds. BBC Worldwide are the distributing service of materials outside the BBC, apart from the Sound Library material. With the exception of selected archive material, the Library holds work material of film output from the Natural History Unit, cumulatively since 1968. Completed programmes, film items and magazine/studio programmes and selected stock shots programme by programme are held. The rate of expansion matches the Unit's output – currently about 60 hours film and tape programmes per year, plus associated rushes.

Video and film holdings: Video: 1,800 hours programmes. 3,000 hours of selected trims and 5,000 hours of rushes are held. VHS holdings include tapes on relevant material from other parts of the BBC and other sources for research purposes. Masters of programmes are held on video at the BBC Information & Archives – Television Archive, Windmill Road, London. Comprehensive collection of non-transmission formats, plus transmission quality copies of more recent productions. Documentary, science and education.

Video components: VHS Video, lo-band U-matic, Beta/Beta-SP, 1-inch Video, D3, DigiBeta, DV.

Film: 17,000,000 feet, 7,500 hours. All footage is science and natural history documentary material. 98% colour film, 2% black and white film. Documentary, science and education.

Film components: 16mm, positive film, negative film, effects mix, final mix.

Storage: Film vaults in Bristol but all master material of completed programmes, i.e. show prints and A & B cut negatives, are stored at BBC's main Film and Videotape Library in Brentford for repeat purposes; maintenance and distribution by BBC Worldwide Programme Sales and Library Sales section. Uncut negative stored at offsite facility.

Computerised database: Available.

Documentation: Shot lists and scripts for all productions and stock shots; also small vital reference collection of books and relevant journals.

Conservation policy: Liaison with archivist at main BBC Information & Archives – Television Archive, Brentford and through them via National Film and Television Archive.

Access: Limited access. By arrangement via BBC Worldwide Library Sales for commercial film enquiries. Non-commercial enquiries via Film Librarian. Sound: by arrangement with Sound Library. Some assistance is possible.

Viewing and listening facilities: Viewing on premises. Viewing off premises. Duplicating. Sales.

Charges: Charges for research for broadcast productions. Charges for research for academic purposes. Charges for facilities and handling. Commercial research via BBC Worldwide. Only limited assistance available for other research.

Copyright: Copyright held. Some material is bought in; some rights subject to co-production agreements. Clearance via BBC Worldwide Library Sales. Copyright advice available.

BBC RADIO CORNWALL

Phoenix Wharf
TRURO
Cornwall
TR1 1UA
Tel: 01872 75421
Fax: 01872 40674

Contact: Ms Pauline Causey, Editor.

Material held to meet legal requirement, plus large news stories, large features, interviews and special news items. A small archive of local interest programmes/news items, social events, disasters, is held. All news scripts are archived.

Access: The radio station collection is private – for use by BBC production staff only.

BBC RADIO CUMBRIA (formerly Carlisle) SOUND ARCHIVE COLLECTION, CUMBRIA RECORD OFFICE

Cumbria Archive Service
Cumbria Record Office
The Castle
CARLISLE
Cumbria
CA3 8UR
Tel: 01228 706285
Fax: 01228 607299

Contact: Mr David M Bowcock, Assistant County Archivist. Ms Susan Dench, Senior Assistant Archivist.

E-mail: carlisle.records.office@cumbriacc.gov.uk

Collection deposited by BBC Radio Cumbria (formerly BBC Radio Carlisle). The Sound Archive is mostly reel-to-reel tape but also some cassette. Coverage early 1970s onwards with a little pre-1970s material.

Sound holdings: Storage: the Sound Archive is shelved in an out-store.

Conservation policy: The Archive Service has no specialist facilities for conserving audiotape.

Card catalogue: Catalogues/indexes available in the Searchroom.

Access to researchers from outside: Access available Mon-Fri, 09.00–17.00. Access for disabled. The material is accessible to bona fide researchers via BBC Radio Cumbria.

Viewing and listening facilities: There are no facilities for listening to tapes.

Copyright: Copyright is vested in the BBC.

BBC RADIO DERBY

PO Box 269
DERBY
DE1 3HL
Tel: 01332 361111
Fax: 01332 290794
Web: http://www.bbc.co.uk/radioderby

Contact: Mr Mike Bettison.

E-mail: radio.derby@bbc.co.uk

Holdings: Two months' output is kept by the radio station plus major local news stories.

BBC RADIO DEVON

PO Box 5
PLYMOUTH
PL1 1XT

Tel: 01752 260323
Fax: 01752 234599
Web: http://www.bbc.co.uk/radiodevon

Contact: Mr John Lilley, Editor.

Holdings kept as per legal requirement. Also, digital recordings have been made, covering the last 5/6 years, of about 4–5 news stories per week – held on mini disc and CD. This material is held specifically for the use of the Radio Devon Newsroom for annual review programmes, etc. In addition, the radio station holds a large radio archive in Exeter, the contents of which have not yet been logged.

BBC RADIO GLOUCESTERSHIRE

London Road
GLOUCESTER
GL1 1SW
Tel: 01452 308585
Fax: 01452 309491

Contact: Mr Bob Lloyd Smith, Editor.

News items are kept by the radio station if they are considered to be of special historical or local interest.

BBC RADIO GUERNSEY

Commerce House
Les Banques
ST PETER PORT
Guernsey C1
GY1 2HS
Tel: 01481 728977
Fax: 01481 713557
Web: http://www.bbc.co.uk/radioguernsey

Contact: Mr Robert Wallace, Editor.

Material kept by the radio station to meet legal requirement only. But does hold items recorded for *The Century Speaks: BBC Millennium Oral History Project.*

BBC RADIO HUMBERSIDE

9 Chapel Street
HULL
East Yorkshire
HU1 3NV
Tel: 01482 323232
Fax: 01482 621458

Contact: Ms Katy Noone, Broadcast Journalist/Researcher. Mr Derek McGill and Ms Hilary Dean, Broadcast Journalist/Researcher.

Radio station. Holdings: News and programme archive 1971–present day, (includes demise of fishing industry).

Sound holdings: Approx. 5,000 1/4-inch tape reels.

Printed catalogue: Yes.

Computerised database: Yes.

Digitised collection: No.

Access: BBC access restrictions apply.

Access to researchers from outside: Only by prior arrangement.

Viewing and listening facilities: Limited.

Copyright: BBC copyright applies.

BBC RADIO LANCASHIRE

26 Darwen Street
BLACKBURN
BB2 2EA
Tel: 01254 262411
Fax: 01254 841043

Contact: Mr John Clayton, Deputy Editor.

Local news features are kept on minidisc (on discretion). Oral history sound recordings also kept. Some material other than news is kept but not filed. Regional studies may keep own items. In the past the *North West Sound Archive*, q.v., received many items from Radio Lancashire and other radio stations throughout Lancashire. Producers keep personal archives as well. Since digitisation producer decides what to keep.

BBC RADIO LEEDS

Broadcasting House
Woodhouse Lane
LEEDS
LS2 9PN
Tel: 0113 244 2131
Fax: 0113 242 0652

Contact: Mr Ashley Peatfield, Editor.

Material is kept by the radio station to meet general legal requirement. Local interest news and programmes, as well as *The Century Speaks: BBC Millennium Oral History Project* programmes, are also held.

BBC RADIO MERSEYSIDE

55 Paradise Street
LIVERPOOL
Merseyside
L1 3BP
Tel: 0151 708 5500
Fax: 0151 794 0988
Web: http://www.bbc.co.uk/radiomerseyside

Contact: Mr Mick Ord, Editor. Mr Eric Wise.

E-mail: mick.ord@bbc.co.uk

Sound holdings: Thousands of hours worth of local audio held by the radio station.

Access: Mon-Fri, 19.00–17.00.

Access to researchers from outside: No.

Viewing and listening facilities: No listening facilities.

Copyright: BBC copyright. Commercial companies are occasionally allowed to purchase dubs of material.

BBC RADIO NEWCASTLE

Broadcasting Centre
Barrack Road
NEWCASTLE UPON TYNE
NE99 1RN
Tel: 0191 232 4141
Fax: 0191 261 8907

Contact: Ms Sarah Drummond, Editor.

Material held by the radio station to meet legal requirement. And there is a 30–year archive of news items, items of major interest and interviews.

Access: The collection is private – for in-house use by BBC production staff only.

BBC RADIO NORTHAMPTON

Broadcasting House
Abington Street
NORTHAMPTON
NN1 2BH
Tel: 01604 239100
Fax: 01604 233027

Contact: Mr John Ryan, Editor.

Local news stories going back 18 years are held by the radio station at the discretion of news editors. A lot of audio of breakfast shows is kept. All interesting stories (3–4 minutes) of local interest, interviews with local celebrities, etc. are held.

Access: Private access – for use of BBC production staff only.

BBC RADIO OXFORD

269 Banbury Road
OXFORD
OX2 7DW
Tel: 01865 311 444
Fax: 0645 311 555

Contact: Mr Phil Ashworth.

All output is held by the radio station for three months. Major local news items are also kept. In addition, there is a music library.

Access: Private access – for the use of BBC production staff only.

BBC RADIO SHROPSHIRE

2–4 Boscobel Drive
SHREWSBURY
SY1 3TT
Tel: 01743 248484
Fax: 01743 271702

Contact: Mr Tony Fish, Editor. Ms Elaine Muir, Archive.

BBC Shropshire's Radio Archives include news and local interest stories, interviews and a variety of programmes. The radio station also holds items recorded for *The Century Speaks: BBC Millennium Oral History Project.*

Copyright: BBC copyright applies.

BBC RADIO STOKE

Cheapside
Hamley
STOKE-ON-TRENT
ST1 1JJ
Tel: 01782 208080
Fax: 01782 289115

Contact: Mr Mark Hurrell, Editor.

Various and many radio programmes from the last 32 years are held by the radio station.

Access: The archive is an internal facility and not really available to outsiders. A charge would be made for any exceptions.

BBC SCOTLAND, INFORMATION & ARCHIVES

BBC
Queen Margaret Drive
GLASGOW
G12 8DG
Tel: 0141 338 2880
Fax: 0141 337 6460

Contact: Ms Noreen Adams, Manager, Information & Archives.

Television came to Scotland in 1952. Very little BBC Scotland output survives from the 1950s. Since the 1960s, a representative sample of output from drama, light entertainment, current affairs, sports, music and arts, Gaelic and religious programmes has been held either in Scotland or in the main BBC Library in Brentford.

Video and film holdings: Video: 20,000 reels/cassettes. BBC Scotland holds about 10,000 titles in a wide range of formats.
Documentary, news and current affairs, science and education, sports, drama.
Video components: VHS Video, hi-band U-matic, Beta/Beta-SP, 1-inch Video, 2-inch Video, 3/4-inch and 1/2-inch, C-Format, Quad, DigiBeta and Beta SX.
Film: 20,000 cans. BBC Scotland holds about 4,000 programmes. 55% colour film, 45% black and white film. Documentary, news and current affairs, science and education, sports, drama.
Film components: 16mm, 35mm, negative film, final mix.

Storage: 90 square metre vault space. Not purpose-built.

Card catalogue: Available, indexed.

Computerised database: Available.

Cataloguing: 1) Stock control systems: 75% automated – providing access to title, transmission date, credits, technical data.
2) Analytical catalogue: 10% automated – providing subject and biographical access (modified form of Sears Subject Headings).

Documentation: P as Cs (Programme-as-Completed); script, shotlist, press release (when available). This typewritten documentation is held separately in BBC Scotland's Records Centre.

Conservation policy: BBC Scotland archive policy provides a framework for selecting a representative sample of output in tandem with Central BBC policy. Non-transmission material is junked/wiped two months post-transmission.

Access: Limited access available for commercial and non-commercial requests. Charges may apply. Contact as above. Limited wheelchair access.

Viewing and listening facilities: Viewing on premises, various formats. DigiBeta plus Beta SX.

Charges: Charges for research for broadcast productions. Charges for research for academic purposes. Charges for facilities and handling. A price list is available upon request.

Copyright: Copyright held. Unless programmes contain bought-in footage. Copyright advice available.

BBC SOUND ARCHIVE

G008 Broadcasting House
Portland Place
LONDON
W1A 1AA
Tel: 020 7765 4230
Fax: 020 7765 5417

Contact: Mr Simon Rooks, Sound Archivist. Research – BBC Radio and Television Archives, Picture Library, Music Libraries Information Resources, Information and Archives Commercial Unit.

E-mail: simon.rooks@bbc.co.uk

The Sound Archive is part of BBC Information and Archives. I&A also manages the BBC's Television Archive, picture, commercial CD and printed music collections and information research resources which contain numerous specialist collections. All research enquiries regarding any of these resources are welcomed by the Commercial Unit as above. The BBC Sound Archive has more than 750,000 recordings acquired over nearly 80 years. The collection reflects the unique role of BBC Radio in the cultural and political life of the nation since 1922. Broadcast speech and music, both complete programmes and selected extracts form the core of the collection, but the Archive also comprises sound effects, actuality and specially commissioned recordings. The Archive's BBC recordings date from 1924. Archiving began to be more systematic from the mid-1930s. Selection policy has developed with changing demands and expectations of archive use and is continually reviewed. A Preservation Project is ensuring the security of the collection and, crucially, improving accessibility through digital technology.

Collection Highlights: *Selected BBC Radio broadcasts since 1924*: Complete programmes and extracts representing all genres of speech and music broadcasting. *News*: Selected news from 1931, daily since 1982. *Drama*: BBC Radio's unique contribution to radio drama with many original productions from notable twentieth century playwrights. *Music of all genres* reflecting the BBC's long established association with major artists and commitment to broadcasting music. *Poetry*: Many of the most significant poets of our times reading their own work. *Second World War* home and foreign broadcasts reflecting the unique role of the BBC between 1939 and 1945. *The BBC Sound Effects Collection. Dialect, accent and language recordings* from the British Isles and the World. *Ethnic music and traditional customs* from Great Britain and from all cultures from Afghan to Zulu.

Masters holdings: More than 750,000 complete programmes, programme extracts and sound effects. Does not include numbers of duplicate access/lending copies. 1/4-inch analogue tape, CDs. DATs, audiocassettes. Collection represents all genres of BBC radio broadcasting, including more than 60,000 hours of original music recordings.

Computerised database: INFAX – BBC Radio and Television Archive catalogue and stock management system. An Informix-based system, INFAX is developed and maintained internally by the BBC. Contains BBC Network Radio and Television holdings. Available internally only. Not Z39.50 compliant. A web browser interface is available on the BBC's Intranet only. There are no externally available catalogues.

Digitised collection: Preservation Projects currently underway: *BBC Radio 1 Archive of pop and rock content* (sessions, concerts, interviews). Transferring 14,000 ours of recordings on analogue tape and DAT to CD and b.wav files on DVD. *Sound Archive discs* (LP and 78s) to CD and b.wav on DVD. A three-year project.

Access: On site access by arrangement. Contact Information and Archives Commercial Unit as above to discuss your requirements.

Copyright: Varied. BBC Copyright and/or associated contributor rights. Use of BBC Material – Radio and Television Archives: BBC material must be licensed for non-BBC use – please contact BBC Worldwide Library Sales at Tel: 020 8576 2861/2; Fax: 020 8576 2939; E-mail: ukls@bbcfootage.com. Please note that it is the customer's obligation to seek permissions and clearances from contributors and rights holders before BBC material can be used.

BBC SOUTH EAST (ELSTREE) RECORDED MATERIALS LIBRARY

Elstree Centre
Clarendon Road
BOREHAMWOOD
Hertfordshire
WD6 1JF
Tel: 020 8228 8705 General number: 020 8228 8714.
Fax: 020 8953 4445

Contact: Mr Chris Purkiss, Senior Librarian.

E-mail: chris.purkiss@bbc.co.uk

Note: *The Library will be moving to new premises in London in 2001.*

Formed as a result of the move of South East Regional TV in early 1989. The Library serves *Newsroom South East, First Sight* and *Metropole*. It holds complete programmes and stock-shots and selected rushes. The Library holds a copy of all transmitted material generated by South East Regional TV from March 1989 to the present and a wide range of stock footage of buildings, people and places in the South East.

Masters holdings: Components: *Newsroom South East*: master and back-up, plus rushes held as well as cut story compilations. *First Sight*: two Beta copies of each programme. Stockshots: compiled and held entirely on Beta.

Junking: All transmitted material is permanently retained: rushes are kept only if they have re-use potential or some strong archival significance.

Storage: Permanent storage space.

Computerised database: From April 1995 to the present all cataloguing of regional output is on the STRIX free-text system. There is also a post-coordinate subject index.

Access: Information can be given on holdings where time constraints permit; requests to borrow or re-use sequences or programmes should always be directed to BBC Information & Archives, BBC White City, Wood lane, London W12 7TS. Tel: 020 8752 5824. Fax: 020 8752 5585. E-mail: infoarch.marketing@bbc.co.uk

---

BBC SOUTH RECORDED MATERIALS LIBRARY

Broadcasting House
Havelock Road
SOUTHAMPTON
Hampshire
SO14 7PU
Tel: 023 8037 4247/8
Fax: 023 8037 4247

Contact: Mr Sunil Bali, Recorded Materials Librarian.

E-mail: sunil.bali@bbc.co.uk

BBC TV South has been serving Southern England (roughly 60 miles round Southampton) since 1961. Film has been used and kept since then, but only selectively covers the 1960s period. Holdings include *South Today* news items (magazine format) and opt-out programmes (30 minute non-fiction features shown locally only, although some repeated nationally.

Masters holdings: Film components: *South Today* and opt-outs (16mm).

Storage: Purpose-built roller stack library with controlled temperature and humidity.

Manuscripts holdings: Documentation kept for virtually all items from 1965 onwards.

Printed catalogue: No published or unpublished catalogues. 1961–81 items indexed by title only, with few cross-references to subjects or people, referring to consecutively numbered items (film) or spools (videotape). 1982 onwards: items in process of being subject classified by TELCLASS (BBC's own system), and catalogued on computer in the BBC TELCLASS network online.

Computerised database: In-house database.

Access: Contact the Librarian.

Access to researchers from outside: Contact the Librarian.

Viewing and listening facilities: By arrangement only.

Copyright: BBC.

BBC SPORTS LIBRARY

Room 5078
Television Centre
Wood Lane
LONDON
W12 7RJ
Tel: 020 8225 6027
Fax: 020 8225 6673

Contact: Mr Phil Gibson, Senior Librarian.

E-mail: phil.gibson@bbc.co.uk

The Library was set up in 1975 by the BBC's TV Sports Department in order to centralise and help control the Corporation's vast use of videotape. Retention policies, determined by the Producer in Charge of VT, form the basis of the current catalogue which indexes BBC-generated material from 1966. Older film material held by the BBC's Film and Videotape Library is gradually being incorporated into the Sports Library system.

Note: *The Library now incorporates the Radio Sports Archive.*

Video and film holdings: The Sports Department's videotape holding is now about 17,000 but is stored separately from the Library's offices. About 5,000 tapes are recorded annually, 70% of which are released for wiping in the first year. Every year, tapes recorded 3 years earlier are reviewed and pruned even further, so that actual growth can be kept down to less than 1,000 per year.
Storage: The handling and storage of Sports tapes is the responsibility of BBC Post Production. Radio tapes and discs are held at the BBC Film and Videotape Library, Brentford.
Junking: The Librarian liaises with Sports production departments to determine a quick release of duplicate and other unwanted material. Remaining tapes are reviewed three years in arrears, together with other areas of the overall holding, by the Producer in Charge of VT.

Books holdings: The Library holds a substantial collection of sports reference books.

Manuscripts holdings: The Library keeps all production paper work relevant to the identification and cataloguing of audio and video tape.

Datasets holdings: A computerised diary of all major sports events was started in January 1991.

Newspapers holdings: Newspaper cuttings and results relevant to BBC Sports output are kept.

Computerised database: The Sports Library catalogue is in four sections: 1) Title (also filed under transmission date); 2) Personality; 3) Team; 4) Subject. The subject catalogue is classified by the BBC's own special scheme for sport which uses a subject heading notation. The catalogue entry itself is a description of events (with timings) that occur on individual spools. The Personality, Team and Subject catalogues are now on an online computer system. Radio tapes and discs and the Sports output of News 24 are included in the catalogue.

Access: All requests for research and access should go through BBC Sports Sales, Rm A3057, BBC Worldwide Ltd, 80 Wood Lane, London W12 0TT. Tel: 020 8433 2573. Fax: 020 8433 2939.

BBC WALES FILM AND VIDEOTAPE LIBRARY

Broadcasting House
Llandaff
CARDIFF
CF5 2YQ
Tel: 029 2032 2198
Fax: 029 2032 2873

Contact: Ms Liz Veasey, Sales and Marketing Manager. Mr Tim Neale.

The Library holds all BBC Wales material post-transmission. In addition to complete programmes a general stock shot collection has been built up on both film and videotape. The subject area covered is of a very general nature with obvious emphasis on Welsh events and personalities; programme title and transmission date are held on an online computer system. In addition to this Library, there are news and sports libraries which catalogue the BBC Wales output in those areas.

Video and film holdings: Video: 33,000 reels/cassettes. Usual broadcasting mix is held on 33,000 video cassettes. Documentary, science and education, sport, arts programmes.
Video components: VHS Video, S-VHS Video, hi-band U-matic, lo-band U-matic, Beta/Beta-SP, 1-inch Video, 2-inch Video, D3, DigiBeta.
Film: 20,000 cans. With the exception of a few early 35mm programmes all film material is held on 16mm. All component parts of a programme are stored in the Library, namely transmission prints and tracks, viewing prints and tracks, cutting copies, original cut negative and music and effects tracks where used. 70% colour film, 30% black and white film. Documentary, news and current affairs, science and education, sports.
Film components: 16mm, 35mm, positive film, negative film, final mix.

Storage: Film and videotape material is held in a central store with the exception of newstape material which is held in the News Library store.

Computerised database: Available.

Cataloguing: All material is catalogued by title, subtitle and transmission date, and selectively by personalities and subjects.

Documentation: Because of the lack of space, the Film Library holds only the bare minimum of production paperwork, e.g. Programme as Broadcast sheets which contain a breakdown of the programme's contents. The BBC has numerous departments which store information such as scripts, Programme as Broadcast and camera and sound dope sheets all of which are available to the Film and Videotape Librarian.

Conservation policy: Shortage of space dictates that some junking is implemented but the material involved are trims and rushes. Transmission material is always retained.

Access: Access available. Mon-Fri 09.30–17.30. Staff are available to assist. Access for disabled. The Library endeavours to deal with all enquiries but priority is given to BBC personnel. Film is not usually released to the public but every effort is made to refer their enquiries to other film sources. Students and researchers are helped as much as possible, but making material available outside BBC premises can be technically and contractually difficult. External customers are now encouraged to contact our Marketing Manager for a 'one stop' access point to the libraries. The contact is Liz Veasley, BBC Wales, Cardiff, tel: 01222 22198.

Viewing and listening facilities: Viewing on premises. Sales. Beta SP & Digi and Film, U-matic, VHS to VHS (other transfers available via Post Production BBC Wales).

Charges: Charges for research for broadcast productions. Charges for research for academic purposes. Charges for facilities and handling. A price list is available upon request.

Copyright: Copyright held. Some programme output includes non BBC copyright material. Copyright advice available.

BBC WRITTEN ARCHIVES CENTRE

Caversham Park
READING
Berkshire
RG4 8TZ
Tel: 0118 946 9281/9282
Fax: 0118 946 1145

Web: http://www.bbc.co.uk/thenandnow/index.shtml

Contact: Mrs Jacqueline Kavanagh, Written Archivist.

E-mail: wac.enquiries@bbc.co.uk

The BBC Written Archives Centre holds the BBC's permanent written records from 1922 to c.1980. These form an important source not only for programmes but also for research into broadcasting history, biography, social and political concerns, music, drama and education. They include the BBC's correspondence with prominent organisations and individuals – politicians, writers, musicians, entertainers and sportsmen, as well as files on radio and television programmes, policy and all other aspects of the Corporation's work. Holdings include BBC publications, radio and television scripts, news bulletins, daily programme-as-broadcast logs of output and indexes for national programmes. Topics include moral standards, popular taste. broadcasting overseas, social issues, wartime propaganda, etc., including information on BBC overseas services, regions, audiences and press reaction, facts, dates, signature tunes and firsts.

Music holdings: Correspondence files covering all types of broadcast music, commissioned works, BBC orchestras and choirs, the Promenade Concerts, etc.

Books holdings: Archival set of all BBC publications; small reference collection of books relating to broadcasting.

Manuscripts holdings: 4.7 miles.

Theses holdings: Holds a few deposited theses based on research conducted at the Written Archives Centre.

Journals holdings: Complete sets of *Radio Times* (including regional editions); *The Listener; BBC Summary of World Broadcasts.*

Newspapers holdings: Broadcasting press cuttings 1922–c.1965.

Posters holdings: BBC publicity posters for radio, television and symphony/promenade concerts.

Ephemera holdings: BBC and broadcasting related souvenirs, tickets, publicity material.

Equipment holdings: Small collection of television and radio equipment.

Access: Wed-Fri, 09.45–13.00 and 14.00–17.00 by appointment only.

Access to researchers from outside: Yes – with some restrictions.

Charges: For commercial use.

Copyright: BBC holds copyright in material written by BBC staff – other copyrights respected.

BEACON FM

267 Tettenhall Road
WOLVERHAMPTON
WV6 0DQ
Tel: 01902 838383
Fax: 01902 838266
Web: http://www.beaconfm.co.uk

Contact: Mr Steve Martin, Programme Director.

The radio station holds 42 days' output only.

BERKSHIRE RECORD OFFICE

9 Coley Avenue
READING
RG1 6AF
Tel: 0118 901 5132
Fax: 0118 901 5131

Contact: Dr Peter Durrant, County Archivist.

County Record Office holding a few films acquired incidentally to the main deposits of written records: (a) Royal Borough of Windsor and Maidenhead, Windsor Borough Freedom Ceremonies: HRH Prince of Wales (ITN 1970); Brigade of Guards (Pathé 1968); Civic Trust Windsor Project 1969 (Pathé). (b) *A Day in the Life of Radio 210* (1977, 17 mins). (c) Festival of Britain activities in Newbury (1951) – original now in Wessex Film & Sound Archive. Berkshire Record Office has video copy.

Video and film holdings: Video: 2 reels/cassettes. VHS videocassette from 16mm original film.
Video components: VHS Video.
Film: 3 cans. 16mm safety print from 35mm original now destroyed. 100% black and white film.
Film components: 16mm, 35mm, positive film.

Storage: Climate controlled strong room.

Cataloguing: No detailed catalogue.

Access: Access available. Tue and Wed 09.00–17.00; Thu 09.00–21.00; Fri 09.00–16.30. Access for disabled. Advance appointment must be made to view this material as the office does not have the necessary equipment to hand.

Viewing and listening facilities: No on-site facilities for viewing.

Copyright: Copyright not held.

BIRMINGHAM CITY ARCHIVES

Central Library
Seventh Floor
Chamberlain Square
BIRMINGHAM
B3 3HQ

Tel: 0121 303 4217
Fax: 0121 464 1176
Web: http://www.birmingham.gov.uk

Contact: Ms Sian Roberts, Senior Archivist. Archives Department.

E-mail: archives@birmingham.gov.uk

Collecting policy covers material concerning or related to the City of Birmingham, although large collections usually have wider implications. There are substantial collections of oral history and folk music revival-related sound recordings, nearly all master copies only. Highlights include the Charles Parker (BBC Radio Producer, writer, actor, etc.) Archive (listening cassettes of Radio Ballad source material available), Banner Theatre Company Archive (MS 1611, permission needed), Philip Donnellan Archive (film material in need of conservation and currently unavailable); oral history material includes that deposited by Dr Carl Chinn, local historian (MS 1902, permission needed) and cassettes made by Digbeth and Deritend Local History Project in 1986, and other smaller collections.

Sound holdings: Yes. See description of collections.

Card catalogue: There are draft catalogues of some collections, but not all.

Access: Opening hours: 09.00–17.00 Monday, Tuesday, Thursday, Friday and Saturday. It is necessary to phone in advance if you want to listen to a recording. All users of the Archives are required to produce official proof of address and signature in order to obtain a County Archive Research Network ticket.

Viewing and listening facilities: None. Viewing of videotapes can be arranged with prior notice. Listening facilities available: restriction is usually due to lack of listening copy/transcript. Prior permission from the depositor is necessary for certain collections.

Charges: None.

BIRMINGHAM LIBRARY SERVICES

Central Library
Chamberlain Square
BIRMINGHAM
B3 3HQ
Tel: 0121 303 4511 or Arts Languages and Literature 0121 303 4227
Web: http://www.birmingham.gov.uk

Reception: Arts Languages and Literature.

Reception: Local Studies and History.

E-mail: arts.library@birmingham.gov.uk

The film, television and radio reference collection in the Central Library is mainly held in the Arts Languages and Literature section of Birmingham Central Library and reflects over a hundred years of collecting. The present policy is to purchase material up to and including undergraduate level. The strengths of the collection include back files of journals including *Radio Times* and *TV Times, The Listener, Sight and Sound,* and the trade directory *Kinematograph Yearbook.* The extensive book collection mainly comprises standard histories, biographies and criticism. Internet and CD-ROM access is available. Also in the Arts Languages and Literature service area, the Birmingham Shakespeare Library contains the complete BBC TV Shakespeare series on video, most other published videos of Shakespeare's plays and an extensive collection of BBC radio scripts and some ITV, BBC TV and film scripts. There are also some Shakespeare film and television production photographs. Material on the technical, sociological and economic aspects of cinema and broadcasting is shelved in the Science and Technology and Social Sciences service areas. The Local Studies service area holds extensive collections of film and video relating to local history and the Music Library has extensive loan collections of music, ballet and opera on video.

Books holdings: Arts Languages and Literature holdings: 2584 volumes.

Journals holdings: 16 current, 28 non-current, 11 annuals. 12 non-current annuals.

Card catalogue: 1879–1971.

Access: Free access to all members of the public. Proof of identity required for some items; some items served under supervision.

Access to researchers from outside: Yes.

Viewing and listening facilities: Video and tape cassette players available.

Charges: Photocopying, photographic, access and reproduction fees.

BLACK WATCH ARCHIVES

RHQ The Black Watch
Balhousie Castle
Hay Street
PERTH
PH1 5HR
Tel: 01738 621281 ext 8530
Fax: 01738 643245

Contact: Lieutenant Colonel S J Lindsay, Regimental Secretary.

The collection consists of copies of films given to the

Regiment over the years. Only one appears to have been specially commissioned. The remainder are straightforward reporting of events. There are 17 films or bits of film. All films concern life in The Black Watch, mostly ceremonial parades but some training and barrack life.

Video and film holdings: Video: All film has been copied to videotape. Documentary.
Video components: VHS Video.
Film: 17 films/part films are held in the archive. All positive film. Documentary.
Film components: Positive Film.

Printed catalogue: Available, indexed.

Conservation policy: The films have already been copied.

Access: Access available. By arrangement only.

Viewing and listening facilities: Viewing on premises.

Charges: Charges for research for broadcast productions. Charges for research for academic purposes. Charges for facilities and handling.

Copyright: Copyright held. Copyright advice available.

BODLEIAN JAPANESE LIBRARY

University of Oxford
27 Winchester Road
OXFORD
OX2 6NA
Tel: 01865 284502
Fax: 01865 284500
Web: http://www.bodley.ox.ac.uk/dept/oriental/bjl.htm

Contact: Mrs I K Tytler, Bodleian Japanese Librarian.

E-mail: ikt@bodley.ox.ac.uk

A collection of over 150 videotapes, consisting of educational materials on Japan (for anthropologists), Japanese films and Japanese television dramas.

Library OPACs with major holdings on moving image and radio: Catalogued on OLIS (Oxford University Libraries OPAC: Telnet: olis.ox.ac.uk; http://www.lib.ox.ac.uk

Catalogue(s) available via the Internet: A list of videotapes is available.

Access: Accredited readers of the Bodleian Library only.

Viewing and listening facilities: Television/video system capable of playing US and UK standard videotapes.

Charges: None.

Copyright: No copyright held.

BORDER TELEVISION NEWS AND ARCHIVE LIBRARY ▣

Border Television plc
Television Centre
Harraby Industrial Estate
CARLISLE
Cumbria
CA1 3NT
Tel: 01228 525101
Fax: 01228 541384

Contact: Mr Tony Steer, Film Research Manager. Mr Adrian Mallinson, Film Research Assistant.

Border Television serves all but the extreme south of Cumbria, the Isle of Man, Dumfries and Galloway, and Scottish Borders. Holdings include news and current affairs, sport, documentary, light entertainment, music, children's programmes, travel and local interest material.

Video and film holdings: Film, 1-inch, VHS, Beta and Digi formats. Studio footage is limited and there are no full broadcast quality examples of the regional news programme in existence, though VHS logs have been kept since 1997. (Attempts are underway to build a Lookaround digital log library, however.)

Storage: 1-inch tapes of programmes and camera rushes are stored in a nearby warehouse, and recorded on computer, while all 2-inch programmes are held by the National Film and Television Archive. Again, the prior system for recording programmes and camera rushes was haphazard and, as such, items have been lost over time. However, a full stock-take of what is in existence has now been taken and all current programmes in production are recorded under a system that records individual camera tape, what is on each tape, where it is located, or by whom it is currently being used.

Computerised database: The Library has documented on a new computer system all regional news and sports packages held on Beta since 1987, along with all programmes produced and in production since 1999. All items and programmes prior to that are held on film or Beta and are registered on a manual system which is slowly being transferred to the computer system.
Documentation in the past has been somewhat lax and, as such, locating older programmes can take time. This again is constantly being improved upon and entered on the computer. The Library has undergone restructuring and re-staffing in the last two years and now a full cataloguing and classification project is underway, along with a strict policy on data storage and information retrieval.

Access: Access is available but limited. Both film research staff are involved closely with the newsroom whose requirements take priority as such research for outside bodies is done when there is available time. In situations where very old or obscure items are being sought the research time required can be considerable, although as more data is transferred onto the computer system it is projected that this should improve.

Copyright: Copyright advice and costings can be gained from either Tony Steer, Adrian Mallinson or Ken Wynne. There are charges for research for broadcast purposes, VHS viewing off premises, research for academic use, for facilities and handling, viewing on site, broadcast rights and other services. Please note that blooper footage is limited and that use of such footage must be agreed upon by the Director of Programmes. Equally so, all Border footage of sporting events must be cleared for broadcast with the relevant sporting body before it can be used.

BORDER TELEVISION NEWSFILM COLLECTION, CUMBRIA RECORD OFFICE ▣

Cumbria Archive Service
Cumbria Record Office
The Castle
CARLISLE
CA3 8UR
Tel: 01228 607285
Fax: 01228 607299

Contact: Mr David M Bowcock, Assistant County Archivist. Ms Susan Dench, Senior Assistant Archivist.

E-mail: carlisle.records.office@cumbriacc.gov.uk

Collection deposited by Border Television Ltd between 21 May 1969 and 7 December 1971, and held on permanent loan.

Video and film holdings: Film: 49 cans. News items. No accessions since 1971. 100% black and white film. Film components: Negative Film.

Storage: Tin trunk in strong room.

Cataloguing: Listed in accession order. No index catalogue list available.

Conservation policy: The archive service has, at present, no special facilities for conserving film and video.

Access: Access available. Mon-Fri 09.00–17.00. Access for disabled. The material is accessible to bona fide researchers.

Viewing and listening facilities: There are no facilities for viewing film. Viewing copies not available.

Copyright: Border Television.

BOSTON COLLEGE

Learning Resource Centre
Skirbeck Road
BOSTON
Lincolnshire
PE21 6JF
Web: http://www.boston.ac.uk

Contact: Mr David Cunniffe, Learning Resource Centre Manager.

E-mail: enquiry@boston.ac.uk

Video and film holdings: Approx. 200 feature films and documentaries on VHS.

Books holdings: 2,000 volumes.

Journals holdings: Small collection.

Computerised database: Uses AUTOLIB software.

Digitised collection: N/A.

Access to researchers from outside: Guest users may join.

Viewing and listening facilities: VCRs.

BOULTON-HAWKER FILMS LTD

Consult *Index Stock Shots*

BOURNEMOUTH UNIVERSITY

Dorset House Library
Talbot Campus
Fern Barrow
POOLE
Dorset
BH12 5BB
Tel: 01202 595460
Fax: 01202 595475

Contact: Mr Matt Holland, Subject Librarian. University Library.

E-mail: mholland@bournemouth.ac.uk

The archive comprises collections of journals, reports, series and annuals connected with British broadcasting and broadcasting organisations. Interest in broadcasting history within Bournemouth University centres on research led by Prof John Ellis within the Bournemouth Media School. The archive is in the very early stages of development. It contains four key journals: *BBC Record, BBC Lunch-time Lectures, The Listener,* and the *Radio Times.* It is supported by an extensive range of texts, journals and other material in the area of broadcasting and media research located in the Dorset House Library.

Video and film holdings: 2,500 items, plus BUFVC Off-air Recording Back-up Service archive.

Masters holdings: 150 virtual reality animations on videotapes. Various formats.

Sound holdings: 900 items, BBC Radio 4 *Analysis.*

Books holdings: *c.*4,000 monographs.

Manuscripts holdings: Radio scripts. *c.*300 BBC Radio 4 *Analysis* and *Archive,* Flashback Productions, and *Producer Choice* 20 files.

Datasets holdings: FIAF CD-ROM.

Journals holdings: 67 subscriptions including *Radio Times* 1927–, *Ariel* 1936–1991 (incomplete), *The Listener* (complete set).

Computerised database: Yes.

Library OPACs with major holdings on moving image and radio: Yes.

Catalogue(s) available via the Internet: Yes, including catalogue of BBC Radio 4 *Analysis* at http://www.analysis.bournemouth.ac.uk

Digitised collection: No, but planned.

Access: Prior permission is required, limited to library opening hours.

Access to researchers from outside: Yes.

Viewing and listening facilities: VHS video.

Charges: None.

Copyright: Off air recording licence, BBC agreement to hold BBC Radio 4 *Analysis* material.

BPVL

25–26 Poland Street
LONDON
W1V 3DB
Tel: 020 7734 6134
Fax: 020 7734 0807

Contact: Mr David Smith, Film & Video Librarian.

E-mail: bpvl@bp.com

Originally a collection of oil company archives from the early 20th century, the Library has since expanded to include historic and current activities of BP's operations worldwide in oil exploration, production and chemicals. It also includes general footage of the locality and population in areas where BP operates, and a wide selection of events BP has contributed to, such as motor racing and bike racing and land speed record attempts. It also holds material of companies now owned by BP such as Super National, National Benzole, Arco, Amoco, Gulf and Sohio. The Library offers a record of the last century through one of Britain's' largest industrial companies.

Harding Rig (photo courtesy of BPVL)

Video and film holdings: Video: 3,000 hours. Both master material and extensive rushes from most productions. Advertising, documentary, history, science and education.
Video components: VHS, U-matic, Betacam/Beta-SP, DigiBeta, DV.
Film: All material originated on film has been transferred and is available on videotape, 85% colour, 15% black and white.

Storage: All video holdings are stored in temperature and climate controlled vaults in Soho.

Conservation policy: No material is junked.

Access: Mon-Fri, 09.30–17.00, by arrangement. Staff are available to assist.

Viewing and listening facilities: Viewing on premises. Time code VHS viewing copies on request.

Charges: Charges for research, duplication and handling.

Copyright: Copyrights reside with The British Petroleum Company plc and BP Amoco plc.

BREEZE 1521 AM

The Stanley Centre
Kelvin Way
CRAWLEY
West Sussex
RH10 2SE
Tel: 01293 519161
Fax: 01293 565663
Web: http://www.mercuryfm.co.uk

Contact: Mr John Kershaw, Managing Director. Mr Simon Osborne, Programme Controller.

E-mail: studio@mercuryfm.co.uk

The radio station holds output to meet legal requirement only.

BRETTON HALL

Library & Learning Resources
West Bretton
WAKEFIELD
West Yorkshire
WF4 4LG
Tel: 01924 832020
Fax: 01924 832077
Web: http://www.bretton.ac.uk/library/front.htm

Contact: Ms Janet Morton, College Librarian.

E-mail: jmorton@bretton.ac.uk

Film and television are not taught as subjects in their own right. Materials are purchased on these subjects to support the BA (Hons) English, Drama and Education courses. Two special collections are housed in the National Arts Education Archive (see separate entry) and the National Media Education Archive.

Video and film holdings: Feature film: 753 titles; Film: 32 titles; Television 19 titles.

Sound holdings: Radio: 38 titles.

Books holdings: Film: 697 titles; Television 124 titles; Radio 9 titles.

Journals holdings: Film and broadcast media: 12 titles (8 of which are current subscriptions).

Library OPACs with major holdings on moving image and radio: Talis (holdings are minor).

Access: Mon, Wed, Thu, 08.30–20.30. Tue, 09.00–20.30. Sat, 09.00–17.00. Access (vacations); Mon-Fri, 08.30–17.00.

Access to researchers from outside: Yes.

Viewing and listening facilities: 7 video playback machines and 6 audio tape decks.

BRIAN TRENNERY'S ARCHIVE

47 Leyborne Avenue
Ealing
LONDON
W13 9RA
Tel: 020 8840 2411. Mobile: 07977 142758

Contact: Mr Brian Trenerry.

E-mail: btren@globalnet.co.uk

The basis of the collection is the 16mm Kodachrome film shot by the late Ivo Peters. Filmed between 1959 and 1977, the footage provides a wide coverage of steam-powered railways in Britain. Covers steam-hauled express and freight trains and railways in dockyards, quarries and mines. There is also footage relating to the railways of Britain pre-World War II and modern footage featuring diesel traction. In addition there is a collection of films featuring various aspects of the British way of life during the 1930s and 1950s. Other footage covers the Caribbean, Cuba and Palestine in the pre-World War II era, as well as film of ocean going liners pre- and post-World War II.

Video and film holdings: Video: 5 hours. Amateur.
Video components: S-VHS Video, 1-inch Video.
Film: 40,000 feet. Subjects covered include main line steam on British railways, Isle of Man railways, ironstone lines, colliery railways and general industrial railways, as well as some recent BR diesel footage. 80% colour film, 20% black and white film. Amateur, documentary.
Film components: 8mm, Super 8mm, 9.5mm, 16mm, positive film, negative film, fine grain print.

Storage: Most of the footage is stored in racks at a separate address, the exception being 16mm negative, Super and Standard 8mm and 9.5mm films.

South London street carnival, 1937 (photo courtesy of Brian Trennery's Archive)

Computerised database: Comprehensive database under construction.

Cataloguing: Printed lists available.

Conservation policy: Effort to keep all the films in the best possible condition, preventing excessive wear.

Access: Limited access. 09.00–18.00.

Viewing and listening facilities: Viewing copies supplied on VHS.

Charges: Charges for research for broadcast productions. Charges for academic research. Charges for facilities and handling. Prices available on request.

Copyright: Copyright held for most of the material in the Archive. Copyright adviser: Brian Trenerry.

BRISTOL RECORD OFFICE

'B' Bond Warehouse
Smeaton Road
BRISTOL
BS1 6XN
Tel: 0117 922 4224
Fax: 0117 922 4236

Contact: Mr John Williams, City Archivist.

The collection of films consists of items acquired by, commissioned by or presented to the City, primarily relating to various activities such as the Port and the former Health Department, and special occasions in Bristol. Over 300 films dating from between 1902 and 1980, mostly of Bristol and the surrounding area. A number of civic ceremonies, royal visits, wartime bomb damage and public works. The collection is added to at irregular intervals.

Video and film holdings: Video: No statistics readily available.
Film: No statistics readily available. Over 300 films are held. One 1920 film by Friese-Greene has alternate frames tinted green and red. 10% colour film, 90% black and white film.
Film components: 8mm, 16mm, 35mm, positive film, negative film.

Storage: The films are stored in a strong room where the temperature and relative humidity are controlled.

Printed catalogue: Available, indexed.

Conservation policy: It is the policy of the Record Office to offer the National Film and Television Archive any nitrate films from which safety copies have been made; if not required by the NFTVA they are junked.

Access: Access available. Mon-Thu 09.30–16.45, strictly by arrangement only. Staff are available to a limited degree. Access for disabled.

Viewing and listening facilities: Viewing on premises. Videotape copies of most of the films in the collection have been made.

Charges: Charges for research for broadcast productions. Charges for research for academic purposes.

Copyright: Provisions regarding copyright depend on the conditions under which individual items were acquired.

BRITISH AGRICULTURAL ARCHIVE FILM UNIT

Springs Farm
Edingley
NEWARK
Nottinghamshire
NG22 8DB
Tel: 01623 882223

Contact: Mr A Richard Watts, Archivist.

The private collection was inaugurated in 1981, as the increase in the use of video created the demise of 16mm film. The object of the Archive was to trace, salvage and preserve all gauges of film, amateur and professional, relating to the development of agriculture and allied industries, assembling it into a specialist reference library for the industry. The oldest film dates back to 1908. The main period covered is the 1930s to the 1960s, with others up to the present day. Now also holds the Milk Marketing Board Film Library and a substantial proportion (i.e. some 400 films) of the Massey Ferguson Tractors Ltd collection. Material held by the Archive has been used in the television series *Green and Pleasant Land* and the film *Operation Harvester* (about farming during World War II.)

Video and film holdings: Video: 15 reels/cassettes. Documentary.
Video components: VHS Video.
Film: In excess of 1,000,000 feet. 60% colour film, 40% black and white film, 1% nitrate film. Advertising, amateur, documentary, science and education, agricultural films, material relating to oil industry.
Film components: 8mm, Super 8mm, 9.5mm, 16mm, 35mm, positive film, negative film, fine grain print.

Storage: Private house.

Cataloguing: None at present.

Conservation policy: No material is junked.

Access: Access available. By arrangement. Access to all bona fide potential users, students, researchers, etc.

Viewing and listening facilities: Viewing on premises. Viewing facilities for very small groups. Film screenings for societies can be arranged. No video facilities at present. Films are not available on loan.

Charges: Charges for research for broadcast productions. Charges for research for academic purposes. Charges for facilities and handling.

Copyright: Copyright not held. Copyright advice available. Copyright adviser: A Richard Watts.

BRITISH AIRWAYS FILM AND VIDEO ARCHIVE LIBRARY

Note: *This Library is under review.*

BRITISH ANTARCTIC SURVEY

High Cross
Madingley Road
CAMBRIDGE
CB3 0ET
Tel: 01223 221400
Fax: 01223 362616
Web: http://www.antarctica.ac.uk

Contact: Ms Joanna Rae, Archivist. For contemporary official material: Roger Kidd, Assistant Information Officer.

E-mail: basarchives@bas.ac.uk

The British Antarctic Survey (BAS), a constituent institute of the Natural Environment Research Council, undertakes a world class programme of scientific research in the Antarctic and related regions. BAS has its origins in 1943, in a British wartime expedition in the Antarctic called Operation Tabarin, which was established on a permanent basis in 1945 as the Falkland Islands Dependencies Survey. It was re-named the British Antarctic Survey in 1962. Since 1944 a number of official and semi-official films about the work of the Survey have been made, often using professional cine photographers. Staff serving in the Antarctic also made amateur films, a number of which have been donated or loaned to the Archives. Since 1990 BAS has been more systematic in keeping a visual record of its activities and infrastructure. Professional staff from the Photographic and Film Unit update footage regularly for use in educational and publicity material. BAS has also worked increasingly with television companies in making programmes. The spectacular scenery and wildlife of Antarctica, and the ground-breaking work of BAS, which is responsible for most of the UK's research in the Antarctic area, are captured in a variety of visual and audio media.

Video and film holdings: Video: Mainly official footage since late 1980s, unedited and complete films, and video copies of cine film held in BAS Archives. Also copies of films and television programmes to which BAS has contributed. Covers scientific and support activities;

interviews with staff about key environmental issues; research stations, aircraft and ships maintained by BAS; living conditions and transport; scenery and wildlife; personnel. Geographical coverage: predominantly British Antarctic Territory, Antarctica; also South Georgia, South Sandwich Islands; Falkland Islands.
Video components: Beta, Beta-SP, S-VHS, hi-band U-matic, VHS.
Film: Professionally-finished feature films and unedited, or partially edited, amateur film. Also off-cuts associated with some of the feature films. Covers similar subject matter to video but pre-dating 1980s, with much footage of husky sledge dogs and some of commercial activities, such as whaling in South Georgia.
Film components: 8mm, 16mm, positive film, negative film, 35mm film strips.

Storage: Special room in purpose-built accommodation, with environmental monitoring and control system. Capacity adequate for foreseeable expansion.

Sound holdings: Mainly oral history recordings of former members of staff, but including some more unusual items, for instance the 'singing' of a hundred huskies. Some recordings of radio broadcasts.
Components: Audio cassette tape, open reel tape, shellac disc.

Stills holdings: In excess of 26,000 images in the Archive Collection (dating from 1944), taken mainly by members of staff serving in the Antarctic, but also including those by professional photographers. Subject matter as described under video. The Photograph Library holds more than 10,000 high quality images of contemporary subject matter, many by BAS's professional photographers.
Components: Glass plate, 2.25 x 3.25 ins; 35mm, negatives, prints, contact prints, enlargements, digital images.

Iceberg, Rothera Point, Adelaide Isalnd, Dec 1997
(photo by P Bucktrout courtesy of British Antarctic Survey)

Computerised database: Depth of description varies but indexing is generally extensive. Catalogue entries are held on a PC-based database. A separate database exists for more recent official material, providing more detail. Over 90% of film and sound holdings are included. About one third of the historical photographs are catalogued.

Cataloguing: Commentary scripts are available for some full-length films. For others there are sequence notes of varying detail. Shot lists exist for recent official film. Original lists of photographs exist for those historical photographs not catalogued. A few transcripts are available for sound recordings.

Conservation policy: Poor quality and repeat film and stills are destroyed following appraisal. Copying cinefilm to video for ease of access and preservation has been a priority. Currently, emphasis is on digital scanning of still photographs.

Access: Access available. Consultation of finding aids and viewing access are by appointment only. Access to material less than 30 years old may be restricted.

Viewing and listening facilities: Viewing of films on premises – VHS or Beta video. Duplicating available by arrangement.

Copyright: Copyright is generally, but not invariably, held by the Crown or the Natural Environment Research Council. The position regarding copyright of photographs is more complex. Some assistance with copyright identification available.

BRITISH BOARD OF FILM CLASSIFICATION COLLECTION

3 Soho Square
LONDON
W1D 3HD
Tel: 020 7440 1570
Fax: 020 7287 0141
Web: http://www.bbfc.co.uk

Contact: Mr Robin Duval, Director. Xandra Barry, Personal Assistant to Director. Mr Craig Lapper, Personal Assistant to Director.

Media regulation. Classification of film, video and some interactive works.

Video and film holdings: Film: All video works and some interactive works classified by the British Board of Film Classification.

Computerised database: On website.

Cataloguing: *Annual Reports* (1985–1999).

Access: Full access on website.

BRITISH DEFENCE FILM LIBRARY

Chalfont Grove
Narcot Lane
CHALFONT ST PETER
Buckinghamshire
SL9 8TN
Tel: 01494 878278
Fax: 01494 878007
Web: http://www.ssvc.com

Contact: Mr Robert Dungate, Librarian.

E-mail: robert@ssvc.com

The Services Sound & Vision Corporation (SSVC) has long been associated with the armed forces, providing both radio and television broadcasting for military personnel around the world. In addition to this the company has also produced hundreds of training films commissioned by the Ministry of Defence for the Royal Navy, Army, and Royal Air Force. It is these programmes along with others, spanning nearly 40 years, that provide an excellent source of military footage. This material is now available to broadcasters and programme-makers. With unequalled access to the military and covering a wide range of subject matter the British Defence Film Library is one of the official suppliers of Ministry of Defence footage, providing unique contemporary material. The Library continues to expand each year as new material is constantly being added.

Video and film holdings: Video: 16,000 cassettes. Approximately 4,000 titles and 12,000 rushes. Military training programmes; edited programmes and rushes.
Video components: VHS, S-VHS Video, hi-8, hi-band U-matic, lo-band U-matic, 1-inch, D3, DVC Pro, Betacam, Beta SP, DigiBeta.

Storage: All material stored on mobile racking system in a controlled air-conditioned environment.

Printed catalogue: Available, indexed.

Computerised database: Available. Access on site.

Conservation policy: All material is stored and archived. World War II and post-war material along with all original film material is held by the Imperial War Museum Film and Video Archive.

Access: Access available. Mon-Fri, 09.00–17.00, by arrangement only. Access for disabled.

Viewing and listening facilities: Viewing facilities available on premises or by sending viewing copies on VHS format. Other facilities include: duplicating, multi-format copying, satellite uplinking and digitisation.

Charges: Charges for research for broadcast and non-broadcast productions. Charges for research for academic purposes. Charges for facilities and handling. Charges for other services. Prices available on request.

Copyright: Copyright held. All original material is Crown copyright. Completed programmes contain 'other' library material. Copyright advice available.

BRITISH DENTAL ASSOCIATION

64 Wimpole Street
LONDON
W1G 8YS
Web: http://www.bda-dentistry.org.uk

Contact: Mr Roger Farbey.

E-mail: r.farbey@bda-dentistry.org.uk

Video and film holdings: 300.

Computerised database: Library database.

Catalogue(s) available via the Internet: Audio-visual catalogue.

Access: BDA members only.

Access to researchers from outside: By appointment, with special permission in writing,

BRITISH EMPIRE AND COMMONWEALTH MUSEUM

Clock Tower Yard
Temple Meads
BRISTOL
BS1 6QH
Tel: 0117 9254980, ext 217
Fax: 0117 9254983
Web: http://www.empiremuseum.co.uk

Contact: Ms Jan Vaughan, Film Archive Co-ordinator. Film Archive Department.

E-mail: film@empiremuseum.co.uk

Established in 1991 to preserve, explore and interpret the history and heritage of the British Empire and Commonwealth from the late 15th century to the present, the Museum aims to stress the ways in which the legacy of Empire and the living relationship with the Commonwealth continue to influence both today's multicultural Britain and the Commonwealth countries. The first collections were received in 1993 but, due to funding restrictions, partial opening of the Museum took place only in 2000. Full opening is planned for 2002. The Museum's holdings currently total more than 38,000 items, including large photographic, oral history, document and costume collections, which are complemented by the steadily growing collection of moving images dating from the 1920s onwards, reflecting the lives of indigenous peoples, settlers and colonial administrators. The film collection is strong on footage of countries in East, West and Central Africa and the Indian sub-continent, including government-produced information and travel films (particularly the Central African Film Unit and the Northern Nigerian Information Service); newsfilm (especially political events and independence struggles in Central and East Africa); and amateur films from private collections (particularly good at portraying local ways of living, customs and industries, together with vanished colonial lifestyles). The Museum also holds a number of collections of television material reflecting current interest in the last years of British rule from the point of view of the governed. These include: *The Raj through Indian Eyes* (2 parts); *Sex Race and Empire*; and *The Mau Mau Emergency*.

Video and film holdings: Currently 30 DigiBeta, 20 Beta and 200 VHS cassettes. Plans for the collection include further creation of submasters and viewing copies on VHS.

Masters holdings: Approx. 550 cans of 16mm and 8mm film.

Sound holdings: Over 1,000 oral history audiocassettes.

Stills holdings: Approx. 40,000 photographic images.

Books holdings: Approx. 7,000 books.

Manuscripts holdings: Approx. 20,000 paper archives.

Datasets holdings: Related material on the Museum's Accessions and Oral History Catalogues.

Ephemera holdings: Research collection of materials acquired in the production of *The Raj through Indian Eyes*.

Tailor at work in Simla. From a film of Simla, India, taken in 1931 by Major General William Clavering Hartgill CB, OBE, MC. (photo courtesy of British Empire and Commonwealth Museum)

Computerised database: Moving image database currently being compiled.

Digitised collection: Digital copies of *The Raj through Indian Eyes* are held. Further digitisation is dependent on budgetary constraints.

Access: By arrangement only. Normally 10.00–17.00, Wed, Thu, Fri.

Viewing and listening facilities: 16mm and 35mm Steenbecks and VHS viewing facilities available on premises.

Charges: Charges for research and viewing. Price list available on request.

Copyright: Copyright held to large part of collection. Information on request.

BRITISH FILM INSTITUTE: BFI NATIONAL LIBRARY

British Film Institute
21 Stephen Street
LONDON
W1P 2LN
Tel: 020 7957 4806
Fax: 020 7436 2338
Web: http://www.bfi.org.uk

Contact: Mr Ray Templeton, Head. Sean Delaney, Library Services Manager BFI National Library.

E-mail: ray.templeton@bfi.org.uk

The BFI National Library provides access to the world's largest collection of information on film and television. As a major national research collection, the main priority is to provide comprehensive coverage of British film and television, but the collection is international in scope. The Library collects books, pamphlets, periodicals and other printed materials, as well as published resources on microfilm and electronic media. The purpose of the collection is to provide a major resource to meet the widest range of information, research and study needs relating to all aspects of the moving image (film, television – regardless of delivery method – video, video games, interactive multimedia, virtual reality); as culture and as industry, as social indicator and influence.

Video and film holdings: See entry for National Film and Television Archive.

Masters holdings: See entry for National Film and Television Archive.

Sound holdings: 1,500.

Stills holdings: See separate entry for British Film Institute Special Collections.

Books holdings: 41,500.

Manuscripts holdings: See separate entry.

(photo courtesy of British Film Institute: BFI National Library)

Theses holdings: Substantial holdings: not counted separately from books.

Datasets holdings: 500,000 title records; 750,000 personalities records; 1 million periodical references.

Journals holdings: 5,000 titles, of which 400 are currently received.

Newspapers holdings: 2.1 million cuttings (estimate); reviews, obituaries, festivals, subjects, etc. Film and name cuttings held on microfilm.

Card catalogue: Index to 19,000 unpublished scripts.

Computerised database: *SIFT – Summary of Information on Film and Television* is an international database of film and television production, and incorporates the catalogue of the NFTVA, as well as an index to the Library's journals and other materials.

Library OPACs with major holdings on moving image and radio: Yes. OLIB for books etc: Z39.50 compliant.

Websites relating to radio and moving images: http://www.bfi.org.uk. (Includes information about collections, and database of films for children.)

Digitised collection: Under consideration.

Access: Opening hours: Mon and Fri, 10.30–17.30; Tue and Thu, 10.30–20.00; Wed, 13.00–20.00.

Access to researchers from outside: Yes.

Charges: Yes. Scale of charges leaflet available.

Copyright: BFI holds rights to BFI-published materials only.

BRITISH FILM INSTITUTE   ☐
SPECIAL COLLECTIONS

---

21 Stephen Street
LONDON
W1P 2LN
Tel: 020 7957 4772
Fax: 020 7436 2338

Contact: Ms Janet Moat, Special Collections Manager. Collections.

E-mail: janet.moat@bfi.org.uk or speccoll@bfi.org.uk

The Special Collections holdings of the BFI incorporate the main collection of approx. 20,000 unpublished scripts, a similar number of press (campaign) books, donations of personal and company papers from the film and television industry, and extensive sequences of ephemera such as cinema programmes (London, the regions and some for abroad), souvenir brochures, autographed letters and general publicity and promotional material. The collections focus mainly on British film and television production, and range from the 1890s to the present. The personal and company papers include production records, scrapbooks, diaries, notebooks, ledgers, minutes and correspondence. Major donors include Joseph Losey, Michael Balcon, Powell & Pressburger, Carol Reed, Anthony Asquith, David Puttnam, Derek Jarman, London Film Productions, and several documentary filmmakers. In addition to the above, there is a random collection of sound recordings – a mixture of interviews, radio promotional spots and some soundtracks. Finally, some complete film music scores and a large amount of sheet music is also held, together with a separate sequence of music cue sheets.

Music holdings: Large quantity of sheet music.

Sound holdings: Approx. 200 cassettes, approx. 150 reels.

Manuscripts holdings: Approx. 500 collections + 20,000 scripts.

Ephemera holdings: Approx. 20,000 press books, also available on microfiche, and thousands of items of cinema ephemera.

Card catalogue: Unpublished script collection.

Printed catalogue: Typescript listings only for majority.

Computerised database: SIFT, Idealist.

Catalogue(s) available via the Internet: No.

Access: Only two study places available, appointment system operated; advance notice needed.

Access to researchers from outside: Open to annual BFI Library members.

BRITISH FILM INSTITUTE STILLS, POSTERS & DESIGNS

First Floor
21 Stephen Street
LONDON
W1P 2LN
Tel: 020 7957 4797
Fax: 020 7323 9260
Web: http://www.bfi.org.uk

About 7 million black and white original photographs, colour transparencies, posters, set and costume designs, illustrating the history of world cinema from *c*.1895 to the present day, and including a comprehensive collection of television stills (approx. 1 million). The stills are catalogued by original film/television title, also personality files, film studios, pre-cinema, cinema buildings, awards, equipment, etc. Special emphasis throughout on British cinema and television.

Stills holdings: Approx. 7 million.

Posters holdings: Approx. 20,000.

Design holdings: Approx. 1,000.

Printed catalogue: Yes.

Computerised database: *SIFT – Summary of Information on Film and Television.*

Digitised collection: No. Possibilities being investigated.

Access: Tue-Thu, 10.30–16.30.

Access to researchers from outside: Yes.

Viewing and listening facilities: By appointment.

Charges: On application.

Copyright: Copyright seldom held; clearance is user's responsibility.

BRITISH GEOLOGICAL SURVEY LIBRARY

Kingsley Dunham Centre
Keyworth
NOTTINGHAM
NG12 5GG
Tel: 0115 936 3205
Fax: 0115 936 3200
Web: http://www.bgs.ac.uk

Island of Staffa. Columnar jointing in Tertiary volcanic flows. Fingal's Cave on the right (photo number D2218 courtesy of British Geological Survey)

Contact: Mr Graham McKenna.

E-mail: libuser@bgs.ac.uk

BGS Library holds a geoscience information resource of worldwide significance. Developed over 150 years, it contains the extensive holdings of the former Geological Survey and Museum as well as those of the Overseas Geological Surveys and its predecessors. The archives contain material of historical and national interest. There are 200,000 maps and atlases of the UK and overseas. The photographic collection which dates back into the last century includes both BGS and deposited collections.

Stills holdings: 80,000.

Computerised database: CD-ROM database searching. A spatial graphic display is being developed for the Survey's own information database.

Catalogue(s) available via the Internet: http://www.geolib.bgs.ac.uk

Websites relating to radio and moving images: External access via Internet.

Access: Material held in the Archives is subject to the provisions of the Public Records Act.

Charges: Charges usually apply to services which employ library staff in selection or advisory work. Fee-based information services available to commercial and industrial clients.

BRITISH LIBRARY NATIONAL SOUND ARCHIVE

96 Euston Road
LONDON
NW1 2DB
Tel: 020 7412 7440
Fax: 020 412 7441
Web: http://www.bl.uk/collections/sound-archive

Contact: Mr Crispin Jewitt, Director, British Library National Sound Archive. Ms Jane Harvell.

E-mail: nsa@bl.uk

The National Sound Archive, a department of the Special Collections Directorate of the British Library, holds the national collection of sound recordings and collects video recordings in selected areas. The Archive aims to receive copies of all sound recordings commercially published in the UK, and to maintain major research collections of published recordings from elsewhere in selected subject areas. Recordings of interviews, performances and events are made or commissioned by NSA staff, and unpublished recordings made by others are acquired. The NSA provides access to the holdings of the BBC Sound Archive and holds significant additional BBC material recorded off the air and from other sources such as the Kenny Everett collection. Among holdings of independent radio material are the complete annual entry for the Sony Radio Awards competition, the IBA radio archive, the AIRC programme sharing scheme tapes, and the Capitol Radio archive. Video recordings are collected in specific areas such as pop music, and limited off-air television recording is carried out, in order to complement and enhance audio holdings. The collection currently includes more than a million discs and around 200,000 sound tape items, and is strong in all subject areas covered by sound recordings. Subjects which receive specific curatorial coverage at present are Western Art Music, Jazz, Popular Music, 'International' music (folk and non-western classical music), Oral History (e.g. *The Century Speaks: BBC Millennium Oral History Project)*, Drama and Literature, and Wildlife Sounds. The collection also includes major holdings of language and dialect and sound effects recordings. The NSA operates an open-access reference library at St Pancras, which includes a very wide range of audio-related periodicals and books from many countries, microfilm of record company archives, record company published catalogues including many rare early editions, and a wide range of discographies in all subjects.

Video and film holdings: The NSA holds an estimated 50,000 tapes of recordings made off-air.

Masters holdings: The NSA does not hold 'masters' in the film sense, though in some cases it holds the original video recordings of performances (perhaps 1,000 tapes in all). Almost all our video holdings are on VHS format.

Music holdings: Approx. 1,050,000 discs and 140,000 tapes.

Sound holdings: Approx. 85,000 discs and 60,000 tapes.

Books holdings: A proportion of the NSA open access library relates to radio recordings. Other areas of the British Library obtain a much wider range of publications relating to moving image.

Manuscripts holdings: None. However, significant BBC-related material is held in the BL Music Library and Manuscripts Department.

Journals holdings: Some UK radio periodicals are held. Also UK and foreign periodicals relating to sound recordings. See above re the BL's overall more systematic coverage.

Newspapers holdings: Ditto. The BL Newspaper Library at Colindale is the main repository for this material.

Ephemera holdings: Minor items of radio ephemera are held. (However, the NSA has a very significant collection of record company ephemera such as release sheets.)

Equipment holdings: The NSA has no moving image (or, specifically, radio) equipment but holds one of the two major public collections of audio recording artefacts in the UK.

Library OPACs with major holdings on moving image and radio: The NSA operates its own online collections management system CADENSA which can be consulted at present only in the BL Humanities 2 Reading Room (St Pancras Floor 2) and the Rare Books and Music Reading Room (which houses the NSA Listening and Viewing Service, Floor 1). It covers all areas of NSA holdings except BBC Sound Archive recordings which are covered by separate catalogues available in the NSA Library in the Humanities 2 Reading Room.

Catalogue(s) available via the Internet: The National Sound Archive's catalogue CADENSA is now available via the Internet on http://www.cadensa.bl.uk. This includes entries for almost two-and-a-half million recordings, making it one of the largest catalogues of its kind anywhere. Subject coverage includes published and unpublished recordings in all genres from pop, jazz, classical and world music to oral history, drama and literature, dialect, language and wildlife sounds.

(photo courtesy of British Library National Sound Archive)

Websites relating to radio and moving images: See NSA pages on BL website (address above).

Digitised collection: Almost all the NSA's current audio intake is digital. Total holdings of digital discs and tapes amount to about 600,000 discs and tapes. It is the NSA's policy to digitise its entire holdings as soon as possible, and various strategies to achieve this are in progress.

Access: All videos are available for viewing. The NSA operates the only public listening facility for BBC programmes. Any programme in the BBC Sound Archive or in the NSA's holdings of BBC and independent radio recordings can be heard in the Listening and Viewing Service. Opening hours: Mon, 10.00–20.00; Tue-Thu, 09.30–20.00; Fri-Sat, 09.30–17.00. For admission to BL reading rooms, including the Listening and Viewing Service, a BL reader's ticket is needed. The Listening and Viewing Service operates by appointment only (direct line: 020 7412 7418).

Access to researchers from outside: Yes.

Viewing and listening facilities: NSA Listening and Viewing Service on the premises at the British Library, St Pancras.

Charges: Free of charge.

Copyright: The NSA has only carried out a very small amount of video recording, mainly of theatrical events. The recording copyright in these events would be owned by the NSA but no other rights. The NSA does not hold any copyright in most of its audio or video holdings.

BRITISH LIBRARY OF POLITICAL AND ECONOMIC SCIENCE

London School of Economics Library
25 Southampton Buildings
LONDON
WC2A 1PH
Tel: 020 7955 7951
Fax: 020 7955 7454

Contact: Mr Rupert Wood, Assistant Librarian, User Education Team. Information Services and Collection Development.

E-mail: r.wood@lse.ac.uk

Note: *The Library will be moving to 10 Portugal Street, London WC2A 2HP after 31 March 2001. Telephone number and fax will remain the same.* A video collection is maintained largely of videos required for teaching purposes. A selection of off-air recordings is also made from British broadcasting channels of programmes which have a documentary or public affairs interest.

Video and film holdings: The BLPES's video collection consists largely of off-air recordings and some bought videos suggested by academic staff for inclusion in its Course Collection (reading list materials). Strengths of the collection are in the general subject areas of Politics (particularly political documentaries) and International History, with some sociological and economic coverage.

Computerised database: http://www.blpes.lse.ac.uk.

Library OPACs with major holdings on moving image and radio: Unicorn catalogue.

Catalogue(s) available via the Internet: Unicorn catalogue.

Copyright: The Library has an ERA licence to record programmes off-air.

BRITISH MEDICAL ASSOCIATION LIBRARY

BMA House
Tavistock Square
LONDON
WC1H 9JP
Tel: 020 7383 6690
Fax: 020 7388 2544
Web: http://www.bma.org.uk

Contact: Ms Fiona Robertson, Film & Video Librarian. The Library.

E-mail: frobertson@bma.org.uk

Note: *The BMA prefers not to have a detailed entry in this edition of the Researcher's Guide as, owing to major departmental reorganisation, it is not currently providing footage and research services.*

BRITISH MOTOR INDUSTRY HERITAGE TRUST FILM & VIDEO ARCHIVE

Heritage Motor Centre
Banbury Road
GAYDON
Warwickshire
CV35 0BJ
Tel: 01926 641188
Fax: 01926 641555

Contact: Ms Gillian Bardsley, Archivist.

The Film Archive of the British Motor Industry Heritage Trust has been assembled from the film collections of the many motor companies and factories which combined to form British Leyland in 1968. These include Rover, Morris, Austin, Triumph, Standard, MG, Riley, Wolseley, and Vanden Plas.

Video and film holdings: Video: 1,000 hours. Advertising, documentary.
Video components: Hi-Band U-matic, lo-band U-matic, Beta/Beta-SP, 1-inch Video, 2-inch Video.
Film: 3,000 cans. 60% colour film, 40% black and white film, 10% nitrate film. Advertising, documentary, training films, crash tests, travelogues.
Film components: 16mm, 35mm, positive film, negative film, fine grain print.

Storage: Purpose-built temperature controlled vault at Gaydon Headquarters.

Computerised database: Available.

Conservation policy: Original film copied onto video masters.

Access: Limited access. By appointment. Access for researchers.

Viewing and listening facilities: Duplicating.

Charges: Charges for research for broadcast productions. Charges for facilities and handling.

Copyright: Copyright held. Copyright advice available. Copyright adviser: Gillian Bardsley.

BRITISH MOVIETONEWS FILM LIBRARY

Head Office
Denham Media Park
North Orbital Road
DENHAM
UB9 5HQ

Tel: 01895 833071
Fax: 01895 834893
Web: http://www.movietone.com

Contact: Ms Barbara Heavens, Senior Librarian.

E-mail: library@mtone.co.uk

British Movietonews is one of the great 35mm newsreel collections of the world, covering the period 1929–1979. The Library also has the Henderson Collection with film material from 1895 to World War I and the Pinewood Feature Film Stock Shot Library. Also the TV-am News Library, rushes of news stories from the period 1983 to 1990.

Video and film holdings: Film: There is no accurate figure but the total footage is estimated to be around 80 million feet, rising possibly to 100 million feet of 35mm film. This figure includes the Pinewood stock shot material. The film preservation programme is now complete and all nitrate newsreels are now on 35mm Master positive.
Video: All the newsreels are now held on DVC Digital tape and can be transferred to VHS, Beta SP and DVC in-house. Early in 2001 the Library will have completed the transfer of over 500 hours of unissued material and out-takes to DVC. The TV-am News Library is also held on DVC tape.

Storage: The film material is stored in 33 vaults adjacent to the Library. The vaults were built in 1961 to the specification of the Home Office and were approved by the factory inspectors. The master tapes are stored in secure fireproof cabinets, with a duplicate set stored off-site at Security Archives.

Computerised database: All the newsreels, the Henderson Collection and the TV-am News Library have been entered onto the Library's Concordance database. Print-outs of items can be faxed or e-mailed from the database. The same information can be searched on the website. The database for the unissued material and out-takes is being compiled at the present time. Pinewood Feature Film Stock Shot Record Books – these are in various volumes in which stock shots are illustrated as well as being described.

Documentation: Movietone issue sheets, 9 June 1929 to 29 May 1979 are now entered on the database. There are also commentary sheets from 1936 to 1979. Printed text of speeches are not available.

Conservation policy: The only material junked is badly decayed nitrate stock. Newsreel preservation programme is now complete. Preservation of film to digital tape nearing completion.

Access: Access available. 09.00–17.30. Staff are available to assist.

Viewing and listening facilities: Time-coded VHS viewing cassettes are available direct from the Denham Office. Viewing on premises.

Charges: Charges for research for broadcast purposes. Charges for research for academic purposes. Charges for facilities and handling. A price list is available upon request.

Copyright: Copyright held.

BRITISH MUSEUM – ETHNOGRAPHY DEPARTMENT

Burlington Gardens
LONDON
W1X 2EX
Tel: 020 7323 8065
Fax: 020 7323 8013

Contact: Staff, Audio-Visual Unit.

E-mail: ethnography@thebritishmuseum.ac.uk

Over 100 different film and video programmes are held. Most of the films have been purchased since 1970, primarily for use in public shows at the Museum, but others are kept mainly for reference. Subjects relevant to cultural anthropology and some archaeology are included.

Video and film holdings: Video: Includes videotapes of some public showing films (listed under film holdings) and other films, including some of Granada TV's *Disappearing World* series. Acquisition rate of five or ten per annum. Documentary.
Video components: VHS Video.
Film: The holdings include 16mm films for public showings (about 50); 12,000 ft of film dating from the 1930s and earlier including film of Aborigines made in 1930s, of Veddas (Ceylon) in the 1930s or earlier and of New Guinea, perhaps 1904; Dr William Sargent's collection on trance, spirit possession, etc., provisionally edited and catalogued; and original unedited reject film material from the BBC *Tribal Eye* series.
Film components: 16mm, positive film.

Storage: Storage in standard cupboards and cabinets.

Printed catalogue: No published catalogue presently available.

Documentation: File of basic information on origin, acquisition and content, plus additional documentation where available, may be viewed by appointment at the Students' Room, British Museum, Ethnography Department, Burlington Gardens, London W1S 2EX, (Tel: 020 7323 8041/8044. Fax: 020 7323 8013).

Viewing and listening facilities: By public shows or by appointment with the Audio-Visual Unit, British Museum, Great Russell Street, London WC1 (Tel: 020 7323 8505/8214. Fax: 020 8323 8827.) Films and videos cannot be loaned.

Charges: Charges for facilities and handling. Handling charges may be made for the reproduction of the few items for which copyright is held.

Copyright: In most cases information on copyright holders may be researched from acquisition information. The Museum itself does not hold copyright on more than two or three items and its collection is held for theatre and research viewing rather than to supply footage to filmmakers.

BRITISH PATHE PLC

New Pathe House
57 Jamestown Road
Camden
LONDON
NW1 7DB
Tel: 020 7424 3636
Fax: 020 7424 3637

Contact: Mr Larry McKinna, Chief Librarian. Paul Gost, Senior Librarian.

E-mail: pathe@britishpathe.com

Pathé's Animated Gazette: started regular bi-weekly publication in London in February 1910. The length of the newsreel at the time was about 300 feet and by 1914 90 copies were being printed. In 1914 up to the start of World War I a daily edition was issued. In the following years, the length and number of copies increased gradually and for several years two newsreels were published weekly, a long one of 600–700 feet and a short one of 300 feet.
Pathé Super Sound Gazette, and *Pathé Gazette*: with the advent of sound in 1930, Pathé had to publish the above three newsreels to cover the period when cinemas were changing from silent to sound projectors. After some years, the first two were discontinued. *Pathé Gazette* continued until the end of 1945.
Pathé News: this was the new title given to the Pathé newsreel from newsreel number 1, 1946. In 1960 Pathé News produced its first reels in colour. The last release of the newsreel was no. 70–17, 26 February 1970.
Pathé Pictorial: first released in March 1918 this cinemagazine continued in production until 27 March 1969.
Eve's Film Review: this news magazine for women began in 1921 and continued until 1933.
Pathétone Weekly: this international production was first released weekly in 1930 with a view to incorporating

all the semi-news events which passed into the Pathé organisation and its news exchanges around the world. It ceased production in 1941.

Astra Gazette: a digest of mainly *Pathé Pictorial* material that was compiled for the RAF. Twelve *Gazettes* were issued.

Video and film holdings: Film: 5,000,000 feet. 100% black and white film.

Film components: 16mm, 35mm, negative film, fine grain print, lavender master, dupe negative film.

Storage: All the film in the collection is stored in temperature controlled vaults at the Pinewood Studios, Iver, Buckinghamshire.

Card catalogue: Available, indexed.

Computerised database: Available.

Cataloguing: The card catalogue is divided into two separate sections: 1) Pre-War (but including the World War II period) and 2) Post-War. The card catalogue is now fully computerised and cross-indexed enabling rapid access to all subject matter by general or detailed search terms. Terminals are available at both the London and Pinewood offices.

Documentation: Issue sheets for *Pathé Super Sound Gazette*, *Pathé Super Gazette*, *Pathé Gazette*, *Pathé News*, *Pathé Pictorial*, *Eve's Film Review*, *Pathétone Weekly*, and *Astra Gazette*. Cameraman's dope sheets, shotlists (from 1940 onwards), commentary sheets etc.

Conservation policy: The Library is involved in a huge preservation programme. The nitrate originals are cleaned, copied and re-catalogued. The programme, which will continue for many years, will be an important contribution to newsfilm records of the 20th century.

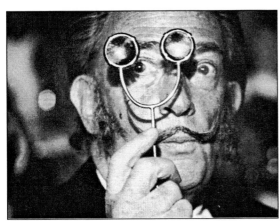

Salvador Dali (photo courtesy of British Pathe PLC)

Access: Access available. Researcher's first point of contact should be the British Pathe's main research office in Charlotte Street, where a large number of video cassettes of the most popular material is held. The actual film is held at the library at Pinewood along with a duplicate database: British Pathe plc, Pinewood Studios, Pinewood Road, Iver Heath, Bucks SL0 0NH, tel: 01753 630361, fax: 01753 655365, e-mail: pathepinewood@enterprise.net. Contact: Ron Saunders, Operations Manager.

Viewing and listening facilities: Viewing on premises. A video and database link between the two sites exists enabling everything to be kept up to date and clients to view film held at Pinewood on this link.

Charges: Charges for other services. Charges are levied for viewing and copying. There are special rates for different types of user. All royalties will be charged at the rates existing, at the time of declaration.

Copyright: All footage is furnished for use in one production only and may not be sub-licensed in isolation. General Conditions and Terms of Trade are sent to all customers and must be read and accepted before material is supplied. British Pathe plc to be given full credit on all productions.

BRITISH RECORD INDUSTRY TRUST SCHOOL

60 The Crescent
CROYDON
CR0 2HN
Tel: 020 8665 5242
Fax: 020 8665 8676
Web: http://www.brit.croydon.sch.uk

Contact: Mrs Valerie Fairbrass, Librarian. Performing Arts and Technology School.

E-mail: vfairbra@brit.croydon.sch.uk

The collection is part of the Performing Arts Library used by students at KS4 and KS5, in particular those studying for BTEC qualifications.

Video and film holdings: 3,000.

Music holdings: 2,000.

Books holdings: 2,000.

Newspapers holdings: 2,000.

Computerised database: Yes.

Library OPACs with major holdings on moving image and radio: Yes.

Digitised collection: No. No plans to do so.

Access to researchers from outside: By arrangement.

BRITISH SOCIETY OF SCIENTIFIC GLASSBLOWERS VIDEO LIBRARY

Kaimes Farm
Dumbarton Road
Oxford Street
STIRLING
FK8 3AB
Tel: 01786 473305
Fax: 01786 446995
Web: (British Society of Scientific Glassblowers) http://www.bssg.co.uk

Contact: Mr Graham Reed.

E-mail: scotiaglasstech@cw.com.net

Started in 1983 by transferring some old (1950) cine film onto video. By 1992, there were over 130 titles in Library.

Video and film holdings: Video: 160 reels/cassettes. The majority are in colour with sound, and cover scientific glassblowing. Other types of glassworking are represented, i.e. ornamental decorative, flat glass, fibre optics and container glass. Collection is expanding at approximate rate of one a month. Advertising, science and education.
Video components: VHS Video, hi-band U-matic.
Film: No film holdings.

Storage: All tapes stored in dust proof cases in cabinet but with no special facilities.

Printed catalogue: Available.

Cataloguing: List of titles available and most titles have been reviewed in the *British Society of Scientific Glassblowers Journal*, 1983, Vol 21, No. 4 onwards.

Access: Access available. By arrangement only.

Viewing and listening facilities: Viewing on premises.

Charges: Charges for facilities and handling. A search fee will be made.

Copyright: Copyright not held. Copyright advice available. Copyright adviser: Ian Pearson.

BRITISH TELECOMMUNICATIONS PLC FILM AND VIDEO ARCHIVE

BT Archives
3rd Floor, Holborn Telephone Exchange
268–270 High Holborn
LONDON
WC1V 7EE
Tel: 020 7492 8792

Contact: Lucy Jones, Archivist.

E-mail: archives@bt.com

Historical film and video library of BT and its predecessor, the Telecommunications Department of the British Post Office. The collection consists of copies of advertisements, training films, promotional and general information films. Films produced up to the date of BT's flotation in August 1984 are classed as public records under the Public Records Acts, 1958 and 1967.

Video and film holdings: Video: 4,400 reels/cassettes. Advertising, in-house productions.
Video components: VHS Video, hi-band U-matic, lo-band U-matic, Beta/Beta-SP, 1-inch Video, 2-inch Video, U-matic S.
Film: 900 cans. 90% colour film, 10% black and white film. Advertising, in-house productions.
Film components: Super 8mm, 16mm, 35mm.

Computerised database: Available.

Conservation policy: Duplicates and low-value material are destroyed.

Viewing and listening facilities: Viewing on premises.

Charges: Charges for research for broadcast productions. Charges for other services. A price list is available upon request.

Copyright: Copyright mostly not held.

BRITISH VIDEO HISTORY TRUST

c/o BUFVC
77 Wells Street
LONDON
W1T 3QJ
Tel: 020 7393 1500
Fax: 020 7393 1555
Web: http://www.bufvc.ac.uk

Contact: Mr Murray Weston, Director. Mr Geoffrey O'Brien, Assistant Director.

E-mail: ask@bufvc.ac.uk

The Trust was established to encourage the collection on videotape of first-hand testimony and scenes of everyday life in Britain. It was set up by the British Broadcasting Corporation and the British Universities Film & Video Council. High-quality video equipment (donated by Sony Broadcast, W. Vinten Ltd and Rank Strand Electric) is lent to groups which have submitted suitable projects for recording. The aim is to enable applicants to gather video recordings of broadcast quality and adequate documentation to allow the widest possible use of the material in future years.

Video and film holdings: Video: 250 hours. Interviews and scenes from projects have covered the life of lighthouse keepers, work at a hand-painted-wallpaper factory, a silversmith making a massive wine cistern, work at an animal hospital, a pie and mash shop, the lifestyle of New Age travellers, and veterans of the International Brigades who fought alongside the Republicans during the Spanish Civil War. Amateur, documentary, raw footage.

Video components: VHS Video, hi-8, Beta.

Storage: Master material held separate from viewing copies. No special humidity controls.

Cataloguing: Groups return documentation with the master tapes. Simple shotlists available for most items. Computerisation is planned.

Access: Access available. Mon-Fri 10.00–17.30, by arrangement only.

Viewing and listening facilities: Viewing on premises.

Charges: The Trust has a scale of charges for use of the material (all proceeds go into the work of the Trust).

Copyright: Copyright held. Copyright advice available. Copyright adviser: Geoffrey O'Brien.

The BRITTEN-PEARS LIBRARY

The Red House
Golf Lane
ALDEBURGH
Suffolk
IP15 5PZ
Tel: 01728 451700
Fax: 01728 453076
Web: http://www.britten-pears.co.uk

Curator for Reader Services.

E-mail: bpl@britten-pears.co.uk

The Britten-Pears Library was originally assembled by Benjamin Britten (1913–1976) and Peter Pears (1910–1986) as a working collection of manuscripts, books, music, and sound and video recordings reflecting their interest and careers. Adjacent to The Red House, where Britten and Pears came to live in 1957, the Library is housed in former farm buildings first adapted in 1963 and greatly expanded in 1993. The collections continue to grow, serving the educational and informational needs of users, school groups and other visitors from all over the world.

Video and film holdings: Video: 420 cassettes. Including home movie, documentary and news material relating to Britten, Pears and their artistic circle; VHS copies of all films for which Britten composed incidental music; many videos of performances of Britten's works, including operas; videos featuring Britten and Pears as performers and material relating to the Aldeburgh Festival and to the Britten-Pears School for Advanced Musical Studies.

Benjamin Britten and Peter Pears at Snape in 1974 (photo by Victor Parker courtesy of The Britten-Pears Library)

Video components: VHS Video.
Film: 15 cans.
Film components: 16mm.

Storage: All material is kept in an audio-visual storeroom in which temperature and humidity are controlled.

Computerised database: Approximately two thirds of the collection is catalogued within the Library's electronic catalogue.

Documentation: Some shooting scripts for key documentaries and operas are available. Files relating to broadcasting history and copyright are also available.

Access: The Library is open Mon-Fri, 10.00–13.00 and 14.15–17.15 by prior appointment only.

Viewing and listening facilities: VHS material may be viewed on-site. There is no facility for viewing film material.

Copyright: Copyright advice available.

BROADLAND 102

St George's Plain
47–39 Colegate
NORWICH
NR3 1DB
Tel: 01603 630621
Fax: 01603 666353
Web: http://www.broadland102.co.uk

Contact: Mr Dave Brown, Programme Controller.

E-mail: sales@broadland102.co.uk

The radio station holds 42 days' output only.

BRUNEL UNIVERSITY

UXBRIDGE
UB8 3PH
Tel: 01895 247000, ext 2787
Fax: 01895 203263
Web: http://www.brunel.ac.uk/depts/lib

Information Librarian, Uxbridge Enquiry Desk Brunel University Library.

E-mail: library@brunel.ac.uk

Video and film holdings: 4,000 videos.

Books holdings: Academic texts on 20th-century film and television.

Theses holdings: Ph.D. and MPL: 1.

Datasets holdings: Check website.

Journals holdings: Check OPAC.

Library OPACs with major holdings on moving image and radio: Yes.

Catalogue(s) available via the Internet: Yes.

Digitised collection: Not currently.

Access: Check Website for current access.

Viewing and listening facilities: Yes.

BUFVC OFF-AIR RECORDING BACK-UP SERVICE

British Universities Film & Video Council
77 Wells Street
LONDON
W1T 3QJ
Tel: 020 7393 1500. Direct: 020 7393 1503
Fax: 020 7393 1555
Web: http://www.bufvc.ac.uk

Contact: Mr Geoffrey O'Brien, Assistant Director.

E-mail: geoff@bufvc.ac.uk

Since June 1998 the BUFVC retains all its off-air recordings from the five British terrestrial television channels. This material accumulates at a rate of around 26,000 hours of transmitted material each year. Staff from any educational institution which has BUFVC membership and which holds an ERA licence can call upon access to this library. It should be noted that at the present time the BUFVC does not supply copies of missed recordings transmitted by the Open University.

Digitised collection: Yes.

Access: Available only to educational institutions which hold an ERA licence and are members of the BUFVC.

Charges: Forms part of membership subscription to the BUFVC.

BULLETIN VIDEO LIBRARY

Bulletin International
5–8 Hardwick Street
LONDON
EC1R 4RB
Tel: 020 7278 6070
Fax: 020 7278 6349
Web: http://www.bulletin.com

Contact: Mr Rabia Bapu, Production Assistant.

E-mail: rabia.bapu@uk.bulletin.com

Bulletin International is a production/PR company making all kinds of promotional material for many different companies, organisations, charities and governmental agencies. Since 1989 a large collection of general and specific images has been built up which Bulletin makes available to producers and broadcasters at competitive rates.

Video and film holdings: Video: 3,000 hours. News and current affairs, science and education, general stock material.
Video components: VHS Video, Beta/Beta-SP.

Storage: Designated tape library on site.

Computerised database: Available.

Cataloguing: A holdings list is available.

Conservation policy: No material is discarded.

Access: Access available. By arrangement. Staff are available to assist.

Viewing and listening facilities: Viewing on premises.

Charges: Charges for facilities and handling. A price list is available upon request.

Copyright: Copyright held.

The BUZZ 97.1

Media House
Claughton Road
BIRKENHEAD
CH41 6EY
Tel: 0151 650 1700
Fax: 0151 647 5427
Web: http://www.thebuzz971.co.uk

Contact: Mr Gavin Matthews, Programme Manager.

The radio station holds 42 days' output only to meet legal requirement.

CADBURY FILM COLLECTION

PO Box 12
Bournville
BIRMINGHAM
B30 2LU
Tel: 0121 458 2000
Fax: 0121 451 4333

Contact: Ms Sarah Foden, Library and Archives.

Cadbury was trading in cocoa on the Gold Coast by 1907 and as early as 1913 began using film for promotional purposes.

Video and film holdings: Film: The Collection includes feature films: 56 films on 16mm, from the 1920s to 1950s, mostly showing the growing and transport of cocoa beans in and around the Gold Coast, and subsequent processing in the Bournville factory, including scenes of daily life at Bournville. (Copies of 26 feature films on 16mm have been deposited with the National Film and Television Archive), and advertising films: 570 cans of film on 35mm, including cinema and television adverts for Cadbury brands from 1950s to 1970s. Advertising, documentary, feature films.

Access: Access limited to loans to major organisations with their own viewing facilities, not to members of the public.

CALDERDALE COLLEGES CORPORATION

Percival Whitley Centre
Francis Street
HALIFAX
HX1 3UZ
Tel: 01422 357357 ext 9028

Contact: Mr Andy Wright, Assistant Librarian. Library and Learning Centre.

E-mail: andyw@calderdale.ac.uk

The videos cover all areas of the curriculum. The book collection covers media studies and the visual arts.

Video and film holdings: c.2,000 VHS video cassettes containing 8,000 programmes.

Sound holdings: 300 audiocassettes.

Books holdings: A few hundred.

Computerised database: M/S access DB for label printing.

Library OPACs with major holdings on moving image and radio: Library catalogue OLIB 7.

Catalogue(s) available via the Internet: No.

Websites relating to radio and moving images: No.

Digitised collection: No.

Access: Mon-Thu, 08.45–21.45. Fri, 08.45–16.00 for college students.

Access to researchers from outside: No.

Viewing and listening facilities: Group viewing. 4–6 individual viewing.

Charges: None for enrolled students.

Copyright: ERA licence.

CAMBRIDGE COUNTY RECORD OFFICE

County Record Office
Shire Hall
Castle Hill
CAMBRIDGE
CB3 0AP
Tel: 01223 717281
Fax: 01223 717201

Contact: E A Stazicker, County Archivist. Dr P C Saunders, Deputy County Archivist.

E-mail: county.records.cambridge@camcnty.gov.uk

The Record Office was established in stages between 1930 and 1958 and acts as an archive for the records of the County Council and a place of deposit for records of other local authorities, societies, businesses, private persons etc. for the county. Film is occasionally received as part of these records.

Video and film holdings: Video: 20 reels/cassettes. Advertising, amateur, documentary, news and current affairs, science and education.
Video components: VHS Video, Beta/Beta-SP.
Film: The archive holds 295 titles. There are five principal collections: 1) County Council planning films, c.1951–65; 2) Cambridge Accident Prevention Council national and local road safety films, c.1950–70; 3) County Council films of schools and educational films, 1934–70; 4) Pye-Unicam, Cambridge and King's Lynn, works, equipment, visitors, etc., 1957–70; 5) Papworth Village Settlement, hospital, village and industries, 1918–81.
30% colour film, 70% black and white film. Amateur, documentary, news and current affairs.
Film components: 8mm, 16mm, 35mm, positive film, negative film.

Storage: Strong room temperature and humidity controlled, but no special area for film.

Printed catalogue: Available.

Conservation policy: Any conservation work would be referred to experts at East Anglian Film Archive.

Access: Access available. By arrangement only. Staff are available to assist. Access for disabled. As the equipment to use the film must be brought from elsewhere, an appointment is essential.

Viewing and listening facilities: Viewing on premises.

Copyright: Copyright held in some cases.

CAMBRIDGE SOUTH ASIAN ARCHIVE

Centre of South Asian Studies
University of Cambridge
CAMBRIDGE
CB2 1SD
Tel: 01223 338094
Fax: 01223 316913
Web: http://www.s-asian.cam.ac.uk

Contact: Dr Kevin Greenbank, Archivist.

E-mail: webmaster@s-asian.cam.ac.uk

The film collection was started in the early 1970s. It comprises principally amateur cinefilm taken by Britons in India and South Asia from the early 1920s to the mid-1950s. 33 collections totalling just over 40 hours of footage depict all aspects of life in colonial South Asia. The collection has just been transferred onto DVD for viewing purposes and DigiBeta for use by researchers and broadcasters wishing to use sections of the films. The collection contains excellent footage of railways, army, engineering and civil service work as well as extensive scenes from South Asian life for both British and Asian inhabitants of the region.

Video and film holdings: Video components: DVDs, DigiBeta tape.

Film components: 16mm positive and negative, Standard 8mm positive.

Storage: DVDs for viewing purposes stored in the Library. The DigiBeta tapes are held by a partner company in London for transfer purposes. The original films are in process of being moved to the National Film and Television Archive for long-term storage.

Computerised database: Brief description in the general archive catalogue. A full shotlist is being prepared as a searchable database which will be put up on the website of the Centre.

Access: The Library is open Mon-Fri, 09.30–13.00 and 14.00–17.30. The Centre does close during certain times of the year, so checking by telephone ahead of a visit is advised. A terms of access contract must be completed by commercial users.

CAMERON LIFE FILM ARCHIVE

92 Manor Road
Manselton
SWANSEA
SA5 9PN
Tel: 01792 417351

Contact: Mr Charles Everest. Mr Nicholas Emery.

The film collection is a subsidiary of the Cameron Life Photographic Archive and contains material relating predominantly to the Solent area and the Isle of Wight from the early 1950s until the mid-1960s.

Video and film holdings: 45 cans containing in total between 10–15 hours of 16mm colour and black and white non-fiction film mostly on transport and maritime subjects (e.g., Isle of Wight railways, ferries, hovercraft, lifeboats, ocean liners, Southampton Docks, etc.) Comprehensive footage of the Britten-Norman Company detailing the development of the Cushioncraft and Islander aircraft projects.

Components: 16mm camera original (negative and positive). Black and white prints, dupes, and sound prints. The material has yet to be transferred to videotape or digitised; it is hoped that this will be done in the near future.

Storage: All films are stored in a semi-controlled environment.

Printed catalogue: Available from Nicholas Emery.

Computerised database: A detailed catalogue is available on request. It is intended to make this available online in the near future.

Documentation: There is some supplementary information.

Junking: Nothing is junked.

Access: By prior appointment.

Access to researchers from outside: Yes, all enquiries welcome.

Viewing and listening facilities: Yes.

Charges: Negotiable – none for viewing.

Copyright: Copyright held on most of the material.

CANAL+ IMAGE UK LTD

Pinewood Studios
Pinewood Road
IVER
Buckinghamshire
SL0 0NH
Tel: 01753 631111
Fax: 01753 655813

Contact: Mr John Herron, Library Manager.

Television series and feature films from British International Pictures, Welwyn Films, Associated British Picture Corporation, Anglo-Amalgamated, Ealing Films, British Lion, EMI, Thorn-EMI and Lumière Pictures. Also available is stock shot footage from the 1920s to the present day.

Video and film holdings: Video: VHS cassettes are available for most of the material held.
Video components: VHS Video.
Film: Original negatives, black and white or colour library prints. Viewing prints are available for most of the material held.

Storage: In vaults at Pinewood Studios.

Stills holdings: There is a stills library.

Cataloguing: All held at Pinewood Studios.

Access: Access available. By arrangement only. Immediate requests by telephone, letter and fax, or if necessary, by personal visit.

Charges: Details of royalty charges and search fees on request.

CAPITAL GOLD (1152)

Radio House
Aston Road North
BIRMINGHAM
B6 4BX
Tel: 0121 245 5000
Fax: 0121 359 1117
Web: http://www.capitalgold.com

Contact: Ms Teresa Mosedale. Marketing Module.

E-mail: info@capitalgold.co.uk

The radio station holds 3 months' output to meet legal requirement. Other programmes have gone to the National Sound Archive, including early programmes from the start of Capital FM. The Capital Group's central library is based in London. A music library is maintained.

Access: No public access.

CAPITAL GOLD (1170 & 1557)

Radio House
Whittle Avenue
Segensworth West
FAREHAM
Hampshire
PO15 5SH
Tel: 01489 589911
Fax: 01489 589453
Web: http://www.capitalgold.com

Contact: Mr Mark Sadler, Programme Controller.

E-mail: info@capitalgold.co.uk

The radio station holds 3 months' output to meet legal requirement. Other Capital Group programmes have gone to the National Sound Archive, including early programmes from the start of Capital FM. The Capital

Group's central library is based in London. A music library is maintained.

Access: No public access.

CAPITAL GOLD (1242 & 603)

Radio House
John Wilson Business Park
WHITSTABLE
Kent
CT5 3QX
Tel: 01227 772004
Fax: 01227 774450
Web: http://www.capitalgold.com

Contact: Mr Tony Fisher, Acting Programme Controller and Head of Music (Dec 2000).

E-mail: info@capitalgold.co.uk

The radio station holds 3 months' output to meet legal requirement. Other Capital Group programmes have gone to the National Sound Archive, including early programmes from the start of Capital FM. The Capital Group's central library is based in London. A music library is maintained.

Access: No public access.

CAPITAL GOLD (1305 & 1359)

West Canal Wharf
CARDIFF
Wales
CF10 5XL
Tel: 029 2023 7878
Fax: 029 2037 3011
Web: http://www.RedDragonfm.co.uk

Contact: Mr Andy Johnson, Programme Director.

E-mail: mail@RedDragonfm.co.uk

The radio station holds 3 months' output to meet legal requirement. Various local audio news and local interest programmes are kept indefinitely on digital recording system. The Capital Group's central library is based in London.

Access: No public access.

CAPITAL GOLD (1323 & 945)

Radio House
PO Box 2000
BRIGHTON
East Sussex
BN41 2SS
Tel: 01273 430111
Fax: 01273 430098
Web: http://www.capitalgold.com

Contact: Mr Andrew Jeffries.

E-mail: info@capitalgold.co.uk

The radio station holds 3 months' output to meet legal requirement. Other Capital Group programmes have gone to the National Sound Archive, including early programmes from the start of Capital FM. The Capital Group's central library is based in London. A music library is maintained.

Access: No public access.

CAPITAL GOLD (1548)

30 Leicester Square
LONDON
WC2H 7LA
Tel: 020 7766 6000
Fax: 020 7766 6100
Web: http://www.capitalgold.com

Contact: Mr Andy Turner, Programme Controller.

E-mail: info@capitalradio.co.uk

The radio station holds 3 months' output to meet legal requirement. Other programmes have gone to the National Sound Archive, including early programmes from the start of Capital FM. The Capital Group's central library is based in London. A music library is maintained.

Access: No public access.

CAPITAL RADIO plc

30 Leicester Square
LONDON
WC2H 7LA
Tel: 020 7766 6000
Fax: 020 7766 6100
Web: http://www.capitalradio.plc.uk

Contact: Mr Richard Park, Group Director of Programmes.

E-mail: info@capitalradio.co.uk

Stations owned by Capital Radio plc hold 3 months' output to meet legal requirement. Other programmes have gone to the National Sound Archive, including early programmes from the start of Capital FM. The Capital Group's central library is based in London. A music library is maintained.

Access: No public access.

CARLTON TELEVISION

Carlton Studios
Lenton Lane
NOTTINGHAM
NG7 2NA

(photo courtesy of Carlton Television)

Tel: 0115 986 3322
Fax: 0115 964 5202
Web: http://www.carlton.com

Contact: Ms Janet Pitts, Library Manager. Mr Rob Peers.

E-mail: library.sales@carltontv.co.uk

Carlton's Library houses one of the country's largest collections, incorporating Midlands regional news from 1956 to the present day; Central Television's programmes from 1982 and Carlton's programming from 1993. The collection is updated daily with news from three regional newsrooms and Carlton's programme output.

Video and film holdings: Video: News from 1981, programmes, viewing cassettes.
Video components: Lo-Band U-matic, VHS, Beta SP, DigiBeta, Beta SX, 1-inch tape, D2, 2-inch Video, D2.
Film: News from 1956 to 1981, programmes.
Film components: 16mm black and white negative film, colour reversal, positive film. negative, effects mix, final mix.

Card catalogue: News 1956–1969, viewing cassettes, programmes on film.

Computerised database: News 1970 to present day, programmes on tape.

Cataloguing: All news is catalogued on either card index or computerised database. All programmes on tape are held on a computerised database; most entries only give production details, but little subject data.

Documentation: Daily printouts of news material, some transmission scripts, some press information and production stills.

Access: Access available by arrangement only. Access

for the disabled. Enquiries should be made in writing and sent by fax, e-mail or post. Research is usually carried out by Carlton's own staff, but arrangements may be made for visits by researchers.

Viewing and listening facilities: Viewing on premises. Viewing off premises. VHS viewing cassettes may be provided on payment of a fee.

Charges: Charges for research, handling and facilities and use.

Copyright: Copyright held.

CASTROL FILM ARCHIVE

Castrol Ltd
Wakefield House
Pipers Way
SWINDON
Wiltshire
SN3 1RE
Tel: 01793 452585
Fax: 01793 513506

Contact: Ms Vanna Skelley, Archivist & Market Information Manager.

Since 1950 Castrol has commissioned two motorsport films annually. Until the 1980s 16mm prints of the films were available to motorcar/cycle clubs for film shows (nowadays, clubs can borrow VHS copies). The Archive collection consists mainly of 16mm prints (not masters), most of which have been transferred onto video format.

Video and film holdings: Video: 876 reels/cassettes. Most of the film material has been transferred onto video. Advertising, documentary, science and education. Video components: VHS Video, hi-band U-matic, lo-band U-matic, Beta/Beta-SP, 1-inch Video.
Film: 546 cans. 98% colour film, 2% black and white film. Advertising, documentary, science and education. Film components: 16mm, 35mm.

Storage: Controlled environment – low temperature, low humidity, basement storage.

Computerised database: Available.

Documentation: Some films have written commentaries.

Conservation policy: Good storage facilities. 16mm prints are being cleaned and transferred on to Betacam tape.

Access: Access available. Mon-Fri 09.00–17.00, by arrangement only. Staff are available to assist. Access for disabled.

Viewing and listening facilities: Viewing on premises. Duplicating. Duplication can be carried out by external agent at researcher's expense. Burmah Castrol will organise and manage duplication.

Copyright: Castrol assumes it owns copyright but does not give warranties or indemnities to filmmakers.

CENTRAL COLLEGE OF COMMERCE

Robertson Trust Resource Centre
Central Business Learning Zone
190 Cathedral Street
GLASGOW
G4 0ND
Tel: 0141 552 3941, ext 4001
Fax: 0141 552 7179
Web: http://www.centralcollege.ac.uk

Contact: Ms Kirsteen Dowie.

E-mail: kirsteen@central-glasgow.ac.uk

A small collection of videos held on various subjects, including management, information technology/computing, secretarial studies, human resource management, and art and design. The collection is used by staff for teaching purposes and by students for general information.

Video and film holdings: Approx. 336 videos.

Computerised database: Yes, Z39.50 compliant.

Digitised collection: No.

Access: Limited to library opening hours. Staff only collection and separate student collection.

Access to researchers from outside: No.

Viewing and listening facilities: 2 televisions.

Charges: None.

Copyright: No.

CENTRAL TELEVISION

see *Carlton Television*

CENTURY 105

Century House
Waterfront Quay
Salford Quays
MANCHESTER
M5 2XW
Tel: 0161 400 0105
Fax: 0161 400 1105
Web: http://www.century105.com

Contact: Mr Paul Jackson, Century Group Programme Controller.

E-mail: radio@century105.com

Radio station holding legal requirement plus special news items and programmes which are kept for in-house use, e.g. in compiling end-of-year review.

CENTURY 106

City Link
NOTTINGHAM
NG2 4NG
Tel: 0115 9106 100
Fax: 0115 9106 107
Web: http://www.century106.com

Contact: Mr Paul Jackson, Century Group Programme Controller.

E-mail: radio@century106.com

Radio station holding legal requirement plus special news items and programmes which are kept for in-house use, e.g. in compiling end-of-year review.

CENTURY RADIO

Century House
PO Box 100
GATESHEAD
NE8 2YX
Tel: 0191 477 6666
Fax: 0191 477 5660
Web: http://www.centurynortheast.com

Contact: Mr Paul Jackson, Century Group Programme Controller.

E-mail: radio@centurynortheast.com

Holds legal requirement plus special news items and programmes which are kept for in-house use, e.g. in compiling end-of-year review.

The CENTURY SPEAKS: BBC MILLENNIUM ORAL HISTORY PROJECT

see *British Library National Sound Archive*

CFM – CARLISLE

PO Box 964
CARLISLE
Cumbria
CA1 3NG
Tel: 01228 818964
Fax: 01228 819444

Contact: Mr Simon Monk, Head of Programmes.

Radio station holding output to meet legal requirement only.

CHAMPION 103 FM

Llys-y-Dderwen
Parc Menai
BANGOR
Wales
LL57 4BN
Tel: 01248 671888
Fax: 01248 671971
Web: http://www.championfm.co.uk

Contact: Ms Eira Davies, Station Director.

The radio station holds 42 days' output only to meet legal requirement.

CHANNEL 4 CLIP LIBRARY

Channel 4 International
124 Horseferry Road
LONDON
SW1P 2TX
Tel: 020 7306 8490
Fax: 020 7306 8362

Contact: Ms Claire Austin, Clip Library Sales Executive.

E-mail: caustin@channel4.co.uk

The Library holds Channel 4's commissioned output since it began broadcasting in November 1982. Some material is originated on film but transferred onto tape and therefore available only on tape.

Video and film holdings: Video: Documentary, news and current affairs, science and education, music and arts, nature.
Video components: 1-inch video, D5, Beta-SP.

Cataloguing: Programme extracts only available.

Access: No access. Programmes are not logged. The Clip Library deals only with broadcast enquiries.

Viewing and listening facilities: No viewing facilities or VHS available for general research.

Copyright: Copyright held. Copyright advice available. Copyright adviser: Claire Austin.

CHANNEL TELEVISION

The Television Centre
La Pouquelaye
ST HELIER
Jersey
JE2 3ZD
Tel: 01534 816816
Fax: 01534 816689
Web: http://www.channeltv.co.uk

Contact: Mr Alan Watts.

E-mail: broadcast@channeltv.co.uk

Channel Television holds all tape and film stock of broadcast items from October 1962. The archive is mostly of local interest, covering Channel Islands events and life. In addition to broadcast news and feature items, rushes of some specific events have been retained. These include: small boy falls into gorilla pit at Jersey Zoo and is protected by male animal, Jambo; passenger ferry hits rocks off Jersey, footage of passengers escaping into life-rafts; the Newall murder enquiry; rare footage of the Liberation of the Channel Islands from German Occupation in 1945 (restricted access); early black and white footage of Channel Island life, including motor racing and aircraft landing on the beach before the airport was built (restricted access); programme items on every Island Games since inception in 1987; restricted access to moving footage of David & Frederick Barclay (owners of Brecqhou, *The Scotsman, The European,* etc.). Other available footage: considerable general view material, including aerial shots of all Channel Islands.

Video and film holdings: Footage can be supplied in a number of formats. Rushes are not generally kept.

The CHANNEL TUNNEL LIBRARY

Hard Hat Archive, C/O Tandem TV & Film Ltd
10 Bargrove Avenue
Boxmoor
HEMEL HEMPSTEAD
Hertfordshire
HP1 1QP
Tel: 01442 61576
Fax: 01442 219250
Web: http://www.tandemtv.com

Contact: Mr Terry Page, Director.

E-mail: info@tandemtv.com

The Library consists of footage of the construction and current operation of the Tunnel from when it was first started in 1986 to its opening in 1994 by Her Majesty Queen Elizabeth and President Mitterand of France. Footage is available of all aspects of construction from tunnelling to aerial footage of terminals and was shot principally in France and the UK, but there is also footage of equipment manufacture in Canada, Italy, Belgium and Germany.

Video and film holdings: Over 100 hours of 16mm and 35mm footage transferred onto 1-inch and Beta SP tapes. Over 50 hours of video on Beta SP.

Storage: Beta SP tapes and programmes stored at Tandem premises. Film negative and programme masters are held at temperature controlled vaults and laboratories.

Computerised database: Computerised database. Printouts can be made available for a small printing fee.

Cataloguing: Computer printouts of all material can be available for a small printing fee.

Access: Access available. 10.00–17.00, by arrangement only.

Viewing and listening facilities: Viewing on premises or supply of duplicates, Beta-SP, Lo or Hi-Band SP U-matic, VHS or Hi-8.

Charges: Charges for research, facilities and handling. Price list available.

Copyright: Construction footage copyright held by Tandem TV & Film. Current operations: Tandem TV & Film is the agent for Eurotunnel. Copyright adviser: Barbara Page.

CHESTER COLLEGE

Parkgate Road
CHESTER
CH1 4BJ
Tel: 01244 375 444
Fax: 01244 392 811
Web: http://www.chester.ac.uk/lr

Contact: Ms Christine Stockton, Director. Enquiries desk Learning Resources.

E-mail: c.stockton@chester.ac.uk

There are 200,000 items in the College Library. Collection of videos includes off-air recordings and bought-in videos and feature films to support courses, e.g. Drama, Art, Languages, European Cinema.

Video and film holdings: 1,000.

Sound holdings: *c.*30 play readings, poetry readings.

Library OPACs with major holdings on moving image and radio: http://libcat.chester.ac.uk

Catalogue(s) available via the Internet: Yes. No major holdings.

Digitised collection: No.

Access to researchers from outside: For reference on application.

Viewing and listening facilities: Video playback on open access. Video presenter by arrangement.

Copyright: All videos are for educational use only.

CHILTERN FM

Chiltern Road
DUNSTABLE
Bedfordshire
LU6 1HQ
Tel: 01582 676200
Fax: 01582 676201
Web: http://www.chilternfm.co.uk

Contact: Mr Trevor James, The Programme Controller.

The radio station keeps 3 months' holdings of all output (full 24 hours).

CHOICE FM

291–299 Borough High Street
LONDON
SE1 1JG
Tel: 020 7378 3969
Fax: 020 7378 3391
Web: http://www.choicefm.net

Contact: Mr Ivor Etienne, Programme Controller.

The radio station holds output to meet legal requirement plus paper file. All news items are kept for one year. Maintains a large private black music library.

CHRIS COPELAND FILM COLLECTION

34 Hall Orchard Avenue
WETHERBY
West Yorkshire
LS22 6SN
Tel: 01937 585990
Web: http://fp.eliteuk.f9.co.uk/television

Contact: Mr Chris Copeland, Proprietor.

E-mail: chris.copeland@talk21.com

A continually expanding collection of mainly 16mm prints relating to British industry and transport. Of particular interest is the collection of British Coal films and titles from the COI, Ford, RAC and other transport related producers.

Video and film holdings: 110.

Masters holdings: 10.

Printed catalogue: Yes.

Computerised database: Yes.

Catalogue(s) available via the Internet: Shortly.

Access: No access.

Viewing and listening facilities: None. Preview tape on VHS available. Beta SP/BVU/DigiBeta tele-cine available.

Charges: Negotiable.

Copyright: None.

CITY BEAT 96.7

Lamont Buildings
Stranmillis Embankment
BELFAST
Northern Ireland
BT9 5FN
Tel: 028 9020 5967
Fax: 028 9020 0023
Web: http://www.citybeat.co.uk

Contact: Mr John Roxborough, Station Director.

E-mail: music@citybeat.co.uk

The radio station holds 42 days' output only.

CLASSIC GOLD AMBER

St George's Plain
47–49 Colegate
NORWICH
NR3 1DB
Tel: 01603 630621
Fax: 01603 666353
Web: http://www.broadland102.co.uk

Contact: Mr Dave Brown, Programme Controller.

E-mail: sales@broadland102.co.uk

Heavily music-based radio station. Holds logging tapes to meet legal requirement. Keeps interviews with music celebrities.

CLASSIC GOLD AMBER (SUFFOLK)

Alpha Business Park
6–12 White House Road
IPSWICH
IP1 5LT
Tel: 01473 461000
Fax: 01473 741200
Web: http://www.amber.radio.co.uk

Contact: Mr Mark Pryke. Programming.

The radio station holds 42 days' radio output only.

CLASSIC HOME CINEMA

7 Taylors Avenue
CLEETHORPES
N.E. Lincolnshire
DN35 0LF
Tel: 01472 603089
Fax: 01472 291934
Web: http://www.home/aol/chcinema

Contact: Mr Phil Sheard, Manager and Owner.

E-mail: chcinema@aol.com

Holds ex-home movies of 1920s – 16mm amateur footage of Lincolnshire, holiday resorts, families, fishing, the sea, seaside, boats, vehicles, wartime, railways, aircraft, mining. There is also a collection of 35mm vintage cinema and television ads, vintage newsreels and trailers to pre-1950s nostalgic films. Holds negatives of B Westerns and 1950s sci-fi films for which limited rights are held.

Printed catalogue: Yes.

Computerised database: Yes.

Catalogue(s) available via the Internet: No.

Access: None.

Access to researchers from outside: No.

Viewing and listening facilities: At above address.

Charges: Going rate per minute or part.

Copyright: Copyright held on all library titles; not for ex-commercial titles.

The CLIP JOINT

31 Dobree Avenue
LONDON
NW10 2AD
Tel: 020 8459 3858
Fax: 020 8459 3895

Contact: Ms Ghizela Rowe. John Brooker.

Includes also John Brooker's Movie Memories started by John Brooker in 1962 primarily for the preservation of 'B' westerns (see separate entry). Extended considerably to include a variety of American and British features as well as shorts, television programmes, cartoons, music films, trailers, commercials, stills etc. Extended in the late '80s to include music footage of the '60s and '70s (*see also separate entry for Maverick*).

Video and film holdings: Video: Most of the above mentioned film holdings are on VHS.
Video components: VHS video.
Film: 1,000,000 feet. Over a million feet of film footage from a thousand different titles from the 1900s to the 1950s with new acquisitions on a regular basis. 20% colour film, 80% black and white film. Advertising, amateur, documentary, feature films, news and current affairs, science and education, television, short films and serials, cartoons.
Film components: 16mm.

Storage: Purpose-built vault.

Card catalogue: Available.

Computerised database: Available.

Cataloguing: Fluent Italian spoken for any information required; French and Spanish a little. Information can be translated into any language if time allows.

Conservation policy: No material is junked.

Access: Access available. By arrangement only. Staff are available to assist. There are no facilities for disabled visitors, but assistance will be provided.

Viewing and listening facilities: Viewing on premises. Viewing off premises. Duplicating. Sales. VHS copies are available on site. Facilities house for any other format.

Charges: Charges for research for broadcast productions. Charges for facilities and handling. Search fees charged for supplying requested material and rates dependent on intended use.

Copyright: Most of the material held is out of copyright control. Copyright advice available. Copyright adviser: Ghizela Rowe.

CLIPS AND FOOTAGE

2nd Floor
80A Dean Street
LONDON
W1V 5AD
Tel: 020 7287 7287
Fax: 020 7287 0984
Web: http://www.clipsandfootage.uk.com

Contact: Ms Alison Mercer.

E-mail: clipsetc@easynet.co.uk

Clips and Footage is a comprehensive film library made up of thousands of hours of archive and modern colour imagery. Collections include aviation from the early days of flight to contemporary commercial and military aircraft; transport footage which covers ocean liners, trucks and cars in detail; archive and contemporary medical footage covering foetal and MRI scans, operations and hospitals; science and business; Americana; a war archive including material on the Korean War; world locations and time-lapse cityscapes, landscapes, flowers and clouds. Special collections: 1) The Hollywood Collection: Clips and Footage holds the largest feature film trailer archive in the UK, many feature films, silent comedies and cartoons, a collection covering the history of production in Hollywood with screen tests of Garbo, Bacall and Audrey Hepburn, interviews with stars and directors, the filming of many feature films and complementary stills and poster libraries. There is also B-movie archive and a sci-fi trailer library. 2) The News Collection: Material on historical personalities such as Eva and Juan Peron, Gandhi, Franco, Krushchev, Helen Keller, Jack Benny, Hitler, Henry Ford, Nixon, Burt Lancaster, Marilyn Monroe, Frank Sinatra, Grace Kelly,

Generals Patton and MacArthur, de Gaulle, J Edgar Hoover and the FBI, Edison, World War I and World War II, disasters, sport, fashion. 3) New Collections: Historical reconstructions of events as diverse as the Peasants' Revolt, the Battle of Culloden and the Napoleonic Wars.

Masters holdings: 35mm, 16mm, DigiBeta, Beta SP.

Stills holdings: Associated movie stills collection – 5,000+ transparencies and prints.

Posters holdings: Movie posters collection – 2,000 items.

Computerised database: FileMakerPro database.

Websites relating to radio and moving images: http://www.clipsandfootage.uk.com

Digitised collection: In progress.

Access: By appointment.

Access to researchers from outside: Yes.

Viewing and listening facilities: NTSC and PAL U-matic; NTSC and PAL VHS.

Charges: Free to researchers. Free research and free viewing at the central London office.

Copyright: All rights held.

CLIVE GARNER VINTAGE RECORDS & FILMS

39 Mosslands Drive
WALLASEY
Merseyside
CH45 8PE
Tel: 0151 638 4711
Fax: 0151 638 4711

Contact: Mr Clive Garner, Owner.

New Brighton Bathing Pool, largest swimming arena in Europe, opened in 1934 – now demolished. (photo courtesy of Clive Garner Vintage Records & Films)

Film collection started in 1960s as an adjunct to a large collection of 78 r.p.m. gramophone records (over 40,000). Films cover same period as the records from the late 1920s to the early 1950s. Emphasis is on films that would form part of 'full supporting programme' at a cinema during the 'golden years' (viz. 1929 to 1949). Included are trailers, special cinema advertising shorts and other similar material, organ interlude films, cinema 'Day Titles', ice cream trailers, interest/documentary films, etc., (all 16mm). Also over 4,000 cinema organ song slides. The archive now also includes audio recordings from pre-war commercial radio and wartime broadcasts from Berlin in English.

Video and film holdings: Film: Also included is a large selection of local films from largely private sources showing scenes on Merseyside from 1929 through to the early 1960s. Earlier material is black and white, but some material from 1936 onwards is colour. Details on compositions of film holdings are not available. 5% colour film, 95% black and white film.

Film components: 16mm, positive film.

Cataloguing: Lists of specific film classifications available on request.

Access: Access available. By prior arrangement only.

Viewing and listening facilities: Viewing on premises. Fully equipped viewing theatre available for use at short notice.

Charges: Charges for research for broadcast productions. Charges are negotiable.

Copyright: Copyright held in most, but not all, cases.

COAST FM

Media House
41 Conwy Road
COLWYN BAY
Wales
LL28 5AB
Tel: 01492 533733
Fax: 01492 535248
Web: http://www.coastfm.co.uk

Contact: Ms Eira Davies, Station Director.

The radio station holds 42 days' output only to meet legal requirement.

COI FOOTAGE FILE

Film Images (London) Ltd
Fourth Floor
184 Drummond Street
LONDON
NW1 3HP

Tel: 020 7383 2288
Fax: 020 7383 2333
Web: http://www.film-images.com

Contact: Mr Tony Dykes, Senior Researcher.

E-mail: research@film-images.com

COI Footage File (Central Office of Information) is a unique visual record of Britain's culture, heritage, way of life and aspirations covering the last 60 years. The collection begins with John Grierson's documentary masterpiece *Drifters*. It moves on to include a wealth of material shot by the Crown Film Unit during the war and today encompasses an outstanding selection of Government-commissioned material that is constantly being updated. Footage File is a kaleidoscope of imagery – social, historical, geographical, scientific and political – including many subjects ranging from landscapes to laser surgery, churches to Churchill, forestry to forensic science.

Video and film holdings: Video and film holdings: 18,500 items.
Video components: DigiBeta, Beta SP, 1-inch, 2-inch, Hi/Lo Band U-matic.
Film components: 16mm, 35mm.

Storage: Custom-made temperature controlled storage off-site in London.

Conservation policy: All material is assessed upon reception and transferred to intermediate formats when required.

Computerised database: Available. A separate part of the site gives the researcher access to the COI Footage File database of shotlists and a catalogue of Crown titles available at regional archives.

Still from 'VILLAGE SCHOOL', 1940 (photo courtesy of Film Images [London] Ltd)

Catalogue(s) available via the Internet: Available online at http://www.film-images.com

Access: Access available (appointments necessary.) Access for disabled. Research can be carried out on behalf of customers.

Viewing and listening facilities: In-house viewing facilities available from VHS PAL reference library and 16mm/35mm Steenbecks available to view from film. Tailor-made VHS or U-matic cassettes can be made for preview purposes. (A fee is payable for this.) Showreels are available on request.

Charges: Fees are charged for research, licence fees and transfers/delivery. All fees are clearly outlined in advance, dependent on the project.

Copyright: Copyright is managed by Film Images on behalf of the Crown.

COLLEGE OF ST MARK AND ST JOHN

Derriford Road
PLYMOUTH
PL6 8BH
Tel: 01752 777188
Web: http://www.marjon.ac.uk

Contact: Dr Bernadette Casey, Subject Group Leader, Media Studies. Mr Frank Clements, Head of Learning Resources Department of Media Studies.

E-mail: stabac@lib.marjon.ac.uk

The main video collection supports the taught modules on Media Studies, and to a lesser extent English Literature and History. The video collection comprises a large number of feature films from the USA, the UK and a collection of foreign language films. Many of these have an historical significance. Also there is a collection of documentaries, some of which are used as teaching aids and others which are studied as media artefacts. The collection includes a large number of popular television programmes, from game shows to soap operas to drama, as well as some corporate work. At present the College is building its archive of films and television programmes directed by women.

Video and film holdings: 3,000 items relating to taught courses.

Masters holdings: No, only material promoting the College.

Music holdings: *c*.200 CDs and 400 cassettes.

Books holdings: Stock of approx. 5,000.

Theses holdings: None. Undergraduate dissertations 2.1 and above only.

Card catalogue: No.

Printed catalogue: No.

Computerised database: Stand-alone machine using Probite.

Library OPACs with major holdings on moving image and radio: No.

Catalogue(s) available via the Internet: No.

Digitised collection: No, and not in the immediate future.

Access: Prior permission by letter preferred.

Access to researchers from outside: Yes.

Viewing and listening facilities: Facilities available in the Learning Resources Centre.

Charges: None.

CONCORD VIDEO & FILM COUNCIL

201 Felixstowe Road
IPSWICH
IP3 9BJ
Tel: 01473 726012
Fax: 01473 274531

Contact: Ms Lydia Vulliamy, Member, Council of Management.

E-mail: concordvideo@btinternet.com

Originally started as 16mm film collection of material on the anti-nuclear weapon activities in Britain and elsewhere in the 1960s. The collection widened to include sociology, arts and general education with specialist collections on anthropology and social work, art and medicine (Graves Medical Audiovisual Library).

Video and film holdings: Video: 3,000 reels/cassettes. Documentary.
Video components: VHS Video, lo-band U-matic.
Film: 2,000 cans. 70% colour film, 30% black and white film. Documentary.
Film components: 16mm.

Storage: Films and videos stored on open shelving.

Printed catalogue: Available, indexed.

Cataloguing: A charge is made for the catalogue.

Documentation: None.

Conservation policy: Material is kept as long as space is available.

Access: Access available. Mon, Tue, Thu, Fri only, 09.00–17.00. Staff are sometimes available to assist.

Viewing and listening facilities: Viewing on premises. Viewing off premises.

Charges: Charges for research for broadcast productions. Charges for research for academic purposes. Charges for facilities and handling. Viewing on premises – charge by the hour; viewing off premises – charge by the programme.

Copyright: Copyright not held. Distribution on behalf of other bodies; clearance requests are referred to them. Copyright advice available. Copyright adviser: Lydia Vulliamy.

COOL FM

PO Box 974
BELFAST
Northern Ireland
BT1 1RT
Tel: 028 9181 7181
Fax: 028 9181 4974
Web: http://www.coolfm.co.uk

Contact: Mr David Sloane, Managing Director.

E-mail: music@coolfm.co.uk

The radio station holds a selection of radio programmes, spanning 25 years, of interest to the Northern Ireland audience.

Music holdings: Record library on disc and CD (not open to outside access).

Sound holdings: Approx. 150 reels of speech and speech/music programmes.

Newspapers holdings: Cuttings relating to Cool FM and Downtown FM, q.v.

Digitised collection: No.

Access: Office hours.

Access to researchers from outside: On application.

Viewing and listening facilities: On application.

Charges: Gratis.

Copyright: Broadcast rights.

CORNISH FILM AND VIDEO ARCHIVE

c/o Cornish Studies Library
2–4 Clinton Road
REDRUTH
Cornwall
TR15 2QE
Tel: 01209 216760
Fax: 01209 210283

Contact: Mr Terry Knight, Principal Librarian/Cornish Studies.

Note: *The Archive will be moving to new premises in September 2001. The Cornish Film and Video Archive was started by volunteer enthusiasts. The Cornish*

Studies Library film and video collection was created as part of the Library's stock. The two are run as one now. The Cornish Film and Video Archive surveyed extant Cornish film and video (report 1990), but collection awaits necessary staffing and funding. Not presently providing a service, but collecting continues.

Video and film holdings: Video: 350 reels/cassettes. Amateur, documentary, feature films, television drama.
Video components: VHS Video.
Film: 15 cans. 75% colour film, 25% black and white film. Advertising, amateur, documentary.
Film components: 16mm.

Storage: No purpose-built storage yet.

Computerised database: Available.

Cataloguing: The material is included in the Library's computerised catalogue, but cannot at present be conveniently separated from non-archive holdings for printout.

Conservation policy: To be determined, but co-operating with TSW Archive and the Cornwall Record Office.

Access: Limited access. Access is not practical at present.

Copyright: Copyright not held.

COSTAIN GROUP FILM & PHOTO LIBRARY

Hard Hat Archive, Tandem TV & Film Ltd
10 Bargrove Avenue
Boxmoor
HEMEL HEMPSTEAD
Hertfordshire
HP1 1QP
Tel: 01442 61576
Fax: 01442 219250
Web: http://www.tandemtv.com

Contact: Mr Terry Page, Director.

E-mail: info@tandemtv.com

The Library started life as a film unit in the 1920s, when Costain was primarily engaged in house building. As the Group's operations have expanded and diversified, so the Library's stock of films and videos has grown. Footage, shot mainly on film around the world, covers the Group's operations in mining, civil and process engineering and construction.

Video and film holdings: Video: 60 hours. Documentary.
Video components: VHS Video, hi-8, Beta/Beta-SP, 1-inch Video.
Film: 180 cans, 180 hours. 75% colour film, 25% black and white film. Documentary.

Film components: 16mm, 35mm, positive film, negative film, fine grain print.

Storage: VHS and hi-8 reference tapes at Tandem premises. 16mm and BVU held at archive vaults. Some programme masters held at labs/video facilities. Temperature controlled vaults.

Printed catalogue: Available.

Computerised database: Available.

Cataloguing: A catalogue of finished programmes is available. Computer printouts of all material can be made available for a small printing fee.

Access: Access available. 10.00–17.00, by arrangement only.

Viewing and listening facilities: Viewing on premises. Viewing off premises. Duplicating. Sales. U-matic, VHS, Betacam-SP, hi-8.

Charges: Charges for research for broadcast productions. Charges for research for academic purposes. Charges for facilities and handling. A price list is available upon request.

Copyright: Copyright not held. Copyright advice available. Copyright adviser: Terry Page.

COVENTRY CITY LIBRARY

Smithford Way
COVENTRY
CV1 1FY
Tel: 024 7683 2314
Fax: 024 7683 2440

Contact: Ms Karen Berry, Librarian.

E-mail: covinfo@discover.co.uk

Music holdings: Film and show soundtracks.

Sound holdings: Radio programmes, e.g. *The Goon Show,* are mostly on sound cassette.

Books holdings: Approx. 3,860 volumes.

Journals holdings: *Sight & Sound* (1991–current), *Monthly Film Bulletin* (1967–1991), *Empire* (incomplete, kept for 5 years), *Radio Times* (1 year kept). *Film Review* (4 copies kept).

Library OPACs with major holdings on moving image and radio: All-purpose OPAC only.

COVENTRY CITY RECORD OFFICE

Mandela House
Bayley Lane
COVENTRY
CV1 5RG
Tel: 024 7683 2418
Fax: 024 7683 2421

Contact: Ms Susan Worrall, City Archivist.

The archive was created by Coventry City Council. Acquisitions were made from 1948 to 1996. It holds several films of local interest, including civic films made by the corporation, one on the consecration of Coventry Cathedral, and some miscellaneous material, including films on the city's reconstruction following wartime bombing, and films on the motor industry.

Video and film holdings: Film: 100% black and white film. Advertising, news and current affairs, science and education.
Film components: 16mm, positive film.

Storage: Normal archival storage, temperature and humidity controlled.

Printed catalogue: Available, indexed.

Cataloguing: List of one-line entries, not indexed, available on request.

Documentation: None.

Conservation policy: Material is retained indefinitely.

Access: Access available. Mon-Thu 09.30–16.45; Fri 09.30–16.15; Mon by arrangement 16.45–20.00 for consultation of list. Access for disabled. By arrangement.

Charges: Charges for research for academic purposes.

Copyright: Copyright resides with Coventry City Council for the 23 films made by that body.

CRESSWELL LTD

Note: *Library has been re-named. See Treadwell Ltd.*

CULTURAL FANTASISTS LTD – MUSIC ARCHIVE

Lower Drumbuie
DRUMNADROCHAIT
Invernesshire
IV63 6XP
Tel: 01456 450155
Fax: 01456 450528

Contact: Ms Jennie Macfie.

E-mail: archive@culturalfantasists.co.uk

Established in 1991, Cultural Fantasists began with a library of about a hundred film clips produced in the early seventies. Since then it has steadily expanded and now includes films and videos by Don Letts, Chris Boger, Peter Whitehead, Tony Palmer, Brian Gibson, Mike Mansfield, Derek Jarman, Ken O'Neil, Jack O'Connell, Brian Simmons, Piers Bedford, Jack Hazan and David Mingay, Lindsey Clennell, Nick Abson, Brian Grant, Russell Mulcahy, Julien Temple and many others,

covering a period from the 1930s to the 1990s. Archive videotape of early 1980s fashion is also held.

Video and film holdings: Mostly British pop and rock artists. Performance clips and full concerts, documentaries, home movies, and interview footage. Extensive and exhaustive collection of punk rock footage.
Video components; VHS, U-matic, Beta SP, Quad video, 1-inch video, D1, D2, DigiBeta.
Film components: 8mm, 16mm, 35mm, positive and negative, magnetic and optical soundtracks.

Storage: Photobition and on site.

Printed catalogue: Available on request. In alphabetical order of band/artist or in date order (please specify).

Conservation policy: Film material is being mastered to Beta or DigiBeta formats. No film material is destroyed unless physically unusable.

Access: By arrangement. Free accommodation for researchers. Staff available to assist.

Viewing and listening facilities: Audition cassettes for viewing off premises are sent on receipt of order. Viewing on premises by arrangement.

Charges: Viewing cassettes are charged for at current rates. Master material is licensed at current rates. Terms and conditions, including rate card, are usually sent at time of enquiry.

Copyright: Copyright is owned by Cultural Fantasists or by the producer or director represented, in most cases. Copyright advice is available.

DAVID FINCH DISTRIBUTION LTD

PO Box 264
WALTON-ON-THAMES
KT12 3YR
Tel: 01932 882733
Fax: 01932 882108

Contact: Mr David Finch, Director.

E-mail: dfa@cwcom.net

A library representing a number of producers. Emphasis on 'reality' with police chases, surveillance camera footage, celebrities, fishing and war.

Video and film holdings: Police pursuits and bad driving (9 hours); film from security cameras – shoplifting, car theft and other crime (9 hours); Interviews with Hollywood celebrities (100 hours). Colour footage of bombing raids over Germany 1943/44 (1 hour). 70 hours of angling from Britain and abroad. Documentary, news and current affairs.
Video components: Beta/Beta-SP.

Printed catalogue: Available.

Computerised database: Available.

Conservation policy: Material kept indefinitely.

Access: Access available. By appointment.

Viewing and listening facilities: Viewing off premises.

Charges: Charges for research for broadcast productions. Charges for facilities and handling. Prices by negotiation.

Copyright: Copyright not held. But David Finch Distribution has the right to act on copyright holders' behalf.

DAVID KENTEN FILM COLLECTION

29 Fishergate
NORWICH
Norfolk
NR3 1SE
Tel: 01603 624255
Fax: 01603 624255

Contact: Mr David Kenten, Owner.

A private hobby that has grown over 35 years into a vast cross-section of subjects, and is still growing as material can be found.

Video and film holdings: Film: 2,000,000 feet. 5% colour film, 95% black and white film, 75% nitrate film. Advertising, amateur, documentary, feature films, news and current affairs, early animation.
Film components: 16mm, 35mm, positive film, negative film, fine grain print.

Storage: Off-site vault for nitrate.

Card catalogue: Card catalogue.

Conservation policy: No material is discarded.

1913 exterior of the Eiko Film Studio, Berlin. Taken from the feature film America/Europa in Luftschiff *(photo courtesy of David Kenten Film Collection)*

Access: Access available. By arrangement. Prospective users should apply in writing prior to making an appointment.

Viewing and listening facilities: Viewing on premises. Sales. Viewing on Steenbeck. Duplicating to any format can be arranged.

Copyright: Only 10% of copyright held by owner.

DENBIGHSHIRE RECORD OFFICE

46 Clwyd Street
RUTHIN
LL15 1HP
Tel: 01824 708250
Fax: 01824 708258

Contact: R K Matthias, County Archivist.

Denbighsire Record Office, formerly part of the Clwyd Record Office, has been collecting films and videos of local history significance since the 1980s. Holdings cover several areas of the former (pre-1974) county of Denbighshire, particularly Colwyn Bay, Denbigh, Ruthin and Wrexham, and while the earliest film dates from 1919, the latest video is from 1990. Subjects include a visit of the Prince of Wales to Colwyn Bay, 1928, Conway Bridge centenary celebrations, 1927, and a royal visit to Ruthin, 1984. The Record Office also holds video tapes of films, mostly relating to Rhyl, and produced by Arthur Cheetham and by the Shannon Film Company. These are part of a deposit received from Philip Lloyd of Mold, formerly the Clwyd Museums Education Officer. The deposit also includes video copies of the following films: part of a football match between Blackburn Rovers and West Bromwich Albion (1898); Queen Victoria's Diamond Jubilee (1897), Lumière Train (1898) and *The Great Train Robbery* (1903).

Video and film holdings: Video: 9 reels/cassettes. Amateur, documentary.
Film: 38 cans. Amateur, documentary.
Film components: 9.5mm, 16mm, 35mm.

Storage: Films and videos are held in the strongroom, which has temperature and humidity control.

Printed catalogue: Available, indexed.

Cataloguing: Index entries appear in the general place/subject index for all the Record Office's collection.

Conservation policy: All nitrate film has been copied onto more stable media and the originals destroyed. Otherwise film is kept even after being copied onto video.

Access: Limited access. Mon-Thu 09.00–16.45; Fri 09.00–16.15. Staff are available to assist. Access to the video collection only. It is not possible to view original film.

Viewing and listening facilities: Viewing on premises. Duplicating. Video copies can be supplied.

Charges: Charges for other services. There is a charge for copying.

Copyright: Copyright advice available. Copyright adviser: R K Matthias.

DEPARTMENT OF CULTURE, MEDIA AND SPORT

Information Centre
2–4 Cockspur Street
LONDON
SW1Y 5DH
Tel: 020 7211 6200
Fax: 020 7211 6032
Web: http://www.culture.gov.uk

Contact: Miss Felicitas Montgomery, Information Centre Manager.

E-mail: enquiries@culture.gov.uk

Small collection covering DCMS subjects.

Computerised database: Catalogues for internal use only.

Digitised collection: No.

Access: By appointment only if material not available elsewhere.

DIAMOND TIME

2nd Floor, Foframe House
35–37 Brent Street
Hendon
LONDON
NW4 2EF
Tel: 020 8203 3303
Fax: 020 8203 3222
Web: http://www.diamondtime.net

Contact: Mr Lee Taylor, Head of Programmes.

E-mail: lee.taylor@diamondtime.co.uk

A comprehensive collection of music on video from the 1970s to the present with historic additions going back to the 1930s.

Video and film holdings: Video: 1,500 hours. Music. Video components: VHS Video, lo-band U-matic, Beta/Beta-SP, 1-inch Video, 2-inch Video.

Storage: Climate controlled warehouse.

Computerised database: Available.

Conservation policy: Regular testing and checking. Slow transfer to Beta.

Access: No access.

Charges: Charges for research for broadcast productions. Charges for research for academic purposes. Charges for facilities and handling. A price list is available upon request.

Copyright: Some rights are held. As a clearance house the company can effect clearances. Copyright advice available. Copyright adviser: Diamond Time.

DIXONS CITY TECHNOLOGY COLLEGE

Ripley Street
BRADFORD
West Yorkshire
BD5 7RR
Tel: 01274 776777
Fax: 01274 391928

Contact: Ms Lynn Barrett, Information Sources Manager.

E-mail: lynn@dixonsctc.org.uk

This very small collection is for use within the College's curriculum.

Video and film holdings: Under 200 titles.

Access: Overnight borrowing.

Access to researchers from outside: No.

Viewing and listening facilities: Videos are issued to users (students) overnight. Teachers show videos in whole classes.

DOCUMEDIA INTERNATIONAL FILMS

19 Widegate Street
LONDON
E1 7HP
Tel: 020 7625 6200

Contact: Mr Steve Goddard, Director.

Documedia International is a European company, a film and video producer and distributor of international broadcast programming – documentaries: programme specials and series on art, science, wildlife, culture, sport, history and the humanities: drama: family entertainment, feature films and short drama.

Video and film holdings: Video: 1,000 plus: Documentaries, drama shorts, drama series and short films.
Video components: All formats: DigiBeta (and all related digi-formats); Beta SP, 1-inch.
Film: 200 hours of completed programming, plus more than 1,000 hours of out-takes and general archives of which 80% is colour.

Film components: Film formats include 16mm and 35mm, negative and film prints, audio relative to filmmaking mediums, such as optical sound (composite prints), 16mm and 35mm magnetic film, 1/4-inch audio and DAT tapes.

Storage: Laboratory storage for negatives. Humidity controlled environment for video master tapes and film prints.

Stills holdings: Photographic library of award winning stills from the films and series owned.

Printed catalogue: Available, indexed. Free of charge.

Computerised database: Available. Database management is for internal use. All enquiries to Documedia will be researched by staff either from the production team or from the sales office.

Documentation: Full transcripts of all completed programmes, dubbing cue sheets, press materials, cast and credit lists, music cue sheets, production and research notes subject to availability, production photographs.

Conservation policy: Restrictions limit access to master film and video tapes and all original materials to staff members only; all production materials available to clients are copies from the masters; back-up master copies of video tapes are retained; film master back-ups are made subject to assessed needs, availability and budget; regulated laboratory access to camera original materials can be arranged in exceptional circumstances; all materials are charged for and all rights under British, European and international copyright laws and conventions related thereto are strictly adhered to and are monitored.

Access: Access available. By prior arrangement. Staff are available to assist.

Viewing and listening facilities: Viewing on premises, or VHS preview tapes can be arranged. Viewing/loan of video preview cassettes charged for at cost, i.e. duplication, dispatch costs.

Charges: Charges for all research banded according to end use, i.e., academic enquiries are charged for at a nominal handling cost, requirements for broadcast use are charged for at the full research rate; charges levied for script copying, VHS tapes (sale or loan) and for general research. Price list available upon request.

Copyright: Owned or controlled by Documedia. The company has a policy of retaining exclusive rights for all materials, i.e. it does not share rights. It does not market or otherwise trade in pd (public domain) materials. Advice on issues relating to ancillary rights clearance (literary rights, music and artists' residuals) given.

DONCASTER COLLEGE

Church View
DONCASTER
South Yorkshire
DN1 1RF
Tel: 01302 553826
Fax: 01302 553838

Contact: Mr Rodney Challis, Video Tutor, Graphics Department. Trevor Bishop.

E-mail: rod.challis@don.ac.uk

Very small collection relating to moving image and radio.

Video and film holdings: Approx. 20–30 videos.

Books holdings: c.200 books.

Journals holdings: 3 or 4 film journals.

Library OPACs with major holdings on moving image and radio: On Genesis computer system.

Catalogue(s) available via the Internet: No.

Digitised collection: No. No plans to do so.

Access: Reference only unless registered staff/student of the college. External membership available.

Access to researchers from outside: Yes.

DORSET FILM AND SOUND ARCHIVE

Dorset Record Office
Bridport Road
DORCHESTER
Dorset
DT1 1RP
Tel: 01305 250550
Fax: 01305 257184
Web: http://www.dorset-cc.gov.uk/archives

Contact: Mr Hugh Jacques, County Archivist.

E-mail: archives@dorset-cc.gov.uk

Although film and photographs have been collected by the County for some time, this film collection could properly be said to date from 1991, when the Record Office moved to its present site incorporating specially designed storage facilities.

Video and film holdings: Video: Most of the collection is uncatalogued. To date 4 hours of material have been catalogued. Amateur, science and education.
Video components: VHS Video, lo-band U-matic.
Film: Most of the collection is uncatalogued.
Film components: 8mm, 16mm, 35mm.

Storage: A purpose-designed film and photograph store designed to meet BS 5454 standards.

Printed catalogue: Available, indexed.

Cataloguing: The majority of the film and video collection is uncatalogued. Catalogues available have been indexed by personal name, place name and by subject.

Conservation policy: To preserve original film stock and to make available VHS video copies.

Access: Access available. Mon-Fri 09.00–17.00; Sat 09.30–12.30. Access for disabled. Access to video holdings only, by appointment. Searches can by made by staff.

Viewing and listening facilities: Viewing on premises.

Charges: A charge for research service by staff is levied.

Copyright: The Record Office's standard deposit agreement allows the Record Office to grant copyright permission for material to be published.

DOWNTOWN RADIO

NEWTOWNARDS
Co Down
Northern Ireland
BT23 4ES
Tel: 028 9181 5555
Fax: 028 9181 8913
Web: http://www.downtown.co.uk

Contact: Mr David Sloane, Programme Controller.

E-mail: programmes@downtown.co.uk

The radio station holds a selection of radio programmes, spanning 25 years, of interest to the Northern Ireland audience.

Music holdings: Record library on disc and CD (not open to outside access).

Sound holdings: Approx. 150 reels of speech and speech/music programmes.

Newspapers holdings: Cuttings relating to Downtown FM and Cool FM, q.v.

Digitised collection: No.

Access: Office hours.

Access to researchers from outside: On application.

Viewing and listening facilities: On application.

Charges: Gratis.

Copyright: Broadcast rights.

DREAM 100 FM

Northgate House
St Peter's Street
COLCHESTER
Essex
CO1 1HT
Tel: 01206 764466
Fax: 01206 715102

Web: http://www.dream100.com

Contact: Mr Gary Ball, Programme Controller.

E-mail: info@dream100.com

The radio station holds output to meet legal requirement only.

DUKE VIDEO POWERSPORT

Champion House
DOUGLAS
Isle of Man
IM99 1DD
Tel: 01624 640022
Fax: 01624 640001
Web: http://www.dukevideo.com

Contact: Mr Jon Quayle, International Sales Director.

E-mail: facils@dukevideo.com

The collection comprises 1,200 titles relating to powersport.

Video and film holdings: Video: 1,200 titles of sport and motorsport.
Video components: VHS Video, S-VHS Video, hi-8, hi-band U-matic, lo-band U-matic, Beta/Beta-SP, 1-inch Video.

Printed catalogue: Available, indexed.

Documentation: Handwritten scripts and press cuttings.

Conservation policy: Material is not discarded.

Access: Access available. 09.00–17.30, by arrangement. Access for disabled.

Viewing and listening facilities: Viewing on premises. Viewing off premises. Duplicating.

Charges: Charges for facilities and handling. Charges for other services.

Copyright: Copyright held. Copyright advice available. Copyright adviser: Jon Quayle.

DUNCAN OF JORDANSTOWN COLLEGE LIBRARY

13 Perth Road
DUNDEE
DD1 4HT
Tel: 01382 345252
Fax: 01382 229283
Web: http://www.dundee.ac.uk./library

Contact: Ms Marie Simmons, College Librarian. Morag Henderson College Library.

E-mail: m.simmons@dundee.ac.uk

Books and videos support the teaching of the School of Television and Imaging, and also support other courses which run film studies options. Areas of strength include animation, video art, cinema films and special effects.

Video and film holdings: 3,000 covering all subjects.

Books holdings: Approx. 1,000.

Library OPACs with major holdings on moving image and radio: DYNIX – available at http://www.dundee.ac.uk/library.

Catalogue(s) available via the Internet: Yes at http://www.dundee.ac.uk/library

Websites relating to radio and moving images: http://www.imaging.dundee.ac.uk (TVI school website)

Digitised collection: No. Not in the near future.

Access: For staff and students only. No outside access. Mon-Thu, 09.00–20.30. Fri, 09.00–17.00, Sat, 12.00–17.00. Reduced hours in vacations.

Access to researchers from outside: Bookstock only. External users have no access to videos.

Viewing and listening facilities: 5 video playback machines for student use.

Charges: Free to University staff and students. External borrowers pay £22 per annum for use of bookstock.

Copyright: None.

DURHAM UNIVERSITY LIBRARY: BASIL BUNTING POETRY ARCHIVE

Palace Green Section
Palace Green
DURHAM
DH1 3RN
Tel: 0191 374 3001
Fax: 0191 374 3002
Web: http://www.dur.ac.uk/library/asc/index.html

Contact: Miss E Rainey. Archives and Special Collections, Durham University Library.

E-mail: pg.library@durham.ac.uk

The University Library's Basil Bunting Poetry Archive is an extensive collection of published works by and relating to the poet Basil Bunting (1900–1985), with manuscripts and papers, photographs, films and sound recordings. Bunting's poetry is deeply rooted in the landscape, history, language and culture of his native Northumbria, where he spent his youth, and to which he returned for the last three decades of his life. He believed that sound was integral to poetic form, and that poetry must be heard. The collection's films are chiefly copies on video of television programmes relating to Bunting, while the recordings include poetry readings and interviews made for television and radio.

Video and film holdings: 7 video copies of television programmes on Basil Bunting; approx. 4 hours.

Sound holdings: 4 cassettes of poetry readings/interviews; approx. 2 hours.

Printed catalogue: Word-processed handlist available locally.

Catalogue(s) available via the Internet: Handlist will eventually be included in the Library's Information System on the Internet.

Access: Open to all bona fide researchers, Mon-Fri, 09.00–17.00. Searchers are required to give prior notice of visits.

Access to researchers from outside: Yes.

Viewing and listening facilities: Facilities for accessing film and sound in the Library.

Charges: None.

Copyright: Copyright in films and sound recordings held by television and film companies.

DURHAM UNIVERSITY LIBRARY: SUDAN ARCHIVE

Palace Green Section
Palace Green
DURHAM
DH1 3RN
Tel: 0191 374 3001
Fax: 0191 374 3002
Web: http://www.dur.ac.uk/library/asc/index.html

Contact: Miss E Rainey, Sub-Librarian. Mrs Jane Hogan Archives and Special Collections, Durham University Library.

E-mail: pg.library@durham.ac.uk

Akasha, Northern Province, Sudan, 1884. (photo courtesy of Durham University Library: Sudan Archive)

The University Library's Sudan Archive includes 133 cinefilms, most of which are the work of amateurs. They record the lives of District Commissioners, doctors and other officials in various regions of the Sudan, and provide a visual record of Sudanese tribal life in the North and South, and buildings of Khartoum, Omdurman and other major centres in the provinces from the late 1920s to the 1960s. Recent accessions have included publicity films produced by the Sudan Government in the 1950s, just before and after independence. The collection provides valuable material for the study of the social and cultural history, anthropology and ethnography of the area.

Video and film holdings: 122 films remastered and copied onto 19 videos (15.5 hours).

Masters holdings: 133 films/31.050 feet.

Stills holdings: Over 46,000 photographs, many closely related to the subject matter of the films.

Books holdings: University library holds strong printed collections on the Sudan.

Manuscripts holdings: Films are often part of larger collections which may include related manuscripts.

Card catalogue: No.

Printed catalogue: Word-processed handlists available locally and also at the National Register of Archives.

Computerised database: Descriptions of pre-1945 films included in the University of Oxford's Haddon database.

Catalogue(s) available via the Internet: All handlists will eventually be included in the Library's Information System on the Internet.

Digitised collection: No.

Access: Open to all bona-fide researchers, Mon to Fri, 09.00–17.00. Searchers are required to give prior notice of visits.

Access to researchers from outside: Yes.

Viewing and listening facilities: Video copies may be viewed in the library. No viewing of original films.

Charges: None for viewing on the premises. Charge for viewing off-premises via loan of video copies to other libraries or suitable institutions.

Copyright: Copyright is held by individual filmmakers.

EAST ANGLIAN FILM ARCHIVE

University of East Anglia
NORWICH
NR4 7TJ
Tel: 01603 592664
Fax: 01603 458553
Web: http://www.uea.ac.uk/eafa

John Waters laying an eel net in a fen channel; from the film AN ENGLISH FEN. (photo courtesy of the East Anglian Film Archive)

Contact: Mr Phil Butcher. Ms Jane Alvey.

E-mail: philip.butcher@uea.ac.uk

The Archive was established in 1976 to locate and preserve films and videos showing life and work in Norfolk, Suffolk, Essex and Cambridgeshire, and to provide a service of access and presentation where copyright allows. The collection spans the years from 1896 to the present day and is continuing to grow rapidly. It aims to reflect all aspects of the region's people, society, economy, geography, history and the work of its film and video makers, both amateur and professional. The Archive is a non-profit making organisation dedicated to the preservation of its collections. Its work is funded by earned income and by grants and donations (Eastern Arts has made an annual grant since 1976). EAFA is also preserving unique and growing collections of regional television output and it now houses the original film collection of the *Hertfordshire Film Archive*. EAFA is home to the unique MA Course in Film Archiving.

Video and film holdings: Video: The video collection comprises *c.*4,000 hours (5,000 items) including both original and duplicated material. Advertising, amateur, documentary, news and current affairs, television programmes.
Video components: VHS Video, S-VHS Video, 8mm Video, hi-8, hi-band U-matic, lo-band U-matic, Beta/Beta-SP, 1-inch Video, 2-inch Video, MII.
Film: The film collection comprises *c.*22,000 titles (*c.*15,000,000 feet; *c.*30,000 cans) including both original and duplicated material. Most of the films are non-fiction, both amateur and professionally made, including documentaries, local and national newsreels, advertising and promotional films, educational and training films,

cinema shorts and home movies. Home movies are a particular strength, with amateur film, most of it unique, accounting for about 50% of the collection. The Archive is actively acquiring contemporary material. There are approximately 2,500 titles in the main catalogued collection, which aims to cover all aspects of East Anglian life, and contains a wide and varied range of material about work, leisure, housing, health, industry, education and domestic and social life in towns and rural areas.

Besides the main collection, there is a sub-collection of educational and miscellaneous films. They are not of East Anglian content but are of related subject interest. An example is a small collection of World War II documentary films dealing with agriculture.

The nightly news magazine programme *Look East* 1976–1985, together with feature and opt-out programmes, are stored on behalf of the BBC regional station in Norwich. Requests relating to this material should be made to the Film Librarian, BBC East, All Saints Green, Norwich. Advertising, amateur, documentary, news and current affairs, science and education, television programmes. Film components: 8mm, Super 8mm, 9.5mm, 16mm, Super 16, 35mm. Original material: positive film, negative film, fine grain print, effects mix, final mix.

Storage: Originals and masters are stored in temperature and humidity controlled environment and their condition is monitored.

Stills holdings: Mostly stills from films in the collection.

Books holdings: Some books relating to film archiving, amateur filmmaking, etc.

Manuscripts holdings: Some documents related to main moving image collection.

Datasets holdings: Own databases.

Equipment holdings: Significant amateur and professional moving image equipment collection.

Computerised database: Available. (In-house only).

Catalogue(s) available via the Internet: Yes, via the EAFA website.

Cataloguing: A printed catalogue in four volumes describes some 1,300 films with subject and place indexes. These catalogues have recently been revised and entered into computerised database. The EAFA catalogue is on University of East Anglia Library database, which is accessible on the Internet.

Cataloguing and database creation is a current four year HEFCE-funded project and entries are continually being added. Work in progress on indexing the entries. Not all films are catalogued yet so researchers are encouraged to contact EAFA to discuss their projects.

Documentation: For each title there is a file holding background information on the history of the film, the filmmaker, subject, etc. where available, and a technical sheet recording the physical condition and duplicating history of the film.

Conservation policy: EAFA has an experienced film conservator to monitor the collection and carry out repair and cleaning of film and preparation for copying. The Archive is committed to preserving original material. Copies are made for preservation and access. No nitrate is stored, as nitrate films are copied immediately onto safety stock and the originals passed to the NFTVA. The Archive specialises in the handling and preservation of small gauges (8mm, 9.5mm, 16mm) and is equipped to print all of these gauges to 16mm film. The Archive offers telecine, optical step printing and separate magnetic track transfer facilities.

Access: Access available. Mon-Fri 09.00–17.00 or by arrangement. Staff are available to assist. Access for disabled. The Archive was originally established so that films of the region would be available for study and research. Individuals and groups may visit the archive by appointment to view films. Film shows (250 a year) are presented at the invitation of groups and societies, schools and colleges throughout East Anglia, and presentations are given in cinemas, arts centres and theatres.

The Archive has produced for sale a series of video compilations of films from the collection: subjects include farming, windmills, rural crafts and industries, railways, US airmen during World War II, the Norfolk Broads, the Fens, and videos on individual towns including Clacton, Lowestoft, Norwich, Southend, Southwood, Thetford and Yarmouth. There are over 40 of these compilation tapes.

Viewing and listening facilities: Viewing on premises. Viewing off premises. Viewing copies are 16mm film and VHS video.

Charges: A price list is available upon request. No charges for non-broadcast research, students, etc. or for supply of information on the collection. There is a viewing and transmission fee for broadcast productions.

Copyright: All copyright observed. Copyright advice available. There are preservation restrictions on some material.

EASTLEIGH COLLEGE

Chestnut Avenue
EASTLEIGH
Hampshire
SO50 5HT
Tel: 02380 911024

Contact: Ms Sheila Tomkins, Central Learning Resources Manager.

E-mail: stomkins@eastleigh.ac.uk

Video and film holdings: Approx. 3,500.

Books holdings: 30.

Digitised collection: No.

Charges: None.

The EBS TRUST

36–38 Mortimer Street
LONDON
W1N 7RB
Tel: 020 7765 5023
Fax: 020 7580 6246
Web: http://www.shotlist.co.uk

Contact: Dr Jim Stevenson, Chief Executive. Shaun J Cannon.

MINET (The Moving Images Network) is made up of a consortium of 21 universities and FE colleges, with academic and technical steering groups. It is a growing bank of over 160 titles of very high quality programmes in the subject areas of Biology, Business Studies, Chemistry, Engineering, Information Systems, Practical Maths, Psychology, and Lectures (Irish Literature and Quantum Physics) – and the *Skillbank* (FE) Collection comprising series on construction, basic engineering, catering, caring and office management. The first stages of developing an entire catalogue to digital format with Web links are under way, but currently all titles are available as PAL VHS or masters. *Shotlist* encourages institutions (and only UK education institutions) to purchase master tapes of the programmes at £150 each) to copy, re-edit and re-version as they see fit. As Shotlist programmes are not only designed stand alone, commentary is often minimal so that they may be a support resource to a lecture. An institution can then change or completely remove this commentary to tailor to its own curriculum requirements.

Video and film holdings: over 160.

Masters holdings: Yes.

Card catalogue: No.

Printed catalogue: Yes, *Shotlist*, and *Skillbank* catalogue.

Computerised database: No.

Library OPACs with major holdings on moving image and radio: No.

Catalogue(s) available via the Internet: Yes. http://www.shotlist.co.uk

Digitised collection: No. Planning to very soon.

Access: Mon-Fri, 09.00–18.00.

Access to researchers from outside: Possibly.

Viewing and listening facilities: Possible, but not established or encouraged.

Charges: None at present as it is not really a service offered. Purchase charges for VHS PAL videos are as follows: £35 (up to 30 min UK HE); £45 (30 mins plus, UK HE); £55, £75 non UK HE).

Copyright: UK Higher Education may purchase masters for £150 to copy and re-edit.

EDINBURGH COLLEGE OF ART LIBRARY

Lauriston Place
EDINBURGH
EH3 9DF
Tel: 0131 221 6033
Fax: 0131 221 6033

Contact: Mr Wilson Smith, Principal Librarian. Library.

E-mail: w.smith@eca.ac.uk

Book, journal and video collection contains material in support of teaching, research and studio work in the College's School of Visual Communication. A small collection of photocopied original film scripts is held.

Video and film holdings: Approx. 500 video cassettes.

Sound holdings: Small number of published audio-cassettes of interviews, etc.

Books holdings: Approx. 1,500 volumes.

Journals holdings: Approx. 12 major film, video, animation journals taken.

Library OPACs with major holdings on moving image and radio: Library OPAC.

Catalogue(s) available via the Internet: http://www.lib.eca.ac.uk

Websites relating to radio and moving images: No.

Digitised collection: No. No plans to do so.

Access: Library opening hours.

Access to researchers from outside: Reference only for outside users.

Viewing and listening facilities: Two video cassette players in Library.

Charges: None.

Copyright: None.

EDUCATIONAL & TELEVISION FILMS LTD (ETV)

247A Upper Street
LONDON
N1 1RU
Tel: 020 7226 2298
Fax: 020 7226 8016
Web: http://www.etvltd.demon.co.uk

May 1st Demonstration 1926 entering Hyde Park, London (photo courtesy of Educational and Television Films Ltd)

Contact: Ms Zoe Moore, Film Librarian. Ginnette Harrold. Jack Amos, Archival Consultant.

E-mail: zoe@etvltd.demon.co.uk

Established in 1950, ETV has amassed a wide and varied range of documentary archive material from the ex-Socialist world, with particular emphasis on the ex-Soviet Union, the former Eastern Block countries and China. Material is also held from Vietnam, Cuba, Chile, Afghanistan and the other Arab Nations. ETV also houses material from the British Labour Movement and the Spanish Civil War.

Video and film holdings: Film: 50% colour, 50% black and white film.

Film components: 16mm and 35mm film, positive.
Video available to hire.

Storage: Films are stored mainly at the library (i.e. Highbury). Surplus material stored in Islington.

Card catalogue: Available.

Printed catalogue: Available, indexed. Lists can be provided.

Documentation: Shot lists available; full lists can be provided. Scripts available for some films.

Access: Access available.

Copyright: Copyright held.

The ELMBRIDGE FILM HERITAGE CENTRE

c/o Elmbridge Museum
Church Street
WEYBRIDGE
KT13 8DX
Tel: 01932 843573
Fax: 01932 846552

Contact: Mr Michael Rowe, Manager.

The Elmbridge Film Heritage Centre was established in 1996. It exists to promote and develop the moving image heritage of Elmbridge. It is building a collection of moving images made in Elmbridge and related to the work of R C Sherriff for use in Elmbridge Museum and the borough. The Centre was created by the South East Film & Video Archive with valuable support from the R C Sherriff Rosebriars Trust.

Access: Access available. By arrangement.

Viewing and listening facilities: Viewing on premises.

Copyright: Copyright held by South East Film & Video Archive. Copyright advice available. Copyright adviser: South East Film & Video Archive.

EMAP RADIO LTD

Mappin House
4 Winsley Street
LONDON
W1N 1AR
Tel: 020 7504 6000
Fax: 020 7504 6021

Contact: Mr Trevor White, Programme Director.

Radio licensee group. Its acquisitions are: 96.3 Aire FM, 96.9 Viking FM, Hallam FM, Key 103, Kiss 100 FM, Magic 105.4 FM, Magic 828, Magic 999, Magic 1152. Magic 1152 MW, Magic 1161 AM, Magic 1170, Magic 1548, Magic AM, Metro FM, Radio City 96.7, Rock FM, and TFM. All its stations hold 42 days' output only to meet legal requirement. The Magic stations share large private music collections.

ENGLISH HERITAGE LIBRARY

Fortress House
23 Savile Row
LONDON
W1X 1AB
Tel: 020 7973 3029
Fax: 020 7973 3001
Web: http://www.english-heritage.org.uk

Contact: Ms Catherine Phillpotts, Librarian.

E-mail: catherine.philpotts@english-heritage.org.uk

Small collection of videos, predominantly about English Heritage – English Heritage historic properties and English Heritage projects. A few items cover other sites, garden history, etc.

Video and film holdings: c.150.

Stills holdings: There is a separate English Heritage Photo Library at the Savile Row office. There is also a large collection of photographs at the National Monuments Record Centre, Kemble Drive, Swindon SN2 2GZ. Tel: 01793 414600.

Digitised collection: No.

Access: By appointment only.

Access to researchers from outside: Yes – to bona fide researchers.

Viewing and listening facilities: Video playback machine in Library.

Charges: None.

Copyright: Copyright held for in-house productions.

ESSEX FM

Radio House
Clifftown Road
SOUTHEND-ON-SEA
Essex
SS1 1SX
Tel: 01702 333711
Fax: 01702 345224
Web: http://www.essexfm.co.uk

Contact: Mr Jeff O'Brien, Programme Director.

E-mail: studios@essexradio.co.uk

Radio station. News programming only kept to meet legal requirement. Maintains large private music collection.

FALKIRK COLLEGE OF FURTHER AND HIGHER EDUCATION

Grangemouth Road
FALKIRK
FK2 9AD
Tel: 01324 403000

Contact: Mr Allan Robertson.

The collection comprises course related materials. 50% of video holdings are off-air recordings.

Video and film holdings: 380 titles.

Books holdings: 50 titles.

Journals holdings: 5 titles.

Digitised collection: No.

Access: College staff and students only.

Access to researchers from outside: No.

FILM IMAGES (LONDON) LTD

4th Floor
184 Drummond Street
LONDON
NW1 3HP

Tel: 020 7383 2288
Fax: 020 7383 2333
Web: http://www.film-images.com

Contact: Mr Tony Dykes, Senior Researcher. James Kearney, Researcher and Ginny Harrold, Acquisitions.

E-mail: research@film-images.com

Film Images was established in 1990 as a comprehensive film and video resource for organisations requiring clips and stock shots for all kinds of productions. It now manages film collections from both America and Europe. It represents the material on behalf of collectors of remarkable, interesting or weird films (whether just one special film or a life-time's work), creating viewing copies for the Library, distributing them to Film Images' international network of offices and indexing films on its fully searchable database. Holds thousands of hours of historical footage from Europe, the USA and Africa: all formats from 16mm/35mm OCN to DigiBeta. Early cinema and actuality, newsreels, educational and instructional films, industrial films, features, commercials, music performance, cartoons, comedies and amateur films. Important collections are: COI Footage File (see separate entry), Film Archives (USA), Historic Films (USA), Lobster Films (France), and the Overseas Film and TV Centre (Africa). There are also thousands of hours of contemporary footage: 90% originates from film, transferred to intermediate video formats. Stock shots of business, locations and science. Contemporary collections are Fast Images (USA), Central Order (Germany), Network Espana (Spain) and Wish You Were Here (USA).

Storage: Custom-made temperature controlled vaults off-site in London for UK collections.

New York taxis, 1990s (photo courtesy of Film Images [London] Ltd)

Computerised database:

Catalogue(s) available via the Internet: Available online via http://www.film-images.com

Cataloguing: All material is catalogued on computer providing very fast access to client's individual needs, including effective yet simple keyword searching.

Conservation policy: Conservation policy: All material is assessed upon reception and transferred to intermediate formats where required.

Access: Access available (appointments necessary). Access for disabled. Research can be carried out on behalf of customers.

Viewing and listening facilities: In-house viewing facilities available from VHS PAL reference library and 16mm/35mm Steenbecks available to view from film. Tailor-made VHS or U-matic cassettes can be made for preview purposes (a fee is payable for this.) Showreels are available upon request.

Charges: Fees are charged for research, licence fees and transfers/delivery. All fees are clearly outlined in advance, dependent upon the project.

Copyright: Copyright is managed by Film Images on behalf of the owners/originators of the footage.

FILM RESEARCH & PRODUCTION SERVICES LTD

Rooms 211–213
Mitre House
177–183 Regent Street
LONDON
W1B 4JN
Tel: 020 7734 1525
Fax: 020 7734 8017

Contact: Mr James Webb, Researcher.

A complete research company specialising in providing stock material and clearance of feature film extracts for commercial purposes.

Video and film holdings: Video: 1,000 reels/cassettes, 170 hours. Advertising, documentary, news and current affairs, stock shots.
Video components: VHS Video, hi-band U-matic, lo-band U-matic, Beta/Beta-SP, 1-inch Video.
Film: 50 cans, 12.5 hours. 99% colour film, 1% black and white film. Science and education.
Film components: 16mm, 35mm.

Storage: Purpose-built shelving at the office.

Printed catalogue: Available, indexed.

Cataloguing: Titles and contents catalogued under general headings (e.g. personality) but only main system is numerical by acquisition.

Documentation: Significant collection of catalogues and reference works.

Access: Access available. 09.30–17.30. Staff are available to assist. Company biased towards commercial rather than academic enquiries, but all requests welcome.

Viewing and listening facilities: Viewing on premises. Viewing off premises. Duplicating. Sales. Off-line VHS.

Charges: Charges for research for broadcast productions. Charges for research for academic purposes. Charges for facilities and handling. Charges for other services.

Copyright: Copyright not held. Copyright advice available. Copyright adviser: A Dunne and J Webb.

FILMFINDERS LTD

61 The Hall
Blackheath
LONDON
SE3 9BG
Tel: 020 8852 4156
Fax: 020 8318 0334

Contact: Mr Philip Jenkinson, Director.

Vintage (1900 to about 1934) feature, interest, documentary material covering most aspects of silent cinema and introduction of sound.

Video and film holdings: Video: 180 hours. Now 75% of the library is on either 1-inch or Betacam, with VHS viewing cassettes.
Video components: VHS Video, Beta/Beta-SP, 1-inch Video.
Film: 200 hours. The film holdings include material on early transport (railroad, stage-coaches), 1920s' and 1930s' novelty acts, vintage car comedy compilations and house-produced compilations on various subjects e.g. cliff-hangers, custard pie battles and syncopated black and white cartoons (150 hours). 10% colour film, 90% black and white film. Feature films, other material.
Film components: 16mm.

Storage: Purpose-built vault.

Cataloguing: No catalogues or lists – material too diverse to classify. Full information on particular requirements available upon application.

Conservation policy: Nothing is junked.

Access: Access available. 10.00–17.00, by arrangement only.

Viewing and listening facilities: Viewing off premises. Anything can be put on VHS for client, usually within 12 hours notice.

Charges: Charges for research for broadcast productions. Charges for research for academic purposes. Charges for facilities and handling. A price list is available upon request. Viewing tapes are available at a standard search fee of £40 plus VAT per title.

Copyright: Copyright held. Various rates apply depending upon use to which film is put. Copyright advice available. Copyright adviser: Philip Jenkinson.

FILMS ON ART

Arts Council Films
14 Great Peter Street
LONDON
SW1P 3NQ
Tel: 020 7973 6820
Fax: 020 7973 6851
Web: http://www.artsonline.com

Contact: Ms Belinda Foulds, Assistant Officer.

E-mail: bnm@artscouncil.org.uk

The Arts Council film and video collection was established in 1981 and is the largest collection of documentaries on the arts in Great Britain. It represents 20 years of Arts Council commitment to the production of high-quality arts programmes with an enduring value to education.

Video and film holdings: Video: 250 hours. Documentary, dance and animation.
Video components: VHS Video, hi-band U-matic, lo-band U-matic, Beta/Beta-SP, 1-inch Video, D3.
Film: 100 hours. 95% colour film, 5% black and white film. Documentary, dance and animation.
Film components: 16mm, negative film.

Printed catalogue: Available, indexed.

Catalogue(s) available via the Internet: A selection from the film collection will be available online via the website over the next 12 months.

Documentation: Publicity cards.

Access: Limited access. By arrangement.

Viewing and listening facilities: Viewing off premises. Duplicating.

Charges: Charges for research for broadcast productions. Charges for facilities and handling.

Copyright: Copyright held. Copyright advice available. Copyright adviser: Belinda Foulds.

FILTON COLLEGE

Filton Avenue
BRISTOL
BS34 7AT

Tel: 0117 931 2121
Fax: 0117 931 2233

Contact: Mr Adam Ranson, Media Lecturer. Communications and Media.

E-mail: adam@adamranson.freeserve.co.uk

Video and film holdings: 700 three-hour video cassettes.

Music holdings: Copyright-free Bruton music collection.

Books holdings: 500–600 media-related textbooks in Library.

Computerised database: Text file only.

Digitised collection: No.

Access: College hours.

Access to researchers from outside: On application.

Viewing and listening facilities: VHS VCRs in Learning Centre.

Charges: None worked out.

Copyright: ERA and Open University licences.

FIRE SERVICE COLLEGE

Moreton-in-Marsh
Gloucestershire
GL56 0RH
Tel: 01608 650831
Web: http://www.fireservicecollege.ac.uk

Contact: Miss Marion Barnes, Acquisitions & Cataloguing Librarian, Library. Mrs D Kiey.

E-mail: library@fireservicecollege.ac.uk

The collection covers fire, fire disasters and firefighter training.

Video and film holdings: 1,000+.

Digitised collection: No.

Access: Closed access. Apply in writing.

Access to researchers from outside: Yes, by visit only.

Viewing and listening facilities: 3 video playback machines and multiple headsets.

Charges: Apply to Reference and Reader Services Librarian for details.

Copyright: ERA licence.

FIRST GARDEN CITY HERITAGE MUSEUM

296 Norton Way South
LETCHWORTH GARDEN CITY
Hertfordshire
SG6 1SU

Tel: 01462 482710
Fax: 01462 486056

Contact: Ms Elizabeth Cummings, Assistant Curator.

E-mail: fgchm@Letchworth.com

Local archive film has been collected since the 1950s.

Video and film holdings: Video: 20 reels/cassettes. Documentary.
Video components: VHS Video, Beta/Beta-SP.
Film: 40 cans. Footage of royal visits, celebrations and festivals dating back to 1928. 90% colour film, 10% black and white film. Amateur, documentary.
Film components: 8mm, 16mm.

Storage: Humidity-controlled store.

Conservation policy: Copying from film onto video-tape.

Access: Access available. By arrangement only. Access for disabled.

Viewing and listening facilities: Viewing on premises.

Charges: Charges for facilities and handling.

Copyright: Copyright held. Copyright held for part of the collection. Copyright advice available. Copyright adviser: Robert Lancaster.

FLASHBACK LIBRARY

Flashback Television Ltd
11 Bowling Green Lane
LONDON
EC1R 0BD
Tel: 020 7490 8996
Fax: 020 7490 5610

Contact: Ms Aileen McAllister. Mr Tim Ball.

E-mail: mailbox@flashbacktv.co.uk

Independent production company Flashback Television has been producing continually since 1982. Over these years it has retained rights to much of the material shot, which has now been catalogued.

Video and film holdings: Video: 700 hours. Land and townscapes throughout Great Britain and Ireland from the vitality of Spitalfields Market (before its refurbishment) to beautiful scenics of Glencoe and the Isle of Skye. Historically important locations from Dunotter Castle, the scene of Cromwell's siege in 1651, to the First World War graves at Tyncote and the Somme. Material of contemporary political importance including Orange Marches through Belfast, the comings and goings at Downing Street (1990), and Princess Diana's funeral (1997). A large collection of garden and gardening-orientated material from the UK, USA and Japan.

Video components: VHS Video, lo-band U-matic, Beta/Beta-SP and DigiBeta.

Storage: All video tapes are stored in specially prepared vaults.

Computerised database: Available.

Cataloguing: Word searches on our computer database enable us to check any queries rapidly.

Access: Access available. By arrangement. Staff are available to assist.

Viewing and listening facilities: Viewing on premises. Viewing off premises. Duplicating. Sales. Any material can be supplied on VHS with BITC.

Charges: Charges for research for broadcast productions. Charges for facilities and handling. A price list is available upon request.

Copyright: All footage Flashback Television makes available is own copyright.

FLIGHT ON FILM LTD

Rush Green Airfield
London Road
Langley
HITCHIN
Hertfordshire
SG4 7PQ
Tel: 01438 726969
Fax: 01438 726969
Web: http://www.flightonfilm.co.uk

Contact: Mr Jonathan Kent, Director. Chris Bonass, Director.

E-mail: flightonfilm@beeb.net

Assembled from 50 years of aviation filming, with emphasis on British aircraft, engines, and aircraft factories. World-wide coverage of British/US aircraft at airports in most countries. Air-to-air footage of Airbus, Boeing and BAe aircraft.

Video and film holdings: Video: 1,000 reels/cassettes, 200 hours. Advertising, amateur, documentary.
Video components: VHS Video, S-VHS Video, 8mm Video, hi-8, hi-band U-matic, lo-band U-matic, Beta/Beta-SP, 1-inch Video, 2-inch Video.
Film: 50 cans, 25 hours. 90% colour film, 10% black and white film. Advertising, amateur, documentary.
Film components: 8mm, Super 8mm, 9.5mm, 16mm, Super 16, 35mm, positive film, negative film, fine grain print, effects mix, final mix.

Storage: Stored at company premises.

Card catalogue: Available, indexed.

Conservation policy: Film regularly transferred to Beta-SP format for long term archive access.

Access: Access available. By appointment. Staff are available to assist.

Viewing and listening facilities: Viewing on premises. Viewing off premises. Duplicating. Sales.

Charges: Charges for research for broadcast productions. Charges for research for academic purposes. Charges for facilities and handling. A price list is available upon request.

Copyright: Copyright held. Copyright advice available. Copyright adviser: Jonathan Kent.

FLINTSHIRE RECORD OFFICE

The Old Rectory
Hawarden
FLINTSHIRE
Wales
CH5 3NR
Tel: 01244 532364
Fax: 01224 538344

Contact: Mr Rowland Williams, County Archivist.

The county of Flintshire was formed in April 1996 out of the former county of Clwyd and comprises the central area of the historic county of Flintshire.

Video and film holdings: Film: Together with documents of local interest there are films of local interest at Rhyl, Holywell and Flint, 1913–*c*.1935; the enthronement of the first Archbishop of Wales, the opening of Queensferry Bridge 1926; and three reels of wildlife in the Prestatyn area *c*.1945–50.
Film components: 16mm, positive film.

Storage: Temperature and humidity controlled.

Cataloguing: Brief lists available.

Access: Researchers are advised to enquire before visiting.

Viewing and listening facilities: Video monitor; no other viewing facilities.

FLR 107.3

Astra House
Arklow Road
LONDON
SE14 6EB
Tel: 020 8691 9202
Fax: 020 8691 9193
Web: http://www.ukrd.com/flr

Contact: Mr Warwick Franklin, Station Manager.

E-mail: flr1073@globalnet.co.uk

The radio station holds 3 months' output of all radio recordings.

FM 102 THE BEAR

The Guard House Studios
Banbury Road
STRATFORD-UPON-AVON
Warwickshire
CV37 7HX
Tel: 01789 262636
Fax: 01789 263102
Web: http://www.thebear.co.uk

Contact: Mr Simon Harding, Head of Programming.

E-mail: thebear@thebear.co.uk

The radio station holds output to meet legal requirement.

FM 103 HORIZON

PO Box 103
Crown Hill
MILTON KEYNES
Buckinghamshire
MK8 0ZP
Tel: 01908 269111
Fax: 01908 564063
Web: http://www.mkweb.co.uk/horizon

Contact: Mr Paul Greene, Programme Controller.

E-mail: win@horizon.music.radio.com

The radio station holds 42 days' output to meet legal requirement.

Access: Happy to point researchers in the right direction if looking at the Milton Keynes area.

FORTH FM/FORTH AM

Forth House
Forth Street
EDINBURGH
EH1 3LF
Tel: 0131 556 9255
Fax: 0131 558 3277
Web: http://www.forthonline.co.uk

Contact: Mr Sandy J Wilkie, Programme Director.

E-mail: forthfm.co.uk

The radio station holds 42 days' output to meet legal requirement. **Note:** *Quality not suitable for rebroadcasting.* Various news and local interest programmes are kept for both stations.

FRANK SMITH 'GRIMSBY FILM PRESERVATION SOCIETY' ◪

28 Barry Avenue
GRIMSBY
Lincolnshire
DN34 5LS
Tel: 01472 878623

Contact: Mr Frank Smith.

An extensive collection of 16mm film, obtained from second-hand dealers, or from the families of the person who shot the films, dating from 1903 onwards. Most of the films have been reprinted in the form of documentaries with magnetic sound tracks and music etc. In some cases the music was composed especially. There is also 16mm material from the Hull area. Negatives from much of the material are also available. Some of the collection has been used by Anglia Television, the BBC, Channel Four, Yorkshire Television and Sky Television.

Video and film holdings: Video components: VHS Video.
Film: The collection includes amateur films made in the mid-1920s. One full-length feature, *The Last Adventurers*, which was made in 1937 in Grimsby. The editing was done by David Lean. Stars: Niall McGinnis, Kay Walsh and Linden Travers. Cleethorpes material discovered at the Theatre Royal, Cleethorpes, prior to its demolition in 1963. Dates from early 1900s to late 1930s.
Film components: 16mm, positive film, negative film.

Storage: Negative stored apart from the main collection.

Card catalogue: Available, indexed.

Cataloguing: 70% of the collection is listed on card index.

Conservation policy: No films are ever discarded.

Access: By arrangement.

Viewing and listening facilities: The films are only loaned out to regional film theatres, television companies and other responsible bodies.

Copyright: Copyright held.

FRED GOODLAND FILM & VIDEO ARCHIVES ◪

Fred Goodland Film and Video Services
81 Farmilo Road
Leyton
LONDON
E17 8JN
Tel: 020 8539 4412 (24 hours)
Fax: 020 8539 4412

Contact: Mr Fred Goodland MBKS.

These ever-expanding, privately owned, archives of film, video and sound recordings are the result of over 50 years of enthusiast collecting and personal restoration work. Mr Goodland joined the film industry as a laboratory technician in 1959. Many years were spent preparing 35mm nitrate negatives and master positives for preservation onto safety stocks. Following years working as a picture and sound editor of film and video documentaries, he now utilises modern restoration facilities in maintaining image and sound materials held in his own collections.

Video and film holdings: Video 8 and Hi8 Video, plus re-copyrighted American archive materials on deleted NTSC Laserdiscs.
Video components: DigiBeta, Beta SP, Beta, VHS, Betamax, Hi-Band U-matic,
Film: Almost 600,000 feet of film, offering a wide range of entertainment and actuality material (1890s–1990s). Subjects include performances of popular music (1920s–1960s), early sound films and colour systems, technical film developments, vintage fashions, trailers, personalities, dance, amateur films, travel, amusing oddities and silent shorts.
Film components: 16mm, Super and Standard 8mm and some 35mm. Positives and dupe negatives, re-recorded magnetic masters and optical sound negatives.
Specialist sound components: Cinema 16-inch 33 1/3rd rpm shellac early talkie Vitaphone type sound-on-disc film tracks. Subjects include various musical shorts, a boxing documentary, feature extracts, plus a trailer and overtures for classic early musicals.

Storage: All film, sound and video materials are held in temperature controlled conditions.

Sound holdings: See entry for *Fred Goodland Sound Archives*.

Computerised database: Enquiries are researched from databases and personal catalogues – due to the diverse nature of the materials they are not published.

Cataloguing: Due to the diverse nature of the collections, no catalogues are available. All enquiries personally researched.

Conservation policy: Nothing is junked. Deteriorating material is copied where possible.

Access: All research enquiries are welcomed but there are no facilities for visitors. Fast access to most material is available on VHS with BITC. Subsequent transfers to professional broadcast formats are personally supervised.

Charges: Rate sheets are available. Charges for research, viewing, VHS transfers, etc., are dependent on time taken. Licence or access fees are dependent on client's usage and status of copyright.

Copyright: Public domain footage is licensed. Where copyright control is known to exist, rights must be cleared and royalty charges paid by the production company prior to use. Assistance will be given to identify current owners of film and music rights if known.

FRED GOODLAND SOUND ARCHIVES

Fred Goodland Film and Video Services
81 Farmilo Road
Leyton
LONDON
E17 8JN
Tel: 020 8539 4412 (24 hours)
Fax: 020 8539 4412

Contact: Mr Fred Goodland MBKS.

These ever-expanding, privately owned, archives of film, video and sound recordings are the result of over 50 years of enthusiast collecting and personal restoration work. Mr Goodland joined the film industry as a laboratory technician in 1959. Many years were spent preparing 35mm nitrate negatives and master positives for preservation onto safety stocks. Following years working as a picture and sound editor of film and video documentaries, he now utilises modern restoration facilities in maintaining image and sound materials held in his own collections.

Video and film holdings: See entry for *Fred Goodland Film and Video Archives.*

Sound holdings: The Sound Collection: Forty original 16-inch 33 1/3rd radio transcription discs are held as part of this privately owned archive collection. They include mainly American World War II star comedy and drama shows, dance music, vocalists, classical material and a later Civil Defence show-biz celebrity spot disc. Condition of discs is variable. Other Sound Recordings and Background to the Collection: The record collection began back in the 1940s and consists of many kinds of recorded material (1900–2000). There are more than 7,000 discs, including over 4,000 original 78s in fine condition. These include thousands of examples of musical styles of the 20th century, including popular tunes, jazz, light orchestral plus documentary material.
Sound components: Shellac and vinyl discs, CD/CDR, 1/4-inch two track and cassette tapes.

Computerised database: 78rpm discs are all fully detailed on a database. Other materials are being worked on. Catalogues are not available but enquiries are welcomed and personally researched.

American World War II 16-inch radio transcription disc (photo courtesy of Fred Goodland Sound Archives)

Cataloguing: Due to the diverse nature of the collections, no catalogues are available. All enquiries personally researched.

Conservation policy: Nothing is junked. Deteriorating material is copied where possible.

Access: There is no visitor access.

Charges: Rate sheets are available. Charges for research, viewing, VHS transfers, etc. are dependent on time taken. Licence or access fees are dependent on client's usage and status of copyright.

Copyright: Where copyright control is known to exist, rights must be cleared and royalty charges paid by the production company prior to use. Assistance will be given to identify current owners of rights if known.

G B ASSOCIATES

80 Montalt Road
WOODFORD GREEN
IG8 9SS
Tel: 020 8505 1850
Fax: 020 8505 8094

Contact: Mr Malcolm Billingsley, Administrator.

E-mail: filmview@dial.pipex.com

Three private archives are the basis of this collection. For the convenience of researchers it is administered from one central point. The collections are still being added to, so there is not cut-off point.

Video and film holdings: Video components: VHS Video.

Film: The total collection, mostly 35mm, is estimated to be in excess of 6 million feet, 80% nitrate, 10% colour. Special collections include advertising films, feature film extracts and cartoons. Examples of different colour systems are held. Documentary/non-fiction probably represents 40% of the collections. Over 700 features and 500 trailers.

Film components: 16mm, 35mm, positive film.

Storage: Prints are stored off the premises at various locations in the London area.

Computerised database: Available.

Cataloguing: Besides a guide of the collection, all material is comprehensively indexed on a database. Print-outs of all categories in the collections are available on request.

Access: The collection is available to all researchers. Research and viewing fees are payable depending on the amount of material involved. Material may be viewed on VHS cassettes.

Viewing and listening facilities: Viewing off premises.

Copyright: Copyright not held. In most cases copyright must be cleared with the copyright owner.

GALAXY 102.2

1 The Square
111 Broad Street
BIRMINGHAM
B15 1AS
Tel: 0121 695 0000
Fax: 0121 696 1007

Contact: Mr Neil Greenslade, Head of Programmes.

Music-based radio station. Holds output to meet legal requirement. Other than this keeps no programming unless individual radio DJs want copies of particular shows.

GEMINI FM

Hawthorn House
Exeter Business Park
EXETER
Devon
EX1 3QS
Tel: 01392 444444
Fax: 01392 444433
Web: http://www.geminifm.com

Contact: Mr Kevin Kane, Programme Controller.

Music-based radio station. Holds output to meet legal requirement. Also keeps interviews with celebrities.

GLASGOW CALEDONIAN UNIVERSITY

Cowcaddens Road
GLASGOW
G4 0BA

Tel: 0141 331 3858
Fax: 0141 331 3005

Contact: Ms Anne Ward, Assistant Librarian. Anne Ward Library.

E-mail: a.ward@gcal.ac.uk

Books holdings: Approx. 400 books on film, television and radio.

Journals holdings: Back runs of major journals, e.g. *Sight & Sound*.

Library OPACs with major holdings on moving image and radio: Telnet and Web-based catalogues available, both Z39.50 compliant.

Catalogue(s) available via the Internet: Telnet and Webpac available.

Websites relating to radio and moving images: Film, Television and Radio web-based subject guides available – no in-house material, links to outside sources.

Digitised collection: No, not in the near future.

Access: Videos cannot be borrowed by students but can be viewed in the library.

Access to researchers from outside: Yes, on application.

Viewing and listening facilities: 8 video viewers.

Charges: None.

GLASGOW SCHOOL OF ART LIBRARY

167 Renfrew Street
GLASGOW
G3 6RQ
Tel: 0141 353 4500
Web: http://www.gsa.ac.uk/library

Contact: Mr John McKay, Head of Information Services.

E-mail: j.mckay@gsa.ac.uk

The collection covers art, design and architecture.

Video and film holdings: 200 VHS tapes, purchased and off-air.

Sound holdings: 50 audiotapes.

Books holdings: 500.

Catalogue(s) available via the Internet: Yes.

Digitised collection: No.

Access to researchers from outside: By application.

Viewing and listening facilities: VHS.

Copyright: ERA licence.

GLASGOW UNIVERSITY MEDIA GROUP   ▣
TELEVISION NEWS ARCHIVE

c/o Professor John Eldridge
Department of Sociology
University of Glasgow
GLASGOW
G12 8RT
Tel: 0141 339 8855 ext 4684
Fax: 0141 330 4925

Contact: Prof John Eldridge.

The collection is a product of the research work undertaken by the above Media Group and constitutes the industrial and economic news from all channels for the period January-June 1975. There are also some specimen examples of whole news bulletins from this period. Later research projects on a number of themes have led to the collection of news and current affairs on a range of topics. The collection is ongoing.

Video and film holdings: Video components: VHS Video.

Storage: The collection is housed in the University of Glasgow.

Cataloguing: Each videotape is suitably indexed and the collection is in chronological order.

Documentation: There is an extensive newspaper file of both popular and quality newspapers which complements the collection.

Access: Researchers wishing to make use of the material can apply to Professor Eldridge at the above address.

GLOBAL SCENES   ▣

4 St John's Road
TUNBRIDGE WELLS
TN4 9NP
Tel: 01892 544043
Fax: 01892 544043
Web: http://www.globalscenes.co.uk

Contact: B R Ware, Proprietor.

Global Scenes maintains and loans out promotional travel videos on behalf of twenty tourist boards, covering Europe, the USA and the Far East. The collection is being constantly updated. The company also represents embassies which supply video material for educational purposes. Pollock Collection, covering Kenya, India, Pakistan, Sri Lanka, and other far eastern countries, held along with transparencies.

Video and film holdings: Video: 100 reels/cassettes, 75 hours. Travel footage. Documentary.
Video components: VHS Video, hi-band U-matic, lo-band U-matic, Beta/Beta-SP.

Printed catalogue: India, Pakistan and full lists.

Viewing and listening facilities: Viewing off premises.

Copyright: Copyright not held.

GLYNDEBOURNE FESTIVAL OPERA   ▣

LEWES
East Sussex
BN8 5UU
Tel: 01273 812321
Fax: 01273 812783

The collection consists of commercially released videos of Glyndebourne operas from 1972 to date.

Video and film holdings: Video: 100 hours. Documentary, feature films, opera productions.
Video components: VHS Video.
Radio. Radio recordings are also held.

Storage: Acid-free boxes.

Printed catalogue: Available, indexed.

Computerised database: Available.

Cataloguing: The printed catalogue of Glyndebourne videos has been published in *Glyndebourne Recorded* by Paul Campion and Rosy Runciman (Julia Macrae Books, 1994), pp. 187–228.

Access: Access available. By arrangement only. Staff are available to assist.

Viewing and listening facilities: Viewing on premises. Sales.

Charges: Charges for research for broadcast productions. Charges for research for academic purposes. Charges for facilities and handling. A price list is available upon request.

Copyright: The copyrights situation varies from video to video (see list published in *Glyndebourne Recorded*; details given above). Copyright advice available.

GOLDSMITHS' COMPANY   ▣

The Worshipful Company of Goldsmiths
Goldsmiths' Hall
Foster Lane
LONDON
EC2V 6BN
Tel: 020 7606 7010
Fax: 020 7606 1511

Contact: Mr David Beasley, Librarian.

Collection of 16mm film and video material of aspects of silversmithing and jewellery trade including assaying and hallmarking for loan to interested groups including institutions, colleges, manufacturers and retailers.

Video and film holdings: Video: 6.5 hours. The collection comprises 12 titles. Documentary.
Video components: VHS Video.
Film: 5 hours. The collection comprises 13 titles. 100% colour film. Documentary.
Film components: 16mm.

Cataloguing: A printed handlist which gives a short summary of the content the titles held is available.

Conservation policy: None.

Access: Limited access. Material available for loan to institutions and groups but not individuals.

Viewing and listening facilities: Arrangements of viewing, sale and duplication are subject to discussion.

Copyright: Copyright not held in most cases. Two films on VHS are company copyright. Copyright advice available. Copyright adviser: The Librarian.

GRAMPIAN TELEVISION LTD

Queen's Cross
ABERDEEN
AB15 4XJ
Tel: 01224 846551
Fax: 01224 846877
Web: http://www.grampiantv.co.uk

Contact: Mr Bert Ovenstone, Head of Public Relations. Mr Bill Moir, Library Public Relations.

E-mail: bert.ovenstone@grampiantv.co.uk

Grampian Television holds a library containing complete programmes, news stories and production rushes. The programmes date back to the 1960s and cover a wide range of documentary, entertainment and sports topics. Production rushes include material shot and edited for Grampian's programmes. News stories are specifically those occurring in the North and North East of Scotland, dating back to the 1960s.

Video and film holdings: Dating back to 1960s: Film, U-matic, Beta SP.

Masters holdings: Television programmes made by GTV. Since 1960s held on film, 1-inch tape, Beta SP, DigiBeta.

Computerised database: In-house designed database.

Library OPACs with major holdings on moving image and radio: Moving images held on various formats.

Access: By appointment.

Viewing and listening facilities: On application.

Charges: On application. Anyone wishing to purchase

film or video material should contact Charles Masson or Bill Moir.

Copyright: Depends on usage requested.

GRANADA MEDIA CLIP SALES – GRANADA TELEVISION

Granada Television
Clip Sales Department
Quay Street
MANCHESTER
M60 9EA
Tel: 0161 827 2207/2332
Fax: 0161 827 2006

Contact: Ms Christine Rimmer, Senior Manager, GM Clip Sales. Christine Rimmer, Deputy Manager.

E-mail: christine.rimmer@granadamedia.com

Material dates back to Granada's first transmission in May 1956. Specialities: Anthropology, music (an eclectic collection), political and social documentaries concerning the UK and international affairs, varied arts collection, North West of England material and prestigious drama productions.

Video and film holdings: Video: Extensive collection of material on video.
Video components: VHS Video, Hi-band U-matic, Beta/Beta-SP, 1-inch Video, 2-inch Video, DigiBeta.
Film: The Library holds over 5,000 programmes. 75% colour film, 25% black and white film.
Film components: 16mm, positive film, negative film, effects mix, final mix.

Storage: The material is stored in vaults.

Card catalogue: Available; indexed for stock footage collection.

Computerised database: Available.

Cataloguing: Card catalogue for stock shot film collection only. Computerised Granada Media corporate database. Printouts are made available.

Conservation policy: All programmes are kept now, but in the past not all videotape programmes were retained. Also, some very early programmes went out live, and, of course, pre-dated video recording.

Access: Access available. By arrangement. Access for disabled. Access by arrangement if there is material available to view.

Viewing and listening facilities: Viewing on premises. Viewing off premises. Duplicating. There will be a fee for viewing on premises. For viewing off premises there would be a charge for copying material.

Charges: Charges for research for broadcast productions. Charges for facilities and handling. Charges for other services.

Copyright: Copyright held.

GRANADA MEDIA CLIP SALES – LONDON WEEKEND TELEVISION

Communications House
48 Leicester Square
LONDON
WC2H 7FB
Tel: 020 7389 8545
Fax: 020 7930 8498

Contact: Ms Julie Lewis, Manager. Jane Snell, Extract Sales. Ms Jo Collerton, Sales. Ms Jane Snell, Sales.

E-mail: julie.lewis@granadamedia.com

The library contains all of LWT's productions for local and network UK transmission since 1968: drama; entertainment; comedy; game shows; pop music; classical music; opera; ballet; chat shows; magazine shows; documentaries; politics; current affairs; arts. Local programmes cover a rich social history of London including transport, housing, police, news, politics, history and wildlife.

Video and film holdings: Video: 150,000 reels/cassettes. Current affairs, entertainment, drama and arts.
Video components: VHS Video, S-VHS Video, hi-8, hi-band U-matic, lo-band U-matic, Beta/Beta-SP, 1-inch Video, 2-inch Video, DigiBeta, D1, D2 and D3.
Film: 45,000 cans. Current affairs, entertainment, drama, arts, sport. 95% colour film, 5% black and white film.
Film components: 16mm, Super 16, 35mm, positive film, negative film, fine grain print, effects mix, final mix.

Storage: Purpose-built vault of 8,000 square feet on three floors, temperature and humidity controlled. The archive is growing at approximately 30,000 units p.a.

Computerised database: Available.

Cataloguing: All programme details on Granada Media corporate database.

Documentation: Camera scripts, transcripts, production as transmitted forms held on file or on optical disk.

Conservation policy: Some transmitted tapes were junked earlier on. The policy is now to hold two transmitted copies on separate sites. Field tapes are junked after review. 2-inch tapes transferred to D2 and DigiBeta for preservation, then given to NFTVA.

Access: Access available. By arrangement. Access for disabled. Lifts are available.

Viewing and listening facilities: Viewing on premises. Viewing off premises. Duplicating. Sales. Most duplicating done in-house or material is sent down the line direct to client.

Charges: Charges for facilities and handling. Flexible rates, discussed by phone.

Copyright: Copyright held. There are limitations on the sale of some items, but clients are generally advised in advance if there is a clearance problem. Copyright advice available. Copyright adviser: Julie Lewis.

GRANADA MEDIA CLIP SALES – TYNE TEES TELEVISION/CHANNEL 3 NORTH EAST

The Television Centre
City Road
NEWCASTLE UPON TYNE
NE1 2AL
Tel: 0191 261 2693648/2693647
Fax: 0191 2612302

Contact: Mr John Davison, Supervisor/VTR and Programme Librarian. Ms Gillian Robinson, News and Archive. Mr Michael Irving, Assistant Librarian.

E-mail: clips.newcastle@granadamedia.com

Tyne Tees Television is the ITV contractor for the North East of England. Its collection includes 16mm film of local news from 1960–80 (black and white and colour), hi-band U-matic news tapes from 1980–1992 with current news output on Beta-SP. Local sport, especially football, is also well represented. There is also a collection of local documentary (current affairs, farming, arts, etc.), features and drama programmes available from various sources (film, 1-inch, 2-inch and Beta-SP). Some non-TTTV material, both amateur and newsreel footage from *c.*1912–1960s is held in the company's Flashback Library on Beta and VHS.

Video and film holdings: Video: News and magazine items form the bulk of the library material – now stored on Beta-SP. Other material includes complete programmes mostly of a local nature but covers current affairs, farming, drama and especially music. *The Tube* collection includes many pop bands from the late 1970s and 1980s.
Video components: Hi-Band U-matic, Beta/Beta-SP, 1-inch Video, Beta SX and DigiBeta.
Film components: 16mm, 35mm.

Storage: Most news/sports material is stored in-house as are all recent programmes. The 1-inch tapes are stored at YTV Leeds. The film material is kept at Teesside University. News material if also held at the company's Billingham studio. They can all be accessed when necessary.

Cataloguing: The in-house cross-reference filing system is used for all news/sports and archive programmes and a computer system (RECALL) has the last 10 years' information on it. Some shotlists or print-outs are available. A listing of 1-inch and Beta programmes is available on card index and computer but shotlist details are not available.

Documentation: Some shotlists, print-outs and card index information available.

Conservation policy: As space is becoming a premium, there is selective pruning of material.

Access: Access is available. Enquiries for any particular item can be made to the library.

Viewing and listening facilities: There are limited facilities for researchers to view news items and programmes.

Charges: Film or tape items can be obtained for commercial use subject to certain conditions and copyright.

GRANADA MEDIA CLIP SALES – YORKSHIRE TELEVISION

The Television Centre
LEEDS
West Yorkshire
LS3 1JS
Tel: 0113 222 8050
Fax: 0113 222 7165

E-mail: clips.leeds@granadamedia.com

Yorkshire Television started broadcasting programmes on the ITV network and locally in the Yorkshire, Humberside, North Lincolnshire and North Derbyshire area in July 1968. The Library contains all transmitted programmes and regional news items produced since its inception. The complete holdings amount to over 60,000 film cans and tape spools which increase according to the number of programmes YTV transmits each year. Production departments cover all subject areas (documentaries, drama, education, light entertainment, science, sport, etc.) including *First Tuesday*, *Whicker's World*, *Jimmy's*, *The Darling Buds of May*, *How We Used to Live*, *Emmerdale*, *New Statesman*, *Heartbeat*, *Rising Damp*, *3D* and *A Touch of Frost*.

Video and film holdings: Video: 40,000 reels/cassettes. Documentary, news and current affairs, science and education, drama and light entertainment.
Video components: VHS Video, S-VHS Video, hi-band U-matic, lo-band U-matic, Beta/Beta-SP, 1-inch Video, D3, DigiBeta, Beta SX.

Film: 25,000 cans. 98% colour film, 2% black and white film. Documentary, news and current affairs, science and education, drama and light entertainment.
Film components: 16mm, Super 16, 35mm, positive film, negative film, effects mix, final mix.

Storage: Temperature and humidity controlled purpose-built vaults on site with mobile racking systems. The area allows for considerable expansion in stock.

Card catalogue: Transferred to database.

Computerised database: Available.

Documentation: Programme-as-Transmitted sheets for all programmes. Calendar news running orders and scripts on microfiche from 1968 to date. AVSTAR news computer terminal directly linked to the newsroom providing news information.

Conservation policy: Insert material is reviewed after six months (where a complete copy of the programme exists). Otherwise, master copies of all transmitted material are retained permanently. All original 2-inch programmes have been transferred to a recent format and include a technical report. The original 2-inch tapes are deposited with the National Film and Television Archive.

Access: Access available. By arrangement only. Staff are available to assist. Access for disabled. But limited facilities for disabled. Access to the collection is available to all researchers and enquirers. Initial enquiries should be made by telephone.

Viewing and listening facilities: Viewing on premises. Viewing off premises. Duplicating. Sales. Viewing copies of requested material on VHS, U-matic or 16mm can be quickly dispatched to any destination. Master material is never released – dupe copies can be made promptly on site.

Charges: Charges for research for broadcast productions. Charges for facilities and handling. A price list is available upon request.

Copyright: Copyright held. Copyright advice available. Copyright adviser: Dale Grayson (Rights and Clips Sales Manager), Jane Chambers.

GREENPARK PRODUCTIONS ARCHIVES

Greenpark Productions Ltd
Illand
LAUNCESTON
Cornwall
PL15 7LS
Tel: 01566 782107
Fax: 01566 782127

Contact: Ms Leonore Morphet, Production Assistant.

E-mail: archives@clips.net

Greenpark Productions, founded in 1938, has kept much of the shorts, documentary and sponsored footage which it shot between 1940 and the present.

Video and film holdings: Video: 73 reels/cassettes. Advertising, documentary, science and education, corporate films.
Video components: VHS Video, lo-band U-matic, Beta/Beta-SP.
Film: 2,000,000 feet. 1,000,000 feet 16mm and 1,000,000 feet 35mm. Documentary material on industrial processes, sports, fishing, finance, insurance, medicine, Africa, Middle East, Germany, Far East, India, Pakistan, British Isles, manufactured products, transport, food, defence, construction, training. Cinema and television commercials. 50% colour film, 50% black and white film, 3% nitrate film. Documentary, science and education.
Film components: 16mm, 35mm, positive film, negative film, fine grain print.

Storage: Vaults on own premises.

Card catalogue: Available.

Access: Access available. By arrangement only.

Viewing and listening facilities: Viewing on premises.

Charges: Charges for research for broadcast productions. Charges for research for academic purposes. A price list is available upon request.

Copyright: Copyright held for some of the material. Copyright advice available.

GUINNESS ARCHIVES

Park Royal Brewery
LONDON
NW10 7RR
Tel: 020 8963 5278
Fax: 020 8963 5173

Contact: Ms Sue Garland, Archivist.

E-mail: sue.garland@guinness.com

Guinness company films and videos produced for internal training and communication, for visitors, for trade promotions and advertising commercials. Mostly British, some Irish and overseas. The material relates to the brewing company and its beer brands, dating from mid-1950s to the present day.

Video and film holdings: Video: 1,000 reels/cassettes.
Video components: VHS Video, lo-band U-matic, 1-inch Video.
Film: Most of the original films are held at the NFTVA.

Storage: Air-conditioned store shared with paper archives and artifacts. Metal shelving.

Computerised database: Available.

Cataloguing: Database for internal use only.

Conservation policy: Copying of original film onto U-matic/VHS/1-inch.

Access: Limited access. Access by appointment with approval of the company. Any requests for broadcast or copying must be approved by the company's Public Relations and Legal Departments.

Copyright: Copyright held. Copyright advice available. Copyright adviser: Legal Counsel at Guinness.

GWR FM – BRISTOL & BATH

PO Box 2000
Watershed
Canon's Road
BRISTOL
BS99 7SN
Tel: 0117 984 3200
Fax: 0117 984 3202
Web: http://www.gwrfm.musicradio.com

Contact: Mr Paul Andrew, Programme Controller.

E-mail: reception@gwrfm.musicradio.com

The radio station holds 42 days radio output to meet legal requirement only.

GWR FM – SWINDON & WEST WILTSHIRE

PO Box 2000
SWINDON
SN4 7EX
Tel: 01793 842600
Fax: 01793 942602

Contact: Mr Steve Fountain, Programme Controller.

The radio station holds 42 days radio output only to meet legal requirement.

GWYNEDD ARCHIVES AND MUSEUMS SERVICE

County Offices
CAERNARFON
Gwynedd
LL55 1SH
Tel: 01286 679095
Fax: 01286 679637

Contact: Ms Ann Rhydderch, Principal Archivist and Heritage Officer.

The collection includes films of railway interest – Penrhyn Railway and Nantlle Tramway, Bangor-Afonwen Railway – film shot on Bardsey Island, *c.*1948 and a small stock of commercial videos of local or professional interest.

Video and film holdings: Video: 20 reels/cassettes. Documentary, science and education.
Video components: VHS Video.
Film: 10 cans. 100% black and white film. Amateur, documentary.
Film components: Positive Film.

Storage: Films have been deposited at the Wales Film and Television Archive.

Catalogue(s) available via the Internet: The Service has plans to have a database of its archival catalogues online on the Gwynedd Archives website in the very near future. However, there will be no audio-visual items online in the foreseeable future with the exception of local stills.

Conservation policy: Nitrate stock is passed on to a willing recipient.

Access: Access available. Access for disabled. Access through the Wales Film and Television Archive.

Copyright: Copyright not held.

The HALAS AND BATCHELOR COLLECTION

67 Southwood Lane
LONDON
N6 5EG
Tel: 020 8348 9696
Fax: 020 8348 3470
Web: http://www.halasandbatchelor.com

Contact: Mrs Vivien Halas, Director.

E-mail: vivien@haba.demon.com

The archive was completed in September 1993 to document the contribution Halas and Batchelor have made to the development of animation in England and Europe. There is also a collection of animation cels from various productions. Films of Bob Godfrey and Lotte Reiniger are now also in the collection. **Note:** *(January 2001) New contact arrangements for the archive are imminent.*

Video and film holdings: Video: Animated films.
Video components: VHS Video, hi-band U-matic, lo-band U-matic, Beta/Beta-SP, 1-inch Video.
Film: The collection comprises 140 titles; many are series. Some negative material is held although this hasn't been checked for deterioration. As the archive is an animation archive, most of the films are series which vary from an hour in length to five minutes. Advertising, animated films.
Film components: 8mm, 16mm, 35mm, positive film, negative film, effects mix, final mix.

Storage: Storage at the National Film and Television Archive and at the Southampton Institute International Animation Research Archive (SIIARA).

Computerised database: Available.

Documentation: Scripts, music cue sheets and credits are available in English for all titles.

Conservation policy: Film and videotape are kept – nothing is thrown out although a fair percentage needs restoration, for which no funds are available as yet. For further information contact John Southall at SIIARA, Tel: 01703 319477.

Access: Access available. Access through the National Film and Television Archive.

Viewing and listening facilities: Viewing on premises. Duplicating. Sales. Duplicating U-matic to VHS.

Copyright: Copyright held.

HALLAM FM

Radio House
900 Herries Road
SHEFFIELD
S6 1RH
Tel: 0114 285 3333
Fax: 0114 285 3159
Web: http://www.hallamfm.co.uk

Contact: Mr Anthony Gay, Programme Director.

The radio station holds output to meet legal requirement. All documents regarding radio are kept for 5 years for financial purposes. News articles are kept for one year.

HAMMERSMITH & FULHAM ARCHIVES AND LOCAL HISTORY CENTRE

The Lilla Huset
191 Talgarth Road
LONDON
W6 8BJ
Tel: 020 8741 5159
Fax: 020 8741 4882

Contact: Ms Jane Kimber, Borough Archivist.

The collection is very small and comprises a miscellaneous group of films transferred to the Archives Department from other departments within the Council.

Video and film holdings: Film: 12 cans. The collection includes films of the following: Re-opening of Gaumont Cinema, Shepherds Bush, after closure due to bomb damage; *Tories Resounding Victory c.*1955; Hammersmith, 1953 (Coronation procession and carnival, etc.); Opening of Fulham Power Station by local Mayor, 1936; 'Merchant Navy' appeal by Mayor of Hammersmith, *c.*1940s (2 copies); Civic procession and memorial

service for George V, 1936 (Hammersmith); and food advertisements. Advertising, documentary.
Film components: 16mm, 35mm.

Storage: Along with all the Borough's archive and local history material, the collection is stored in an environmentally controlled archive strong room.

Conservation policy: These films form part of the Borough's archive collection and are therefore preserved indefinitely.

Access: There are no facilities for viewing films at present. Enquirers should contact the Borough Archivist.

Copyright: Various copyrights.

HASTINGS MUSEUM

Johns Place
Bohemia Road
HASTINGS
East Sussex
TN34 1ET
Tel: 01424 781155
Fax: 01424 781165

Contact: Ms Victoria Williams, Curator.

The material has been acquired by donation over the last 20 years. It includes publicity films passed on by the tourism department and from the Borough Engineer, 1940s–1970s. There is some footage by Harry Furniss (1854–1925) and a collection of amateur film from St Nicholas children's home, also the RAC rally 1956. The video collection includes an amateur survey of the town centre prior to development, a commissioned feature on Grey Owl and recorded talks by a local historian. Most of the film of the collection has now been deposited with the *South East Film and Video Archive* at the University of Brighton, q.v.

Video and film holdings: Video: 24 reels/cassettes. Amateur, documentary.
Video components: VHS Video, Laserdisc.
Film: 13,000 feet, 53 cans. 20% colour film, 80% black and white film. Advertising, amateur, documentary, news and current affairs, science and education, other material.
Film components: 9.5mm, 16mm, 35mm, positive film.

Storage: The collection will eventually be deposited at the West Sussex Record Office through the South East Film and Video Archive. Some film is still currently held at Hastings and Brighton.

Card catalogue: Available, indexed.

Computerised database: Available.

Cataloguing: The film collections are catalogued onto separate databases at Hastings and the South East Film and Video Archive, University of Brighton.

Conservation policy: This is being drawn up through the South East Film and Video Archive.

Access: Enquiries to Hastings Museum or South East Film and Video Archive (q.v.).

Viewing and listening facilities: Viewing on premises.

Charges: Charges for facilities and handling. Charges to be negotiated.

Copyright: Copyright held. Copyright advice available. Copyright adviser: South East Film and Video Archive.

The HAWLEY COLLECTION AT THE UNIVERSITY OF SHEFFIELD

University of Sheffield
196–198 West Street
SHEFFIELD
S1 4ET
Tel: 0114 222 7100
Fax: 0114 222 7001
Web: http://www.sheffield.ac.uk/uni/projects/hp

Contact: Ms Joan Unwin, Research Associate.

E-mail: hawley.tools@sheffield.ac.uk

The Collection is owned by a Charitable Trust (No. 1049003) and stored at the University in a refurbished building. Its film and video material consists of a) material shot by Ken Hawley and other amateurs, filming the last remaining craftsmen working in particular manufacturing processes; b) promotional and publicity materials made by manufacturers, and c) specially commissioned films recording work practices, including hours of interviews, filmed by the university television team. A wide range of subjects is covered by the material, e.g. cutlery making and tool-making – razor forging, scissors forging, forging and manufacture of silver spoons, sickle making, file cutting, grinding and polishing, spokeshave making, hand forging, Beechwood bench planes, thatching (in Hope Cove, Devon), and pewter spinning, And the work and skills of individual craftsmen such as table knife cutlers, pocket and sporting knife cutlers, saw piercers, plane makers, etc., is depicted. The Collection houses trade catalogues, artefacts and graphical material relating to the films. An award-winning video about the Collection and Ken Hawley, *You'll not be wanting this then, will you?*, was made by the University in 1999. This is available for purchase from the University.

Viewing and listening facilities: The Collection has no way of running 8mm and 16mm films though some have been copied on to video.

HERTFORDSHIRE FILM ARCHIVE

see *East Anglian Film Archive*

The original film stock of this film collection has now been transferred to the East Anglian Film Archive for safekeeping. All enquiries to EAFA. A video access collection only is being maintained at Hertfordshire Archives & Local Studies.

HILLCROFT COLLEGE

South Bank
SURBITON
KT6 6DF
Tel: 020 8399 2688
Fax: 020 8390 9171

Contact: Mrs Hannah Kent, Learning Resources Manager.

E-mail: hkent@hillcroft.ac.uk

General collection suited to adult education (women) curriculum.

Video and film holdings: 250 tapes, off-air recordings and purchased videos.

Library OPACs with major holdings on moving image and radio: Yes.

Digitised collection: No.

Access: Prior permission.

Access to researchers from outside: With prior permission.

Viewing and listening facilities: Video presenter.

HILLINGDON HERITAGE SERVICE

Central Library
High Street
UXBRIDGE
UB8 1HD
Tel: 01895 250702
Fax: 01895 811164

Contact: Ms Carolynne Cotton, Local Heritage Co-ordinator.

E-mail: ccotton@hillingdon.gov.uk

Films made for local councils in Hillingdon area since 1950s. Some earlier material donated by members of the public on local events since 1935.

Video and film holdings: Video: 15 hours. Amateur, documentary.

Video components: VHS Video.

Film: 5 hours. 26 reels of film of civic events, mostly from the early 1960s, made by the local authority. 73% colour film, 27% black and white film. Documentary, feature films.

Film components: 8mm, Super 8mm, 16mm, positive film.

Printed catalogue: Available.

Conservation policy: Most film has been copied onto video.

Access: Access available. By appointment. Access for disabled.

Viewing and listening facilities: Viewing facilities only for video.

Copyright: Copyright held for films, but not for most of the video material.

HISPANIC AND LUSO BRAZILIAN COUNCIL

Canning House Library
2 Belgrave Square
LONDON
SW1X 8PJ
Tel: 020 7235 2303
Fax: 020 7235 3587
Web: http://www.canninghouse.com

Contact: Ms Carmen Suarez, Librarian. Library.

E-mail: enquiries.library@canninghouse.com

Video and film holdings: The Council is starting a video collection of films and documentaries specialising in Latin America, Spain and Portugal.

Books holdings: The Library holds a collection about Latin American and Iberian cinema.

Datasets holdings: The Library is starting a collection of CD-ROMs.

Card catalogue: In progress.

Printed catalogue: In progress.

Computerised database: In progress.

Library OPACs with major holdings on moving image and radio: In progress.

Catalogue(s) available via the Internet: In progress.

Websites relating to radio and moving images: In progress.

Digitised collection: No.

Access to researchers from outside: Yes but must become members.

Viewing and listening facilities: In-house viewing; some for loan.

The HISTORY OF ADVERTISING TRUST ARCHIVE

HAT House
12 Raveningham Centre
Raveningham
NORWICH
Norfolk
NR14 6NU
Tel: 01508 548623
Fax: 01508 548478
Web: http://www.hatads.org.uk

Contact: Mr Michael Cudlipp, Secretary. Eve McClure, Archivist.

E-mail: hatadvert@email.msn.com

Founded in 1976 as an archive and educational research organisation (registered UK charity No. 276194). With material dating from 1800 to last month's commercials, the collection contains some two million items: advertising product (print, television, radio); market research; media and public relations; historical archives of advertisers, advertising organisations and agencies. Information and image service; academic and other researchers by appointment.

Video and film holdings: Video: Several thousand television commercials (UK only) from 1955 onwards; currently being recatalogued. Advertising.
Video components: VHS Video, hi-band U-matic, lo-band U-matic, Beta/Beta-SP.

Storage: Archive building.

Card catalogue: Available, indexed.

Printed catalogue: Available, indexed.

Computerised database: Available.

Catalogue(s) available via the Internet: Part listed on the UEA catalogue.

Cataloguing: Video collection currently being recatalogued for inclusion in computerised database.

Documentation: Brochure, annual report, various publications.

Conservation policy: The Archive aims to provide preservation/conservation to highest standards.

Access: Access available. Mon-Fri 09.00–17.00, by appointment only. Closed 25 December–2 January. Staff are available to assist.

Viewing and listening facilities: Viewing on premises.

Charges: Charges for commercial research. Minimum possible charges for 'non-profit' research. Charges for copying, e-mails, etc., services by arrangement.

Copyright: Copyright not held. Client is required to clear copyright. Copyright advice available. Copyright adviser: Secretary.

HOME 1079–FM

The Old Stableblock
Brewery Drive
Lockwood Park
HUDDERSFIELD
West Yorkshire
HD1 3UR
Tel: 01484 321107
Fax: 01484 311107
Web: http://www.home1079.com

Contact: Mr Richard James, Programme Controller.

Holds 42 days radio output to meet legal requirement. Has recently begun archiving news items, local interest programmes and interviews.

HOUSE OF LORDS RECORD OFFICE (THE PARLIAMENTARY ARCHIVES)

House of Lords
LONDON
SW1A 0PW
Tel: 020 7219 3074
Fax: 020 7219 2570
Web: http://www.parliament.uk

E-mail: hlro@parliament.uk

Audio-visual material consists mainly of: (i) film and videotape of the House of Lords Closed Circuit TV Experiment, 1968. A small amount of material connected with the public televising of both Houses is held, but enquiries about material from the Chambers should be directed to the Head of the Parliamentary Recording Unit (Tel: 020 7219 5512). (ii) Films and videocassettes, from the Central Office of Information, broadcasters and others, of material connected with Parliament. The earliest dates from the late 1940s. (iii) Films and videocassettes in deposits received by the Record Office. (iv) Films and videocassettes of events on the Parliamentary Estate.

Video and film holdings: Video components: VHS Video, hi-band U-matic, Beta/Beta-SP, 2-inch Video, Philips 1700.
Film components: 16mm, 35mm, positive film, negative film.

Storage: The collection is stored in air-conditioned accommodation.

Cataloguing: A considerable amount of material is uncatalogued, including a large collection of material received from the BBC in connection with *The Great Palace* series. The collection is being recatalogued.

Documentation: Supplementary documentation is

available, or can be made available, for some items in the collection.

Access: Initial enquiries about all aspects of access (including charges, copyright and viewing) should be made to the Clerk of the Records.

HOVE MUSEUM AND ART GALLERY

19 New Church Road
HOVE
East Sussex
BN3 4AB
Web: http://www.brighton-hove.gov.uk/bhc/libraries/museumtemp.html

Contact: Ms Abigail Thomas, Curator. Carrie Wiltshire, Assistant Curator (Toys, Media and Film).

In 1997 Hove Museum & Art Gallery purchased the portion of the Barnes Collection relating to the South East. This collection reflects the important role the region played in the birth of the film industry. Local film pioneers George Albert Smith, James Williamson, William Friese-Greene, Esme Collings, Alfred Darling and Charles Urban were individually responsible for technical, artistic and commercial practices which underpin today's film industry. Editing and colour image reproduction were developed locally and the results were marketed all over Europe and America. The collection is made up of early apparatus, photographs, programmes, rare publications and other ephemera relating to these pioneers. John and William Barnes began collecting in the 1930s, long before the interest in film history was reflected in universities, museums and heritage centres. They established their own museum in St Ives which became renowned as a resource for film historians world-wide. After its closure the collection was divided into three portions. The portion relating to pre-cinema (lanterns, etc.) was sold to a museum in Turin; Hove Museum has the second and the third is still kept by the Barnes Brothers.

Stills holdings: 300. Mostly portrait photographs and images of early technology. There are also some early lantern slides for the cinema dating from c.1910–1915, and some other pre-1900 examples.

Books holdings: 10, relating to early film pioneers.

Journals holdings: *Film History*.

Ephemera holdings: The Barnes Collection archive relating to South East film pioneers.

Equipment holdings: Early film equipment, such as film projectors. 30 approx.

Card catalogue: Yes.

Printed catalogue: Not yet.

Computerised database: Being developed.

Catalogue(s) available via the Internet: No.

Digitised collection: No. Trying to find funding.

Access: Mon-Fri, 10.00–17.00, by prior appointment.

Access to researchers from outside: Yes, open to all.

Viewing and listening facilities: The Museum does not hold film material. The collection is object based.

Charges: None, except for photographic costs.

HTV WALES

The Television Centre
Culverhouse Cross
CARDIFF
CF5 6XJ
Tel: 029 2059 0177 ext 731
Fax: 020 2059 7183
Web: http://www.htvwales.com/archive/

Contact: Ms Angela Jones, Librarian.

The library holds all transmitted material from Wales and the West ITV franchise area from 1958 to the present day.

Video and film holdings: Video: 60,000 reels/cassettes. Typical television output – news inserts, current affairs, drama, light entertainment. Holdings increase by at least 10 hours a week. Documentary, news and current affairs, science and education, light entertainment and quiz shows.
Video components: Beta/Beta-SP, 1-inch Video.
Film: 9,000 cans. 60% colour film, 40% black and white film. Documentary, feature films, news and current affairs.
Film components: 16mm, 35mm, positive film, negative film, 2,000 A and B neg rolls.

Storage: Film area has air-conditioning on static racks. A purpose-built air-conditioned vault exists with mobile racking for 1-inch and Beta cassettes.

Card catalogue: Available, indexed.

Computerised database: Available.

Cataloguing: Archive project in progress to computerise card catalogue; date of completion is estimated as 2005. All footage from August 1986 to the present day is catalogued on computer and archive material until 1969 is now accessible on computer.

Documentation: Library holds news scripts on a temporary basis (few months). Most programme documentation is held by the relevant departments.

Conservation policy: All transmitted material kept. Sub-master material is periodically recycled.

Access: No access. Research is undertaken by library staff only.

Charges: Charges for research for broadcast productions. Charges for facilities and handling.

Copyright: Copyright held. Contracts Department stores copyright details. Copyright advice available. Copyright adviser: Sue Jarman.

HUNTLEY FILM ARCHIVES LTD

78 Mildmay Park
Newington Green
Islington
LONDON
N1 4PR
Tel: 020 7923 0990
Fax: 020 7241 4929
Web: http://www.huntleyarchives.com

Contact: Ms Amanda Huntley, Archivist.

E-mail: films@huntleyarchives.com

Huntley Film Archives was founded by John Huntley in the mid-1940s. The collection, therefore, has come together slowly, centred on a catalogue of documentary films. The emphasis has always been on maintaining a film-based archive, mainly 35mm and 16mm, although the Archive holds large numbers of Standard and Super 8mm films as well as 9.5. All footage is mastered and preserved on film to ensure high quality and durability of the images. This is additionally important to this archive as it also presents around 150 films shows annually to audiences around the country who enjoy the opportunity to view documentary film in a cinema context. The footage can also be supplied to researchers and commercial users on their chosen tape or disc format. Viewing copies are available on VHS. The collections are increasing by about 1,000 titles per month. This includes a growing video archive and an increase in feature film holdings, particularly production and behind the scenes type footage. However, the bulk of the holdings are loosely, social history: the life of the ordinary person world-wide – work, domestic lives, transport, food, living conditions, leisure, education, traditions and religion.

Video and film holdings: Video components: Beta-SP, DigiBeta, VHS.
Film: 80,000 titles. 25,000 documentaries. 5,000 advertising films, 8,000 amateur films, 6,000 feature films, 6,000 medical films, 16,000 travelogues, 4,000 educational films and 9,000 industrial films. 50% colour, 50% black and white.
Film components: 8mm, Super 8mm, 9.5mm, 16mm, 35mm, positive film, negative film, fine grain print.

Storage: Large warehouse premises with everything stored at one location i.e. viewing, catalogue, etc. with the exception of nitrate film which is stored at a specialist studio facility outside London. Extra films can therefore be found while a viewing is in progress.

Sound holdings: Sound recordings archive.

Stills holdings: Fully comprehensive stills collection. The Archive represents the Dalton-Nicholson Movie Stills Collection, 250,000 pictures from the best years of Hollywood. This collection includes sub-categories of stars and production.

Books holdings: Reference library maintained.

Manuscripts holdings: Scripts collection.

Posters holdings: There is a posters collection.

Equipment holdings: Old movie projection and production equipment is available for loan to museums or prop departments.

Computerised database: Computer record retrieval is now fairly advanced. The Archive had a programme specially written for the library and it is highly effective at searching very wide or narrow criteria. Print-out of full film synopsis is available. Visiting researchers and students are most welcome to browse the catalogue. The card index system has been retained, although this system is less accessible to the outside researcher. There will always be an experienced in-house researcher to assist, at no extra cost. Cataloguing is ongoing.

Cataloguing: The catalogue is available online to browse and order on http://www.huntleyarchives.com

Conservation policy: The Archive is committed to film as master medium. All nitrate is to be transferred to safety stock and nothing is ever junked. Sometimes, films are deposited with archives more relevant to the subject matter. Safety films are also duplicated as an ongoing process. Research and development of our restoration and conservation techniques is constantly updated.

Access: Access available. By appointment. Access for disabled. Ramp access.

Viewing and listening facilities: Viewing on premises. Viewing off premises. Duplicating. Sales. VHS tapes are available on all holdings.

Charges: Charges for research for broadcast productions. Charges for research for academic purposes. Charges for facilities and handling. A price list is available upon request.

Copyright: Copyright held. Copyright advice available.

I.A. RECORDINGS VIDEO ARCHIVE

PO Box 476
TELFORD
Shropshire
TF7 4RB
Tel: 01907 224509

Web: http://www.iarecordings.org

Contact: Mr Kelvin Lake, Director.

E-mail: info@iarecordings.org

Original material recorded by the self-funded, voluntary organisation I.A. Recordings. From 1982 onwards it covers British industrial activity past and present, e.g. remains of old industries and intensive recording of existing industries, many of which were threatened and have since closed. The work is funded by the sale of compilations and productions based on the archive material. I.A. Recordings maintains an extensive website at http://www.iarecordings.org with general information about industrial archaeology and details of archive recordings including an A-Z subject index.

Video and film holdings: Video: 300 hours. 12,000+ minutes of video tape on 680 lo-band and SP hi-band U-matic cassettes, 100% colour. All is original, non-fiction record material. Rate of acquisition is approximately 60 tapes per year. Own productions.
Video components: Hi-8 Video, hi-band U-matic, lo-band U-matic, 1-inch Video, DV, DVC Pro, Beta-SP.

Storage: No purpose-built or environmentally controlled storage; funds for this not available.

Printed catalogue: Available.

Cataloguing: Detailed shotlists of most of the tapes exist for internal use. Some transcripts have been made. Scripts are held for edited productions but original archive recordings are not scripted. Full printed catalogue of sales material available free of charge. Alphabetical list of main subjects on web pages at http://www.iarecordings.org

Documentation: Shot lists, mostly written used internally. Any detailed information can be produced on request: full archive catalogue is in an abbreviated form for internal use.

Conservation policy: No material is junked.

Access: Limited access. No facilities for visitors, so copies of material are sent to researchers for a nominal fee.

Viewing and listening facilities: Duplicating. Sales. Copies of any material may be supplied on request for a nominal fee.

Charges: Charges for research for broadcast productions. Charges for facilities and handling. A price list is available upon request.

Copyright: Copyright held. Some material is joint copyright in that other organisations can also use the material, but our use is not restricted. Copyright advice available. Copyright adviser: Kelvin Lake.

The IMAGE BANK LONDON

17 Conway Street
Fitzroy Square
LONDON
W1T 6EE
Tel: 020 7312 0300
Fax: 020 7391 9123
Web: http://www.imagebankfilm.com

The Image Bank is a leader in rights-protected film, offering more than 10,000 hours of creatively shot, conceptually driven footage. The collection offers instant access to the work of more than 200 cinematographers, including Academy Award winners and some of the industry's hottest commercial directors. Image Bank Film provides 35mm footage covering landscapes, contemporary lifestyles, industry, wildlife, and sports. Time-lapse sequences are also included.

Video and film holdings: Video components: Lo-Band U-matic, Beta/Beta-SP, 1-inch Video, D1, D2.
Film: 70% colour film, 30% black and white film, 1% nitrate film.
Film components: 16mm, Super 16, 35mm, negative film.

Computerised database: Stock footage site at http://www.imagebankfilm.com includes more than 100,000 full-motion clips.

Cataloguing: The Image Bank created and distributed Image Index, a computer interface which searches and retrieves footage from each office's entire film collection. Using a single keyword (or a combination of up to twenty different keywords), this visual database can locate a film clip in half a second. Information about each image – cinematographer, release and clearance guidelines, detailed captions, and more – appear instantly, along with each clip in a four-window storyboard format. Image Index is available for use at all European film offices.

Access: By arrangement.

Viewing and listening facilities: Viewing on premises. Viewing off premises. Duplicating. 3/4-inch viewing cassettes, with final elements available same day.

Copyright: Held by artists whom The Image Bank represents. Copyright advice available.

IMAGE DIGGERS VIDEO

Image Diggers
618b Finchley Road
LONDON
NW11 7RR
Tel: 020 8455 4564
Fax: 020 8455 4564

Contact: Mr Neil Hornick, Director.

E-mail: zip@phancap.demon.co.uk

An ongoing collection of VHS tapes, mostly recorded off-air since 1986 for personal /academic use. They are available, for research and academic purposes only, as part of the Image Diggers archive, which also includes a substantial collection of stills material (photographs, 35mm slides, postcards, magazine cuttings, etc.), plus sheet music, ephemera, books, magazines and newspaper clippings. The range of videos, currently running to about 500 tapes, covers cinema, theatre, literature, television, and aspects of popular culture; with numerous full-length movies and television plays, anthologies of clips from musicals, and animation shorts. There is also an audiocassette collection, covering 500 drama, radio features, popular music (from all countries and periods, and personal performances and interviews).

Video and film holdings: Video: 1,500 hours. Amateur, documentary, feature films, animated films, clips from musicals, comedy.
Video components: VHS Video.

Storage: Boxed and/or shelved.

Computerised database: Available.

Cataloguing: Selections available on request.

Documentation: Relevant credits, articles, reviews and books.

Access: Access available. No access for disabled. Collection is stored on 2nd floor and there is no lift.

Viewing and listening facilities: Viewing on premises. Viewing off premises.

Charges: Charges for research for broadcast productions. Charges for research for academic purposes. Charges for facilities and handling. All prices by negotiation.

Copyright: Copyright not held except in a few cases.

IMPERIAL WAR MUSEUM DEPARTMENT OF DOCUMENTS

Imperial War Museum
Lambeth Road
LONDON
SE1 6HZ
Tel: 020 7416 5220
Fax: 020 7416 5374
Web: http://www.org.uk/docs-hp.htm

Contact: Mr R W A Suddaby, Keeper. Mr R W A Suddaby Department of Documents.

E-mail: docs@iwm.org.uk

The Department of Documents holds an extensive and important collection of primary source material relating to warfare in the twentieth century, largely composed of British private papers and captured German records. The Department's holdings in relation to film include the papers of Lord Bernstein, the Film Adviser to the Ministry of Information during the Second World War, which consist of official correspondence and reports containing much detail on the production and distribution of films made under their aegis, and the public reaction to them. Also held are a small number of film and television scripts, a few collections of papers of individuals who served with the Film Units of the armed forces, and within the holdings occasional references can also be found in personal diaries and letters to filmgoing since 1914.

Manuscripts holdings: 20–30 collections of personal papers.

Card catalogue: Subject and name-based card index.

Printed catalogue: Printed catalogues for larger collections.

Computerised database: InmagicDB/TextWorks database.

Digitised collection: No.

Access: Prior appointment requested.

Access to researchers from outside: Yes.

Viewing and listening facilities: Reading room, capacity approx. 30 seats.

Copyright: Copyright in most collections held by private individuals.

IMPERIAL WAR MUSEUM DEPARTMENT OF EXHIBITS AND FIREARMS

Imperial War Museum
Lambeth Road
LONDON
SE1 6HZ
Tel: 020 7416 5270
Fax: 020 7416 5374
Web: http://www.iwm.org.uk

Contact: Mr David Penn, Keeper.

E-mail: kgale@iwm.org.uk

The Department of Exhibits and Firearms collections cover three-dimensional objects, including artillery, vehicles and small craft, uniforms, medals and insignia, weapons, flags, communications equipment, models, medical equipment, cameras, toys, currency and ephemera.

Ephemera holdings: Yes.

Equipment holdings: 56 items which include cine cameras, film projectors and wireless equipment. Projectors are American, French, German and British. Wartime cameras of similar origin include Arriflex 25mm, Zeiss Ikon high speed camera, Vinten Model K Mk1 'Normandy', Bell and Howell Eyemo (single lens) 'Bomb Spot', Newman Sinclair, De Vry Standard 35mm film camera, Type G45 cine gun camera, Millikan Camera Type DBM-5C (American), German BSK 16 gun camera, as well as Sedic S-2 16mm cine camera (Japanese), Canon Scoopic 16MS (Japanese), Bolex Paillard B8L 16mm (Swiss), etc. Wireless equipment includes an HMV Mains Radio, Marconi receiver Model No 556, the British Model AC Receiver. the AC Civilian receiver, British domestic radios, and a German domestic radio from the 1939–1945 period.

Digitised collection: No. A digitising programme is planned to start this year (2000) but will take 2+ years to complete. It will be selective, beginning with items on display.

IMPERIAL WAR MUSEUM FILM AND VIDEO ARCHIVE

Lambeth Road
LONDON
SE1 6HZ
Tel: 020 7416 5291/5292
Fax: 020 7416 5299
Web: http://www.iwm.org.uk

Contact: Mr Paul Sargent, Deputy Keeper. Jane Fish, Production Information Officer.

E-mail: film@iwm.org.uk

Note: *The above address is the postal one.* The street address for the Film and Video Archive is: All Saints Annexe, Austral Street, London SE11 4SL.

The collection was founded in 1919 when copies of the official films which had been made by Britain during World War I were handed over to the Museum (itself founded in 1917) for preservation. From World War II, the Museum was able to take over all the unedited film shot by the service film units, as well as many documentary and official films, and significant collections of foreign material. The Archive is not, however, limited to the world wars: post-war collections include material from the NATO Film Library and from UNTV in former Yugoslavia. Material is acquired by gift, purchase or exchange from individuals and commercial companies.

Video and film holdings: Video: 6,500 hours. Documentary.

The 'rescue' scene from the likely faked sequence of The Battle of the Somme, *1916 (courtesy of the Imperial War Museum Film and Video Archive)*

Video components: VHS Video, S-VHS Video, hi-8, hi-band U-matic, lo-band U-matic, Beta/Beta-SP, 1-inch Video.

Film: 120,000,000 feet. Practically all the material is non-fiction, and over half of it is unedited record footage, much of which is supported by dope sheets. The principal unedited holdings relate to the three British armed services in World War II, to British and German technological developments, and to Britain's railways during World War II. Other significant subcollections are British newsreels and official films from both the world wars and German and Soviet newsreels from the World War II. 10% colour film, 90% black and white film, 50% nitrate film. Documentary, news and current affairs.

Film components: 8mm, Super 8mm, 9.5mm, 16mm, Super 16, 35mm, positive film, negative film, fine grain print.

Storage: Nitrate film is stored in purpose-built vaults at Hayes, Middlesex. Acetate film is stored in specially converted temperature and humidity controlled stores at the Museum's outstation at Duxford Airfield, Cambridgeshire.

Books holdings: Departmental copies are held for internal reference only.

Manuscripts holdings: Original cameraman's 'dope sheets' (WWII) for Army and Air Force.

Datasets holdings: Slade Film History Register of Newsreels (on microfiche and microfilm.) Newsreel Association of Great Britain and Ireland – Minutes of Council Meetings 1937–1960 (on microfilm).

Journals holdings: *Bioscope* (1914–1920, on microfilm); *Documentary News Letter* (1940–1948); *Film History*

1987–1990, 1993–); *Historical Journal of Film, Radio and Television* (1981–); *Imperial War Museum Review* (1986–).

Equipment holdings: A small exhibition of cine cameras (all gauges, including amateur) dating from 1914 is displayed in the Archive at the All Saints site. The Archive holds a number of projectors (35mm, 9.5mm, 8mm, and S-8mm), but these are mostly maintained as working units for use within the Archive. However, there are a few that are for exhibition, although currently (2000) not on display.

Card catalogue: Covers mostly Second World War collection for armed forces.

Printed catalogue: Available.

Cataloguing: *Vol. 1: The First World War Archive* was published in November 1994. Computerised database covers part of the collection only. It is available for searching by visitors to the Archive, but there is at present no remote access.

Documentation: Dope sheets are held for the British Army and RAF film unit material; shotlists for this material and some other collections are also available. Files including scripts, correspondence and other information relating to some Ministry of Information films from the World War II are also held. The Museum's library has a small section of books on film, propaganda, etc. A handbook to the Archive is available.

Conservation policy: The Museum does not intentionally destroy any material. Occasionally, nitrate material is found on acquisition to have deteriorated beyond redemption, but otherwise no material is destroyed uncopied.

Access: As a public archive it is open to anyone with a bone fide interest. Opening hours: Mon-Fri 10.00–16.45, by appointment only. Access for disabled. There is a lift for researchers with disabilities.

Viewing and listening facilities: Viewing on premises. All material is, in principle, available for viewing by appointment, although there may be practical problems when a film is held in a unique copy.

Charges: Charges for research for broadcast productions. Charges for facilities and handling. A small charge is made for prolonged private research; details of charges, reproduction fees and commercial rates are available on request.

Copyright: Mostly owned by IWM or Crown Copyright which is administered by the IWM. Some material owned by third parties is also held for which the rights have to be cleared. DTI off-air recording licence from

February 1993 to record programmes that fall within the Museum's brief.

IMPERIAL WAR MUSEUM PHOTOGRAPH ARCHIVE

Imperial War Museum
Lambeth Road
LONDON
SE1 6HZ
Tel: 020 7416 5287
Fax: 020 7416 5355
Web: http://www.iwm.org.uk

Contact: Mr Jeremy Richards, Acting Head, Photograph Archive.

E-mail: j.richards@iwm.org.uk

The IWM Photograph Archive contains over six million images illustrating all aspects of twentieth century conflict. A major source of military and civilian, professional and amateur, action and record photographs. Includes work by Horace Nicholls, Cecil Beaton, Bill Brandt and George Rodger. Recent acquisitions include work by Steve Pyke and Tom Stoddart.

Stills holdings: 6 million.

Card catalogue: Although a catalogue of the collection is not currently available lists of photographs on popular topics can be obtained.

Printed catalogue: Yes.

Computerised database: Yes.

Digitised collection: Currently underway.

Access: No charge for access. Opening hours: Mon-Fri, 10.00–17.00.

Access to researchers from outside: Yes.

Charges: Copy prints and/or transparencies are available for a print fee. Reproduction rights are negotiable.

Copyright: Crown Copyright. Some private copyright.

IMPERIAL WAR MUSEUM SOUND ARCHIVE

Imperial War Museum
Lambeth Road
LONDON
SE1 6HZ
Tel: 020 7416 5360
Fax: 020 7416 5379
Web: http://www.iwm.org.uk

Contact: Dr Margaret Brooks, Keeper. Rosemary Tudge, Officer Manager Sound Archive, Imperial War Museum.

E-mail: sound@iwm.org.uk

The Sound Archive was established in 1972 as the national centre for audio recordings relating to twentieth century conflict involving Britain and the Commonwealth. It was a pioneer of oral history and these personal reminiscences dominate the collection, now over 83 million feet (33,200 hours) and growing at the rate of about 3.5 million feet per annum. Historic recordings include speeches recorded by British and international key figures since the 1930s, considerable wartime BBC material, examples of the German High Command's communiqués, ENSA and ORBS light entertainment from the 1940s, daily recordings of the Nuremberg war crimes trials, poetry readings, NATO briefings, relevant recent radio programmes and a very wide range of sound effects.

Sound holdings: 2000: 83+ million feet of sound (33,200+ hours), and growing.

Card catalogue: No.

Printed catalogue: Some parts of the collection.

Computerised database: Entire collection.

Catalogue(s) available via the Internet: Due in the future.

Digitised collection: In progress, commenced 1998.

Access: Mon-Fri, 10.00–17.00.

Access to researchers from outside: Yes.

Viewing and listening facilities: Listening facilities for individuals or groups.

Charges: No charge for browsing the database or listening. All recordings are catalogued and are available for reference and research.

Copyright: Copyright mostly held by the Archive.

INDEPENDENT TELEVISION COMMISSION LIBRARY

33 Foley Street
LONDON
W1W 7TL
Web: http://www.itc.org.uk

Contact: Mr Barrie MacDonald, Librarian. Jan Kacperek, Deputy Librarian.

The strength of the Library is in the special television industry collections, such as the archives, audience reports collection, ITV/Channel 4 programme and company publicity, as well as the more traditional stock of books, journals, official publications, annual reports and press cuttings. The ITC archive collections are important and increasingly well used. The ITC operates the 30-year rule for public records. Some records may be made available earlier, depending on the nature of the records

and purpose of research. **Note:** *(February 2001) This Library is presently under review.*

Stills holdings: Television programme stills.

Books holdings: Book collection on all aspects of non-technical television, UK and World.

Manuscripts holdings: Archive collections are available through the Library: ITA/IBA/ITC archives, 1954–; Cable Authority archives, 1984–90; Associated-Rediffusion archives, 1955–68.

Theses holdings: A few unpublished academic theses on broadcasting topics.

Datasets holdings: *International FilmArchive* CD-ROM (FIAF).

Journals holdings: Journals on most non-technical aspects of television, UK and World.

Newspapers holdings: Press cuttings collection for television and radio, UK and World, 1954–.

Ephemera holdings: Television programme publicity, 1955–.

Card catalogue: No longer.

Printed catalogue: Not of book collection, but ITC Library list of periodical holdings.

Computerised database: The ITC Library computerised catalogue on CAIRS software is available internally.

Catalogue(s) available via the Internet: No.

Websites relating to radio and moving images: Library has pages on the ITC Website at http://www.itc.org.uk

Digitised collection: No. No plans at present.

Access: Mon-Fri, 12.00–17.15 (may change). Please check before visit. Current opening hours may also be checked on the ITC website http://www.itc.org.uk

Access to researchers from outside: Library open to the public.

Viewing and listening facilities: No audio-visual materials held.

Charges: No charge for the use of the Library, except for photocopying.

Copyright: Copyright of ITC publications.

INDEX STOCK SHOTS

12 Charlotte Mews
LONDON
W1T 4EH
Tel: 020 7631 0134
Fax: 020 7436 8737
Web: http://www.index-stockshots.com

Contact: Mr Philip Hinds, Manager.

E-mail: index@msn.com

Index Stock Shots is primarily a source of 35mm colour film footage, a proportion of which continues to be shot specially for library use. The company also maintains an archival collection dating back to the early 1900s. The contemporary collection includes, aerials, aviation, cities, landmarks, lifestyle, time-lapse, wildlife. The historical archive features aircraft, industry, motor racing, Third World, travel.

Video and film holdings: Video: About 300 hours. The bulk of this footage originates on film, although only 150 hours are neg available.
Video components: D1, DigiBeta, Beta SP.
Film: Approx. 500 hours of 35mm negative, of which approx. 150 hours are also available on tape.
Film components: 35mm negative, 35mm interpositive.

Storage: The majority of components are stored in-house.

Card catalogue: Available, indexed. The catalogue for the historical collection is available in-house.

Computerised database: Available.

Catalogue(s) available via the Internet: The catalogue for the contemporary collection is available on the Library's website at http://www.index-stockshots.com

Documentation: Brochure.

Access: Access to these collections is available to professionals working in all areas of film, television and associated production.

Viewing and listening facilities: Viewing is possible in or out of house, subject to availability.

Los Angeles International Airport (photo courtesy of Index Stock Shots)

Charges: A service fee is charged for the use of library footage for reference purposes. Licence fees are charged for the supply of master material.

Copyright: Index owns much of its footage, and controls copyright on behalf of other contributors to the Library.

INSTITUTE OF AMATEUR CINEMATOGRAPHERS – IAC LIBRARY

24c West Street
EPSOM
KT18 7RJ
Tel: 01372 739672
Fax: 01372 739672
Web: http://www.theiac.org.uk

Contact: Ms Janet Smith, Administrative Secretary.

E-mail: icfilmsvideo@compuserve.com

Largest collection of amateur films dating back to 1932. Films are only available for hire.

Video and film holdings: Video: Amateur.
Video components: VHS Video, S-VHS Video.
Film: Amateur.
Film components: 8mm, Super 8mm, 9.5mm, 16mm.

Storage: Shelving in one room on second floor of building.

Printed catalogue: Available.

Cataloguing: Video and Super-8 catalogues are indexed by categories and makers, 16mm catalogue is not indexed.

Documentation: None.

Conservation policy: No material is ever discarded.

Access: No access.

Viewing and listening facilities: Viewing off premises.

Charges: Charges for facilities and handling. A price list is available upon request.

Copyright: Copyright not held. Copyright resides with filmmakers.

INSTITUTE OF COMMUNICATION STUDIES

University of Leeds
Roger Stevens Building
Level 5
LEEDS
LS2 9JT
Tel: 0113 233 5810
Fax: 0113 233 5820
Web: http://www.leeds.ac.uk/ics/archives.htm

Contact: Prof Philip M Taylor, Director. Andrew Thorpe, Technician.

E-mail: p.m.taylor@leeds.ac.uk

The ICS audio-visual holdings comprise individual film and television collections of staff and three principal archives: the Gulf War Archive dating from January 1991 to March 1991 – 24-hour coverage of all UK terrestrial coverage, plus CNN, Sky, TR1, GRD, RAI, Moscow: the ESRC Electoral Archive – television coverage of all UK general elections (embracing the periods from when they were called to when they were completed) from 1971: the Kosovo War Archive dating from March to May 1999 – coverage by BBC World, RAI, TFI and GRD 24-hour coverage.

Video and film holdings: Yes.

Books holdings: These are in the University Library. The book collection relating to media generally amounts to more than 30,000 titles.

Theses holdings: Yes.

Journals holdings: Yes.

Newspapers holdings: Yes.

Card catalogue: The Institute will be applying for funding to catalogue its collection.

Digitised collection: No. Yes.

Access: Mon-Fri, 09.00–17.00. Prior permission.

Access to researchers from outside: Yes.

Viewing and listening facilities: Yes.

Charges: On request.

Copyright: In-house viewing only.

INSTITUTE OF CONTEMPORARY HISTORY & WIENER LIBRARY

4 Devonshire Street
LONDON
W1N 2BH
Tel: 020 7636 7247
Fax: 020 7436 6428

Contact: Ms Rosemarie Nief, Librarian. Christine Patel, Library Assistant.

E-mail: lib@wl.u-net.com

Private library. One of the leading research centres on European history since World War I, with special reference to the era of totalitarianism and to Jewish affairs. Founded by Dr Alfred Wiener in Amsterdam in 1933, it holds material that is not available elsewhere. Books, periodicals, press archives, documents, pamphlets, leaflets, brochures and videos. Much of the material can be consulted on microfilm. The video collection – Oskar Joseph Video Collection – began in approximately 1989.

Video and film holdings: Video: 1,300 videos containing some 5,200 programmes. Material includes Cold War propaganda material, neo-Nazi and revisionist material, German and Allied propaganda films, television documentaries from Europe and the US, feature films of the 1930s and 1940s. Documentary, feature films, news and current affairs.

Video components: VHS Video.

Storage: Videotapes shelved on open shelves in semi-dark room.

Card catalogue: Available, indexed.

Documentation: None.

Access: Access available. Mon-Fri 10.00–17.30. There are four steps to the front door to overcome. By letter of introduction (readers needing to use the Library for any length of time should become members).

Viewing and listening facilities: Viewing on premises.

Charges: Charges for research for academic purposes.

Copyright: Copyright not held. Copyright advice available. Copyright adviser: The Librarian.

INSTITUTION OF CIVIL ENGINEERS

1 Great George Street
LONDON
SW1P 3AA
Tel: 020 7665 2258
Fax: 020 7976 7610
Web: http://www.ice.org.uk

Contact: Ms Claire Delgal, Assistant Librarian.

E-mail: claire.delgal@ice.org.uk

Video and film holdings: Approx. 340.

Stills holdings: 3,600 slides.

Computerised database: Videos are on the Library catalogue.

Digitised collection: No.

Access: Prior permission.

Access to researchers from outside: Yes. Items in the audio-visual collection may be borrowed by members of the Institution and by UK-based organisations or lecturers interested in the work of professional engineers.

Viewing and listening facilities: One playback machine.

Charges: None.

Copyright: Only for the Institution's own videos.

INSTITUTION OF ELECTRICAL ENGINEERS

Savoy Place
LONDON
WC2R 0BL

Tel: 020 7344 8436
Fax: 020 7344 5395
Web: http://www.iee.org.uk/archive

Contact: Ms Sarah Barnard, Senior Archivist.

E-mail: sbarnard@iee.org.uk

The archives of the Institution of Electrical Engineers contain films of scientists who were awarded the Faraday Medal or an honorary fellowship by the Institution, talking about their work. There are also occasional film and video items in other collections, relating to various technological developments such as radar and transatlantic cables. These, however, are not numerous.

Video and film holdings: Video: 25 reels/cassettes. Science and education.
Video components: VHS Video, hi-band U-matic.
Film: 125 cans. Films of scientists talking about their work. 10% colour film, 90% black and white film.
Film components: 16mm, 35mm.

Storage: Temperature controlled strong room.

Card catalogue: Available.

Printed catalogue: Available, indexed.

Cataloguing: Card index to printed lists. Holdings are indexed alphabetically.

Conservation policy: Films and videos are part of the Institution of Electrical Engineers' permanent holdings.

Access: Limited access. By prior appointment only.

Copyright: Copyright held. Copyright advice available. Copyright adviser: Lenore Symons.

INSTITUTO CERVANTES

326–330 Deansgate
MANCHESTER
M3 4FN
Tel: 0161 661 4210
Fax: 0161 661 4203
Web: http://www.cervantes.es/rbic

Contact: Mr Jose Maria Fernandez, Librarian. Library.

E-mail: bibman@cervantes.es

The Library of the Instituto Cervantes in Manchester is a resource centre specialising in the Spanish language and the culture of the Spanish-speaking world. Its collection includes approximately 500 Spanish and Latin-American films on video and about 100 videos of Spanish television drama.

Video and film holdings: Approx. 600.

Books holdings: Approx. 50 books on Spanish and Latin American cinema.

Datasets holdings: Several databases on Spanish cinema on CD-ROM.

Journals holdings: Several Spanish cinema journals.

Newspapers holdings: Yes.

Computerised database: Yes.

Library OPACs with major holdings on moving image and radio: Yes.

Catalogue(s) available via the Internet: Yes.

Digitised collection: No.

Access: Mon-Thu, 12.00–19.45. Fri, 11.00–15.30.

Access to researchers from outside: Yes. The Library is open to the general public.

Viewing and listening facilities: Provided.

Charges: Yes, to obtain a library card for borrowing materials.

INVICTA FM

Radio House
John Wilson Business Park
WHITSTABLE
Kent
CT5 3QX
Tel: 01227 772004
Fax: 01227 771558
Web: http://www.invictafm.com

Contact: Mr Luis Clark, Programme Director.

E-mail: info@invictaradio.co.uk

Radio station. Holds 42 days' output to meet legal requirement.

The IRONBRIDGE GORGE MUSEUM TRUST FILM AND VIDEO COLLECTION

The Ironbridge Gorge Museum Trust
The Wharfage
Ironbridge
TELFORD
Shropshire
TF8 7AW
Tel: 01952 432141
Fax: 01952 432237
Web: http://www.ironbridge.org.uk

Contact: Mr John Powell, Librarian. Ms Joanne Smith, Documentation Manager.

E-mail: library@ironbridge.org.uk

Video and film holdings: Video: 107 reels/cassettes. The video collection consists of local news reports relevant to the Ironbridge Gorge Museum Trust or the Telford area. It includes in-house museum videos and material on subjects relevant to the industrial revolution, etc. Amateur, documentary, news and current affairs, science and education.

Video components: VHS Video, hi-band U-matic, Beta/Beta-SP.

Film: 200 cans. The film collection consists of local news reports relevant to the Ironbridge Gorge Museum Trust and the Telford area and comprises material on subjects relevant to the industrial revolution, etc. It also includes footage on the renovation of the Iron Bridge in the 1970s and also loan collections from British Steel and the Historical Metallurgy Society. 40% colour film, 60% black and white film. Advertising, amateur, documentary, science and education.

Film components: 16mm.

Storage: Films are stored in polypropylene acid-free canisters from USA. Cassettes are stored in original cases, then in video drawer units.

Printed catalogue: Available, indexed.

Computerised database: Available.

Conservation policy: Film masters are copied onto video for use rather than use original. No conservation in-house, but outside conservator used if necessary.

Access: Access available. Mon-Fri 09.00–17.00, by appointment only. Staff are available to assist. Access for disabled. Ramps and toilet.

Viewing and listening facilities: Viewing on premises. Duplicating. Sales.

Charges: The Museum Trust charges a fee for reproduction and postage and packaging.

Copyright: Copyright held. Copyright advice available.

ISLE OF WIGHT RADIO

Dodnor Park
NEWPORT
Isle of Wight
PO30 5XE
Tel: 01983 822557
Fax: 01983 822109
Web: http://www.iwradio.co.uk

Contact: Mr Stuart McGinley, Programme Controller.

Holds 42 days' output to meet legal requirement. Keeps an archive of news items for one year for own use. Chat shows are recorded at presenters' discretion.

ITN ARCHIVE

Independent Television News Ltd
200 Gray's Inn Road
LONDON
WC1X 8XZ

Tel: 020 7430 4480
Fax: 020 7430 4453
Web: http://www.itnarchive.com

Contact: Mr Alwyn Lindsey, Sales Director.

E-mail: archive.sales@itn.co.uk

Worldwide news events from 1955 to the present day and a wealth of associated feature footage, rushes and clip reels. News information service, cuttings and reference. Also UK representation of French Pathé. Represents the entire newsreel archive (from 1896) of the *Reuters Television Library (see separate entry).*

Video and film holdings: Video components: Hi-band U-matic, Beta/Beta-SP, 1-inch Video.

Film components: 16mm, 35mm, positive film, negative film, effects mix, final mix.

Storage: All material, as well as Reuters', is stored on site.

Card catalogue: Available, indexed.

Printed catalogue: Available.

Computerised database: Available.

Catalogue(s) available via the Internet: ITN and Reuters Television Library database is online.

Cataloguing: Card/microfiche index 1955–1981. Computerised database since 1981. Diary of transmitted bulletins from 1955 onwards.

Conservation policy: As resources allow.

Access: Access available. By arrangement. Access for disabled.

Viewing and listening facilities: Viewing on premises. Duplicating. Sales. On site video/film transfer facilities.

Charges: Charges for research for broadcast productions. Charges for research for academic purposes. Charges for facilities and handling. A price list is available upon request.

Copyright: Copyright held. Copyright advice available. Copyright adviser: Alwyn Lindsey.

IVN/QUESTAR – STOCK FOOTAGE LIBRARY

IVN Communications
Centre 500
500 Chiswick High Road
Chiswick
LONDON
W4 5RG
Tel: 020 8956 2340
Fax: 020 8956 2339

Contact: Mr Robert Burgis, Manager/Stock Footage Library.

E-mail: bobburgis@aol.com

Destination-related programmes originally produced for broadcast and video distribution worldwide. Now over 250 titles. Approximately 20 new titles are added to the collection annually.

Video and film holdings: Video: 300 reels/cassettes. Collections comprise: Video Visits – documentary style introduction to cities/countries/regions; *Readers Digest* – wonders of the world, nature and natural history: *Video Expeditions* – destination and adventure; *Lonely Planet* – world-wide adventures of independent travellers; *Gardens* – documentary covering nine famous British gardens; *Great Metros* – city and rail transport systems. Documentary.
Video components: VHS Video, Beta/Beta-SP, 1-inch Video.
Film components: 16mm.

Printed catalogue: Available.

Conservation policy: Items are deleted from the collection if/when rights expire or if replaced by newer material.

Access: Limited access. Telephone enquiries welcome.

Viewing and listening facilities: Viewing off premises.

Charges: Charges for facilities and handling. A price list is available upon request.

Copyright: Copyright not held.

JAZZ FM – GREATER LONDON

26–27 Castlereagh Street
LONDON
W1H 6DJ
Tel: 020 7706 4100
Fax: 020 7723 9742
Web: http://www.jazzfm.com

Contact: Ms Kirsten Macgillivray, Programme Director.

E-mail: info@jazzfm.com

Jazz FM keeps some live sessions and recordings of shows with musicians. The radio station has a large private music library. It does not maintain a news archive as its news is supplied by ITN.

JAZZ FM – NORTH WEST ENGLAND

The World Trade Centre
Exchange Quay
MANCHESTER
M5 3EJ

Tel: 0161 877 1004
Fax: 0161 877 1005
Web: http://www.jazzfm.com

Contact: Ms Kirsten Macgilllivray, Programme Director.

E-mail: info@jazzfm.com

Jazz FM – North West England keeps some live sessions and recordings of shows with musicians. The radio station has a large private music library. It does not maintain a news archive as its news is supplied by ITN.

The JEWISH MUSEUM

The Sternberg Centre
80 East End Road
LONDON
N3 2SY
Tel: 020 8349 1143
Fax: 020 8343 2161
Web: http://www.jewmusm.ort.org/welcome.htm

Contact: Mr C Seigel, Curator. Ms S Jillings, Assistant Curator.

The Museum was founded in 1983. It has a small film/video collection relating to the growth and development of the Jewish community in London.

Video and film holdings: Video: 34 reels/cassettes. Majority of films have been transferred to video. Amateur, documentary.
Video components: VHS Video, 8mm Video, hi-band U-matic.
Film: The holdings consist of amateur and documentary footage on the history of Yiddish theatre in London; footage of Jews in Aden; footage of Cable Street, 1936; a Jewish wedding in East London in 1924. Amateur, documentary.

Card catalogue: Handlist of video and film holdings.

Printed catalogue: Available.

Documentation: The Museum also has an archive collection of approximately 15,000 photographs which can be used as stills. These are stored in negative form with reference contact prints and there is an index to the collection.

Conservation policy: Collection is being monitored.

Access: Access available. By arrangement only. Access for disabled.

Viewing and listening facilities: Viewing on premises.

Charges: Charges for research for broadcast productions. Charges for printing still photographs.

Copyright: Variable. Copyright advice available.

JOHN BROOKER'S MOVIE MEMORIES

Watermead
Bartlow Road
ASHDON
Essex
CB10 2HR
Tel: 01799 584039
Fax: 01799 584039

Contact: Mr John Brooker, Archivist.

Started in 1962 primarily for the preservation of B westerns starring Roy Rogers, William Boyd, etc. Has since been extended to include other B movies (East Side Kids, Jungle Jim, Sherlock Holmes, etc.), serials and assorted features and shorts from the 1930–1955 period. Also selection of early television shows and footage of rock 'n roll and country music artists.

Video and film holdings: All material is 16mm, mostly black and white. Over 700 features and shorts.
Components: Material available for viewing on time-coded VHS video.

Storage: Air-conditioned store room.

Card catalogue: No catalogue – all films on card index system. Full information on particular requirements available on application.

Access to researchers from outside: Yes.

Viewing and listening facilities: At above address by appointment. Time-coded VHS copies available of all titles.

JOHN RYLANDS UNIVERSITY LIBRARY OF MANCHESTER

Manchester University
150 Deansgate
MANCHESTER
M3 3EH
Tel: 0161 834 5343
Fax: 0161 834 5574
Web: http://www.rylibweb.man.ac.uk

Contact: Dr Stella Butler, Head of Special Collections. John Rylands Library, 150 Deansgate, MANCHESTER M3 3EH.

E-mail: spcoll72@man.ac.uk

Stills holdings: A few items, e.g. in L P Hartley archive (*The Go-Between*).

Books holdings: Some material at main site, open access, e.g. American Studies material.

Manuscripts holdings: Robert Donat archive (film star, actor) – new acquisition, uncatalogued; papers of Sir William Mansfield Cooper, former Manchester University Vice-Chancellor, re setting up of Schools Television in the early days of ITV (provisional typescript catalogue). Archive of Basil Dean (theatre impresario and pioneer of the British Film Industry) containing papers relating to Paramount Famous Lasky Corporation, RKO, Associated Talking Pictures Ltd and London Film Productions, 1928–1944.

Card catalogue: Yes (printed books).

Library OPACs with major holdings on moving image and radio: Yes (printed books).

Catalogue(s) available via the Internet: Yes (printed books).

Digitised collection: No, possibility being investigated.

Access: By prior arrangement for those outside the university.

Access to researchers from outside: Yes.

KENT INSTITUTE OF ART AND DESIGN

Oakwood Park
MAIDSTONE
Kent
ME168AG
Tel: 01622 757286
Fax: 01622 621100

Contact: Ms Fay Cooke, Librarian, Maidstone Site. Library & Learning Resources.

E-mail: fcooke@kiad.ac.uk

The Institute's other sites are at Fort Pitt, Rochester, Kent ME1 1DZ, and New Dover Road, Canterbury CT1 3AN.

Video and film holdings: 4418 videos (including off-air), held mainly at the Maidstone and Rochester sites.

Books holdings: Moving images – film/digital collection based at Maidstone site.

Journals holdings: *c.*35 journals are held mainly at Maidstone site.

Newspapers holdings: Small newspaper cuttings collection.

Library OPACs with major holdings on moving image and radio: WebCat.

Catalogue(s) available via the Internet: SIRSI UNICORN – Z39.50 compliant.

Websites relating to radio and moving images: http://www.kiad.ac.uk/library.

Digitised collection: No.

Access: Prior permission for public.

Access to researchers from outside: Yes, for reference only.

Viewing and listening facilities: Video players.

Charges: None.

KING'S FUND LIBRARY

11–13 Cavendish Square
LONDON
W1M 0AN
Tel: 020 7307 2568/2569
Fax: 020 7307 2805 Enquiry Desk
Web: http://www.kingsfund.org.uk/elibrary/html/library_main.htm

The King's Fund is an independent health charity which aims to stimulate good practice in service provision and to influence health policy. It has external links through a number of British-based and overseas networks. The Library collection covers service development and management, particularly in healthcare settings.

Video and film holdings: 100.

Digitised collection: No.

Access: Reference library only. Videos may not be borrowed. Opening hours – Mon-Fri, 09.30–17.30; except Wed, 11.00–17.30. Sat, 09.30–17.00.

Access to researchers from outside: Yes.

Viewing and listening facilities: Yes, one publicly accessible video recorder/television with headphones.

Charges: £10 refundable deposit.

Copyright: None.

KINGSTON-UPON-HULL RECORD OFFICE

79 Lowgate
KINGSTON UPON HULL
HU1 1HN
Tel: 01482 615102
Fax: 01482 613051

Contact: G W Oxley, City Archivist.

Films acquired by donation or made by, or for, Council departments.

Video and film holdings: Film: Local civic events from about 1940. Civic events.

Film components: Positive Film.

Storage: Archive strong room.

Cataloguing: Typed lists.

Access: Access available. By appointment. Mon-Thu 09.00–12.30 and 13.30–17.00, Fri 09.00–12.30 and 13.30–16.30. Access for disabled.

Viewing and listening facilities: Viewing off premises.

Copyright: Copyright not held.

KIRKLEES COMMUNITY HISTORY SERVICE

Kirklees Metropolitan Council
The Stables, Tolson Museum, Ravensknowle Park
Wakefield Road
HUDDERSFIELD
West Yorkshire
HD5 8DJ
Tel: 01484 223800
Fax: 01484 223805

Contact: Mr Brian Haigh, Community History Manager.

Films are acquired from private individuals, local cine clubs and from Council departments. The collection includes over 120 titles relating to the locality which includes Huddersfield, Batley, Dewsbury, Mirfield, the Spen Valley and the Holme and Colne Valleys. Topics covered include transport, industry, historic events and celebrations. Acquisitions are made as they become available.

Video and film holdings: Video components: VHS Video.
Film components: 8mm, 16mm, 35mm, negative film.

Sound holdings: Sound archive of oral history recordings. A catalogue of the Sound Archive has been published and is available from the Community History Service.

Stills holdings: Large collections of photographs.

Cataloguing: The films are listed by title, and a record of the gauge, colour, length and maker is kept together with a summary of contents. The catalogue, covering over 120 titles, may be consulted at the Local Studies Library, Huddersfield Library and Art Gallery, Princess Alexandra Walk, Huddersfield HD1 2SU. Tel: 01484 221965.

Digitised collection: Approx. 50,000 images from the photographic collections have been digitised and are accessible at four libraries and museums via touch screen computers. A selection of images is available on website http://www.hpac.org.uk/Kirklees/index.ntml.

Access: The material is not available for loan and access is by appointment only via Local Studies Library.

Copyright: Copyright in most of the items in the collection rests with the filmmakers.

KISS 100 FM

Mappin House
4 Winsley Street
LONDON
W1N 7AR
Tel: 020 7436 1515

Contact: Mr Keith Rentin, Engineer.

Kiss FM holds programmes on video of the launch of the radio station, a private collection of dance music, a large selection of interviews on DAT in particular with London-based DJs and black musicians based abroad. In addition, Kiss is planning to undertake a large archiving project.

LAUDER COLLEGE

Halbeath
DUNFERMLINE
Fife
KY11 8DY
Tel: 01383 845155
Fax: 01383 845001

Contact: Mr Tom McMaster. Library Resources.

E-mail: tmcmaster@lauder.ac.uk

The College does not teach film and television studies specifically but there is some coverage in media studies generally.

Video and film holdings: Off-air recordings being gradually developed at the moment.

Masters holdings: About 500–600 commercially-produced audio-visual resources.

Sound holdings: Included in figure above for audio-visual resources.

Books holdings: Very small collection related to media studies.

Journals holdings: No film or television journals currently subscribed to.

Library OPACs with major holdings on moving image and radio: Heritage IV OPAC.

Catalogue(s) available via the Internet: Webpac to be online by December 2000.

Websites relating to radio and moving images: Ongoing Website catalogue development.

Digitised collection: No.

Access: Mon-Thu, 08.30–21.00. Fri, 08.30–17.00. Sat, 10.00–13.00.

Access to researchers from outside: Yes. External membership free.

Viewing and listening facilities: Video playback facilities available.

Charges: No charges applicable (under review).

LEEDS ANIMATION WORKSHOP

45 Bayswater Row
LEEDS
LS8 5LF
Tel: 0113 248 4997
Fax: 0113 248 4997

Contact: Ms Milena Dragic, Co-worker.

Holds 25 years of animation on social issues produced by Leeds Animation Workshop.

Video and film holdings: Video: 17 reels/cassettes, 2 hours. The film collection has been transferred onto video.
Video components: VHS Video, lo-band U-matic, Beta/Beta-SP, 1-inch Video.
Film: 4,800 feet, 17 cans, 2 hours. 100% colour film. Animated films.
Film components: 16mm.

Storage: No purpose-built storage.

Printed catalogue: Available.

Cataloguing: Catalogue regularly updated available on request. Notes for most films available on request.

Documentation: Notes for individual films available on request.

Conservation policy: Until now material has not been discarded.

Access: Access available. Mon-Thu 10.00–16.00, by prior arrangement. Staff are available to assist.

Viewing and listening facilities: Viewing on premises. Viewing off premises. Sales. VHS copies are available.

Copyright: Copyright held.

LEEDS INDUSTRIAL MUSEUM

Armley Mills
Canal Road
Armley
LEEDS
LS12 2QF
Tel: 0113 263 7861
Fax: 0113 263 7861

Contact: Mr Martin Gresswell, Curator.

Holdings are described below.

Video and film holdings: Videorecordings of 1888 films of Louis Le Prince, who experimented in Leeds, plus newsreels.

Masters holdings: Approx. 100 16mm films – mainly technical/training.

Equipment holdings: *c.*15 Kalee cameras and projectors.

Printed catalogue: Printed list.

Digitised collection: No.

Access: By arrangement.

Access to researchers from outside: Yes.

Viewing and listening facilities: 35mm and 16mm in the Museum's cinema.

Charges: Admission charge to Museum.

LEEDS METROPOLITAN UNIVERSITY

Woodhouse Lane
LEEDS
West Yorkshire
LS1 3HE
Tel: 0113 283 2600 ext 3382
Fax: 0113 283 3123
Web: http://www.lmu.ac.uk/net.lw/film.htm

Contact: Mrs Sandra McDowell, Learning Adviser. Learning and Information Services.

E-mail: s.mcdowell@lmu.ac.uk

The collection supports postgraduate courses in Film Production and Scriptwriting and undergraduate courses in Animation.

Video and film holdings: 4,700 (of which 1,500 are films).

Books holdings: *c.*2,000.

Datasets holdings: 1 CD-ROM (LMU members only have access).

Journals holdings: 30.

Computerised database: Not available for external users.

Library OPACs with major holdings on moving image and radio: Yes, but not radio.

Catalogue(s) available via the Internet: Soon. A new system is being acquired.

Websites relating to radio and moving images: Yes.

Digitised collection: No.

Access: External users, reference only. 09.00–17.00 only in vacations.

Access to researchers from outside: Yes. Books and journals.

Viewing and listening facilities: No audio-visual access for external users.

Charges: £100 per annum for external borrowers' ticket (books only).

LEEDS REFERENCE LIBRARY

Central Library
Municipal Buildings
LEEDS
LS1 3AB
Tel: 0113 247 8283
Fax: 0113 247 8268
Web: http://www.leeds.gov.uk

Contact: Pat Egan, Central Collections Manager.

Items were donated to the local studies library.

Video and film holdings: Video: 7 reels/cassettes. Documentary.
Video components: VHS Video.
Film: 7 cans. All the films held are black and white. They cover royal visits and celebrations. Documentary.
Film components: 16mm.

Card catalogue: Available, indexed.

Conservation policy: All films have been copied on to VHS tapes.

Access: No access. There are no viewing facilities on the premises.

Viewing and listening facilities: Viewing off premises.

Copyright: Copyright held.

LEEDS UNIVERSITY/SSRC ELECTORAL BROADCASTING ARCHIVE & GULF WAR ARCHIVE

The Edward Boyle Library
Audio-Visual Section
University of Leeds
LEEDS
LS2 9JT
Tel: 0113 233 5540
Fax: 0113 233 5539
Web: http://www.leeds.ac.uk/library/

Contact: Ms Alison Depledge.

E-mail: a.j.depledge@leeds.ac.uk

The Electoral Broadcasting Archive originated in specimens of pre-war party films and newsreel speeches acquired by the School of History, to which were then added a representative selection of the news and current affairs output of television during the February 1974 General Election campaign, with the permission of the broadcasters. Thereafter, grants from the SSRC, ESRC and the IBA, and special licensing arrangements granted by the BBC and ITCA, permitted comprehensive recording of the news, current affairs, discussion, phone-in and similar programme output of all channels received in the region (selectively also of radio) during the periods between the dissolution of Parliament and the declaration of results. Gifts from the Labour Party and others allowed the addition of programmes transmitted only in the London area.

The Gulf War Archive originated from a five-nation comparative analysis research project into the presentation of the war carried out by the Institute and funded by the ESRC, BBC, ITC and BSC. The collection consists of the round-the-clock output of BBC1, BBC2, ITV, Channel 4, BSkyB and CNN, plus the peak-time output of BR2 (Germany), TF1 (France), RAI (Italy) and Gorizout (Russia), from day two of the commencement of the hostilities to the end of the week following the armistice. **Note:** *The Gulf War Archive is kept in the Institute of Communication Studies, University of Leeds.*

Video and film holdings: Video: The national and local news bulletins, party political broadcasts, current affairs and discussion programmes, including phone-in and chat-shows transmitted each day during various General Election campaigns, recorded in context. Also general output mainly for the Gulf War Archive.

Cataloguing: The recordings are simply numbered and listed on mimeographed sheets.

Access: Access is through prior written application stating purpose of the research, position of the researcher and preferred time for viewing. Initial enquiries concerning access should be made to the Director of the Institute of Communication Studies, University of Leeds, Leeds LS2 9JT, tel: 0113 233 5800, fax: 0113 233 5808. These recordings are kept for the purpose of study and research only by bona fide researchers or students within the fields of the political and social sciences and history. They are not for general educational purposes.

Viewing and listening facilities: Viewing on premises. Viewing facilities are available in the library audio-visual area. No copies of the recording in whole or in part, such as still images, may be provided.

LEEDS UNIVERSITY TELEVISION

University of Leeds
LEEDS
LS2 9JT
Tel: 0113 2332651
Fax: 0113 2332655
Web: http://www.mediant.leeds.ac.uk/vtcatalogue

Contact: Mr Peter Coltman, Head of Television and Training Section, Media Services. Miss J A Dartnall.

E-mail: p.h.coltman@leeds.ac.uk

Leeds University Television exists to originate and edit moving images for teaching and learning in higher education. As appropriate, it also makes these available to other institutions, usually through the sale of copies of programmes, occasionally through the sale of individual sequences. It is not an archiving body, nor does it purchase materials except to contribute to its own programmes. It is not therefore generally of interest to researchers and is seldom used by them.

Masters holdings: Master collection of original material on videotape.

Computerised database: Access database of master and insert material.

Catalogue(s) available via the Internet: http://www.leeds.ac.uk/ums/vtcatalogue

Access to researchers from outside: Yes.

Charges: Access to material is charged to external users.

Copyright: Copyright held on most material.

LEICESTER SOUND

Granville House
Granville Road
LEICESTER
LE1 7RW
Tel: 0116 256 1300
Fax: 0116 256 1303

Contact: Mr David Friend, News Editor.

E-mail: leicestersound@musicradio.com

Radio station. All news output and scripts are kept for one year.

LEICESTERSHIRE FILM ARCHIVE

17 Kingsway
LEICESTER
LE3 2JL
Tel: 0116 289 0531
Fax: 0116 289 0531

Contact: Mr Rob Foxon, Director.

The newly established Leicestershire Film Archive provides a clear identity for the Leicester and Leicestershire collection of the TUA Film Archive (see separate entry). It comprises mainly amateur shot material, much of which has been blown up from 9.5mm originals, showing aspects of life in the county from around 1930 to the present day. Film records include the 1932

Pageant of Leicester, the 1935 Silver Jubilee celebrations in Leicester, Coronation parades, royal visits, local industry, transport, farming and country life in an area much neglected by filmmakers. There are also documentary and other productions featuring Leicester and Leicestershire.

Video and film holdings: Film: 200 cans, 80% black and white, 20% colour. Amateur and professional, documentary, news and current affairs, science and education.
Film components: 8mm. 9.5mm, 16mm, 35mm, positive and negative material.

Storage: Special room in purpose-built accommodation.

Card catalogue: Available.

Printed catalogue: No printed catalogue at present.

Computerised database: Partly computerised database.

Conservation policy: Viewing copies made from preservation masters. Repatriation of non-core material to other archives with owners consent. No usable material junked.

Access: Public film shows via the annual Bygone Leicester Moving Image Picture Show. Film shows are also presented at the invitation of groups and societies, schools and colleges. The Archive has also produced a small number of videos of local interest. Films can be made available for film, video and television use, subject to copyright clearance.

Viewing and listening facilities: Viewing on premises by appointment. VHS viewing copy by arrangement.

Civic Parade – Pageant of Leicester, 1932. (photo courtesy of Leicestershire Film Archive)

Charges: Archive search fee. Charges for VHS copies, broadcasting and productions. Enquire for current rates. The archive is self-financing and all income from charges and film shows is used in the restoration and preservation of material held.

Copyright: Some copyright held. Copyright advice available. Copyright adviser: Rob Foxon.

LEICESTERSHIRE MUSEUMS SERVICE FILM ARCHIVE

Record Office for Leicestershire, Leicester & Rutland
Long Street
Wigston Magna
LEICESTER
LE18 2AH
Tel: 0116 257 1080
Fax: 0116 257 1120

Contact: Mr Robin Jenkins, Keeper of Archives.

The collection has been accumulated by various sections of Leicestershire Museums, Arts & Records Service. The majority has been transferred to the Record Office section since c.1968. The technology section at the Snibston Discovery Park collects and copies film for its own holdings.

Video and film holdings: Video: 60 hours. The video collection consists of approximately 60 hours of footage, and includes the Leicestershire Collection of local videos. Advertising, amateur, documentary, news and current affairs, science and education.
Video components: VHS Video.
Film: 150 cans. The Archive holds approximately 150 cans of film covering topics from royal events and celebrations to museum activities such as taxidermy. Material of general and local interest. A small amount of fiction. Symington of Market Harborough factory films, c.1899, 1921–1977. Various pageants, royal events, coronation, funeral, royal visit films 1932–1954, including film of Leicestershire Yeomanry in camp 1937–1938. Civil Defence strips and ten films by Religious Films Ltd. London British Coal instructional films transferred to Record Office from Snibston, 1991. 100% black and white film, 40% nitrate film. Advertising, amateur, documentary, feature films, news and current affairs, science and education, NCB instructional films.
Film components: 9.5mm, 16mm, 35mm, positive film, negative film.

Storage: In controlled and approved archive store.

Card catalogue: Available, indexed.

Cataloguing: Some collections listed in detail.

Conservation policy: Gradual transfer of film to safety stock and video.

Access: Access available. Access for disabled. Staff can conduct preliminary search to establish viability of personal visit. Videos only available, except by special arrangement.

Charges: Reproduction and copyright charges are levied.

Copyright: Some copyright held. Copyright advice available. Copyright adviser: C W Harrison.

LEO & MANDY DICKINSON'S ADVENTURE ARCHIVE

Kalos
Cotswold Lane
Old Sodbury
BRISTOL
BS37 6NE
Tel: 01454 316708
Fax: 01454 327686
Web: http://www.adventurearchive.com/film.htm

Contact: Ms Mandy Dickinson.

Adventure films from the last 25 years, including 80 completed films. Material covers rock climbing, mountaineering, ballooning, skydiving, parachuting, cave diving, caving, ice climbing, kayaking, white water rafting and wildlife in Africa. Interviews with explorers and adventurers and weather shots including time lapse.

Video and film holdings: Video: 300 hours. Documentary.
Video components: Hi-8 Video, Beta/Beta-SP, 1-inch Video, DigiBeta.
Film: 50,000 metres. 100% colour film. Documentary.
Film components: 8mm, Super 8mm, Super 16, positive film, negative film, effects mix.

Storage: Film cans and videos are stored in a vault.

Printed catalogue: Available, indexed.

Computerised database: Available.

Conservation policy: All original film material has been kept and is being transferred onto digital Betacam.

Access: Access available. By arrangement. Access for disabled.

Viewing and listening facilities: Viewing on premises. Viewing off premises. Duplicating. Sales.

Charges: Charges for research for broadcast productions. Charges for research for academic purposes. Charges for facilities and handling. A price list is available upon request.

Copyright: Copyright held. Mainly owned by Leo Dickinson, others jointly but copyright clearance can be arranged. Copyright advice available. Copyright adviser: Mandy Dickinson.

LEWISHAM LOCAL STUDIES & ARCHIVES

Lewisham Library
199/201 Lewisham High Street
LONDON
SE13 6LG
Tel: 020 8297 0682
Fax: 020 8297 1169
Web: http://www.lewisham.gov.uk

Contact: Mr A J Wait, Archivist.

E-mail: local.studies@lewisham.gov.uk

The Local History Centre collects all types of material relating to the history of Lewisham. It was established in 1960. The films held are two short length films on local events (copies supplied by BFI), a collection of 8mm films (49 reels) of local events (particularly boys' clubs), holidays, etc., produced by Mr P D Dannatt, a local resident c.1937–1957, and four other 16mm films of local events. The centre also possesses four VHS videos of local plaque unveiling ceremonies and other local events.

Video and film holdings: Video: 4 reels/cassettes.
Video components: VHS Video.
Film: 62 cans.
Film components: 8mm, 16mm, positive film.

Storage: Stored in archives strong room on steel racking. Humidity is controlled by air handling plant and air circulation.

Access: Limited access. By arrangement only.

LIDDELL HART CENTRE FOR MILITARY ARCHIVES

King's College London
Strand
LONDON
WC2R 2LS
Tel: 020 7873 2015
Fax: 020 7873 2760
Web: http://www.kcl.ac.uk/lhcma/top.htm

Contact: Ms Patricia Methven, Director of Archive Services.

E-mail: archives.web@kcl.ac.uk

The Liddell Hart Centre for Military Archives is principally an archive of personal papers of senior 20th-century British defence personnel, but it includes some film and video material, particularly research material created by television documentary production companies. The centre was founded in 1964, and the first accession of video material from a production company was received in 1989.

Video and film holdings: Video: *The Death of Yugoslavia:* videotapes and transcripts of original interviews and transmitted programmes for the documentary series *The Death of Yugoslavia* made by Brian Lapping Associates, 1995; additional background research material, including press cuttings, books and texts of UN resolutions (244 U-matic tapes). *The Nuclear Age:* video tapes, scripts and interview transcripts for 12 programmes on the history of nuclear weaponry and strategy made jointly by Central Independent Television plc and WGBH Boston in 1989 (12 VHS tapes). *The Washington Version:* videotapes and transcripts of interviews and conference sessions for a BBC television series on the Gulf Crisis, made by Brian Lapping Associates, 1992 (87 NTSC VHS tapes). *Woolly Al Walks the Kitty Back:* videotapes of interviews, and interview transcripts for a BBC television *Timewatch* documentary on US-UK relations during the Falklands War, made by Brian Lapping Associates, 1992 (80 U-matic tapes). Documentary. Videotapes and interview transcripts of filmed interviews for the documentary series *The Fifty Years War: Israel and the Arabs* made by Brian Lapping Associates, 1998; additional background research material, including press cuttings, books and pamphlets (6 VHS tapes). Videotape of programme and copies of documents used for the television documentary *Bad Trip to Edgewood* made by Yorkshire Television Limited in 1993 on the US Army chemical and biological testing programme (1 VHS tape).

Printed catalogue: Summary guide entries and completed catalogues will begin to be available on the Centre's website from autumn 2000.

Cataloguing: Hard-copy lists compiled by depositors are available for consultation in the reading room. Summary guide entries will be available on the centre's website by early 1998.

Access: Access by prior arrangement, including disabled. Researchers are advised to discuss their requirements with staff of the Centre in advance of a visit.

Charges: No charge for research access but charges made for reprographic services, reproduction of materials in broadcast productions and in some instances, for filming within the Centre.

Copyright: Copyright not held. Copyright advice available.

LIDDLE COLLECTION

Brotherton Library
University of Leeds
LEEDS
LS2 9JT

Tel: 0113 233 5566
Fax: 0113 233 5561

Contact: Mr Richard D Davies.

E-mail: r.d.davies@leeds.ac.uk

Founded 30 years ago to collect, preserve and make available for research all forms of evidence of personal experience of World War I.

Video and film holdings: Video: 30 reels/cassettes. Interviews with veterans. Amateur, documentary.
Video components: VHS Video, Beta/Beta-SP.
Film: A small amount of film is held. 100% black and white film.
Film components: 8mm, 35mm.

Storage: Currently stored in main strong rooms; some film suspected of being nitrate has been removed for the time being.

Card catalogue: Available.

Printed catalogue: No.

Computerised database: No.

Cataloguing: The computerised database is not complete.

Access: Access available. Mon-Thu, 09.00–19.00. Fri, 09.30–19.00. Sat, 10.00–13.00 (vacation etc., variations). Access for disabled.

Viewing and listening facilities: Viewing facilities depend on circumstances.

Charges: Charges for research for broadcast productions.

Copyright: Copyright held for most of the collection. A small percentage of copyright retained by donors.

LIGHT HOUSE

The Chubb Buildings
Fryer Street
WOLVERHAMPTON
WV1 1HT
Tel: 01902 716055
Fax: 01902 717143

Contact: Mr Frank Challenger, Chief Executive.

E-mail: lighthouse@light-house.co.uk

Light House houses the region's only dedicated media reference library which comprises a comprehensive selection of film, television and media books, journals, periodicals, industry guides, study packs and film directories. In addition, there is a collection of over 3,000 film portfolios for the 1960s to the present and a collection of film posters. There is also a somewhat eclectic collection of programmes on video tape (various formats) which comprises: the majority of the Arts Council's films about art and related matters, independent productions from the region, documentaries on local issues, and programmes made on the Light House's training courses.

Video and film holdings: Approx. 1,000 videotapes, including the Arts Council's Collection.

Journals holdings: Holds contemporary and historic journals on cinema, television and photography.

Newspapers holdings: Over 3,000 portfolios of newspaper cuttings from the 1960s to the present.

Posters holdings: Film posters collection dates from 1987 onwards.

Digitised collection: No, not at present.

Access: Library is open at specified times and by appointment.

Access to researchers from outside: Yes.

Charges: None.

LINCOLNSHIRE & HUMBERSIDE FILM ARCHIVE

61 Cathedral Drive
SPALDING
Lincolnshire
PE11 1PG
Tel: 01775 725631
Fax: 01775 270204
Web: http://www.lincsfilm.co.uk

Contact: Mr Peter Ryde, Archivist (For general enquiries and details of title contents).

E-mail: info@lincsfilm.co.uk

Formed in 1986 to locate, preserve and make accessible film on all aspects of life and work in historic Lincolnshire (Lincolnshire & South Humberside), especially pre-1960, though later items are not refused. The Archive operates in association with the Museum of Lincolnshire Life, Lincoln.

Video and film holdings: Video: VHS viewing copies of most film titles are held.
Video components: VHS Video, Beta SP.
Film: 81 hours. Documentary and non-fiction film illustrating life and work in the region from 1904 to the early 1970s, with emphasis on the 1930s and 1940s. A good deal was shot as news coverage; some films were produced as publicity films. 475 titles, mainly silent; the collection is steadily expanding. 40% colour film, 60% black and white film, 3% nitrate film. Amateur, documentary.
Film components: 8mm, 9.5mm, 16mm, 35mm, positive film, negative film, fine grain print.

Butlin's girls – Butlins Holiday Camp, Skegness, 1938 (photo courtesy of Lincolnshire Film Archive)

Storage: Temperature and humidity controlled vault storage for master materials.

Printed catalogue: Available, indexed.

Catalogue(s) available via the Internet: Main catalogue, frequently updated, can be accessed on website http://www.lincsfilm.co.uk

Cataloguing: Computer database for search by date, place, region and broad subject. Detailed subject index still in preparation, but information on specific subject content is available on application.

Documentation: Supplementary documentation is available in some cases, e.g. press cuttings, commentary scripts for local newsreel items, etc. General background information can be supplied for most items.

Conservation policy: Once accessioned, no material is normally junked. Nitrate still held after copying unless/until decayed past hope.

Access: Access available. Staff are available to assist. Access for disabled: wheelchair access, but no special toilets, etc. Professional: Viewing on or off the premises (VHS only). Material selected by client supplied on Beta-SP. Charges for facilities and rights available on request. Public: Viewing on premises only, except by special arrangement. Viewings on film or projected video arranged off premises for societies, etc. Numerous compilations on video available for public sale.

Viewing and listening facilities: Viewing will normally be on video in the first instance. Showings of film can be arranged for societies. Films themselves are not available on loan, except to approved production companies. Viewing off premises only by arrangement.

Charges: Charges for facilities and handling. Prices available upon request.

Copyright: In the vast majority of cases copyright is held. Copyright advice available. For rights, licensing and professional facilities contact Steve White.

LIVERPOOL JOHN MOORES UNIVERSITY

Aldham Robarts Learning Resource Centre
Mount Pleasant
LIVERPOOL
L3 5UZ
Tel: 0151 231 3104
Fax: 0151 707 1307
Web: http://cwis.livjm.ac.uk/lea/info/arts/dva.htm

Contact: Ms Sheena Streather, Senior Information Officer. Learning & Information Services.

E-mail: leasstre@livjm.ac.uk

The content of the collection reflects its primary purpose, to support courses in Media & Cultural Studies, Screen Studies, Drama, Musical Theatre, Literature & Cultural History, and Languages. Comprises mainly feature films of which there are over 400, including contemporary popular, plus foreign, classic and silent films; some television series and sample episodes of series, including drama, comedy, BBC Shakespeare productions, televised plays and musicals; also a few documentary and factual videos on these subject areas, including Pathe newsreels and other historical footage, theatrical techniques and film and television production training videos.

Video and film holdings: Approx. 600 videocassettes.

Music holdings: Minor. Approx. 50 CDs of sound effects and recorded music.

Books holdings: Approx. 3,000.

Datasets holdings: *Film Index International* on CD-ROM.

Journals holdings: 22 current journal subscriptions.

Printed catalogue: Regularly updated list.

Library OPACs with major holdings on moving image and radio: Yes, and Z39.50 compliant.

Catalogue(s) available via the Internet: Only to members of the University.

Websites relating to radio and moving images: No.

Digitised collection: No.

Access: Recorded items only available for loan by members of the University. May be viewed on premises on production of HE ID at Learning & Information Services' discretion.

Access to researchers from outside: Yes, for reference purposes only on individual application.

Viewing and listening facilities: 10 individual viewing sets plus 2 group video viewing rooms, bookable by members of the university only.

Charges: No charges to view or borrow recorded material. Fines charged on loaned items returned late.

Copyright: ERA licence. Recorded material available for use by members of staff and students only.

LIVERPOOL RECORD OFFICE & LOCAL HISTORY DEPARTMENT

Liverpool Libraries & Information Services
Central Library
William Brown Street
LIVERPOOL
L3 8EW
Tel: 0151 233 5817
Fax: 0151 233 5886

Contact: Mr David Stoker, Manager, Record Office.

E-mail: recoffice.central.library@liverpool.gov.uk

Note: *Liverpool Record Office prefers not to have a detailed entry in this edition of the Researcher's Guide as its service for film and sound archives is under review. This process is likely to take some time and involves detailed consideration of many options as part of a Merseyside Archives Liaison Group study.*

LLANELLI PUBLIC LIBRARY

Vaughan Street
LLANELLI
Wales
SA15 3AS
Tel: 01554 773538
Fax: 01554 750125

Contact: R H Davies, Llanelli Regional Librarian.

Started in 1957 when a camera was purchased to record the making of tinplate by hand in Llanelli, before the last of a large number of mills, which had operated for almost a century, closed. This arose out of a decision to collect film (movie and still) as local history archive material.

Video and film holdings: Video: Approximately 20% of the video stock are film copies.
Video components: VHS Video.
Film: 110,000 feet. The aim of the collection is to record on film all facets of Llanelli's industrial and social life and, in this respect, it can be said that the scope of the collection is narrow. Films on tinplate, steel, sheet-making, foundry work and other industries, however, have a wider significance as examples of a particular industry at a particular time. Collection currently

expanding at *c*.5,000 ft of 16mm film each year. 80% colour film, 20% black and white film. Amateur, industrial and social history.

Film components: 16mm.

Storage: Film stored in an unheated room in cans which are kept in cupboards. The video collection is also kept in cupboards.

Card catalogue: Available, indexed.

Computerised database: Available.

Cataloguing: The film collection is accessible by a card index. The video collection details have been added to the computerised database.

Access: Access available. Tue, Wed, 09.30–18.00. Mon, Thu, Fri, 09.30–17.00. Sat, 09.30–17.00. The collection is primarily being developed as a film archive of Llanelli for posterity as apart of the extensive collection of conventional local material. Casual enquirers would not be allowed access to material, but bona fide researchers should write to the Llanelli Regional Librarian.

Viewing and listening facilities: Viewing on premises. Viewing off premises. Duplicating. Facilities for copying video available.

Charges: Charges for research for broadcast productions. Charges for research for academic purposes. Charges for facilities and handling. A price list is available upon request.

Copyright: Copyright resides with Carmarthenshire County Council.

The LONDON FILM ARCHIVE

78 Mildmay Park
Newington Green
LONDON
N1 4PR
Tel: 020 7923 4074
Fax: 020 7241 4929
Web: http://www.londonfilmarchive.org

Contact: Mr Robert Dewar, Archivist. Ms Amanda Huntley.

E-mail: info@londonfilmarchive.org

In 1996 the trustees of the London Film Archive became aware that while most of the major parts of Great Britain were served by a regional film archive, Greater London had no film repository and local film focus of its own. Accordingly, the Archive was constituted as a Charity and policy drawn up. As with most other regional archives, the aims of the Trust are to collect, preserve and make accessible moving image materials that document life in the city, since the first films of 1895 to the present day. Filmic images of London are so rich and varied, a source of visual intensity in streets and landmarks and people and communities, and the Archive's holdings will aim to reflect that diversity. With an emphasis on documentary films, both professional and amateur, the archive attempts to illustrate the social and economic changes of the capital, as well as encapsulating London's position as a major centre for the sciences and the arts.

Video and film holdings: VHS viewing copies available of all holdings.

Storage: Basic environmentally controlled storage facility on same site as the viewing room.

Masters holdings: 5,000 master negatives and master positives.

Music holdings: Very extensive 78rpm collection. Music scores also.

Sound holdings: Sound interviews with film directors.

Stills holdings: About 10,000 production stills and stills of London from 1850.

Books holdings: Over 5,000 reference books.

Manuscripts holdings: Movie scripts and production notes.

Journals holdings: About 50 titles.

Newspapers holdings: *Illustrated London News*.

Posters holdings: A collection of about 1,000 posters.

Ephemera holdings: Press books, souvenirs, brochures, pamphlets.

Design holdings: Especially animation cells.

Equipment holdings: Projectors, cameras, pre-cinema toys.

Card catalogue: Old card index still retained as it is the most complete record of the collection.

Printed catalogue: Limited printed catalogue by subject.

Computerised database: Searchable database online from December 2000.

Catalogue(s) available via the Internet: Yes. from December 2000.

Access: By appointment.

Access to researchers from outside: Yes.

Viewing and listening facilities: VHS viewing 16mm/35mm Steenbecks.

Charges: Usually £50 per half day.

Copyright: Copyright held on some films, other require some clearances.

LONDON FILM COMMISSION

20 Euston Square
Regent's Place
LONDON
NW1 3JH
Tel: 020 7387 8787
Fax: 020 7387 8788
Web: http://www.london-film.co.uk

Contact: Dr Daniela Kirchner, Information Manager.

E-mail: daniela@london-film.co.uk

The datastore holds records of over 12,000 locations, 15,000 crew and 8,000 facility companies and local services, and a further 20,000 useful contacts. The locations area covers mainly Greater London. The collection also includes the Home Counties and other parts of the UK for locations such as castles, country houses, farms, and rural and coastal features.

Video and film holdings: Video showreels.

Stills holdings: Location library – c.12,000 locations, c.150,000 pictures.

Books holdings: Small reference library.

Datasets holdings: Datastore of locations, crew and facilities.

Computerised database: Yes – datastore based on XML offers a sophisticated search system.

Digitised collection: Picture collection is in process of being scanned.

Access: Mon-Fri, 08.30–19.00.

Access to researchers from outside: Yes.

Charges: For black and white and colour photocopies.

LONDON FIRE BRIGADE

Room 520
Hampton House
20 Albert Embankment
LONDON
SE1 7SD
Tel: 020 7587 6339
Fax: 020 7587 6086
Web: http://www.london-fire.gov.uk

Contact: Ms Judy Seaborne, Brigade Librarian. Graham de Core, Photographic Library.

E-mail: libraryservices@london-fire.gov.uk

Wartime material is held at the Imperial War Museum. The National Film and Television Archive is holding material of the 1950s. The IWM's and NFTVA's respective charges apply for duplicating and searching. London Fire Brigade charges apply for copyright.

(photo courtesy of the London Fire Brigade)

Video and film holdings: Video: Operational incidents, training programmes.
Video components: VHS Video, hi-8, hi-band U-matic, lo-band U-matic, Beta/Beta-SP, DV (digital video).
Film components: 35mm, positive film, negative film, fine grain print, digital.

Printed catalogue: Available.

Computerised database: Available.

Cataloguing: Printed catalogue available for sale. Computerised database searchable.

Access: Limited access, by appointment only.

Viewing and listening facilities: Duplicating. Sales.

Charges: Charges for research for broadcast productions. Charges for research for academic purposes. Charges for facilities and handling. A price list is available upon request.

Copyright: Copyright held. Copyright advice available.

The LONDON INSTITUTE – CAMBERWELL COLLEGE OF ARTS LIBRARY

Peckham Road
LONDON
SE5 8UF
Tel: 020 7514 6350
Fax: 020 7514 6324
Web: http://www.linst.ac.uk/library/

Contact: Ms Ruth Creamer, Head of Learning Resources. Library and Learning Resources.

E-mail: r.creamer@camb.linst.ac.uk

The London Institute comprises five constituent colleges: Camberwell College of Art, Central St Martin's College of Art and Design, Chelsea College of Art and

Design, London College of Fashion and the London College of Printing.

Video and film holdings: 900 titles.

Books holdings: Thorold Dickinson collection comprises some 2,500 titles.

Journals holdings: *Sight & Sound*: 1950 onwards. *Screen*: 1970 onwards (incomplete).

Posters holdings: Incidental items as part of poster collection.

Card catalogue: Subject index.

Printed catalogue: Relating to film and video titles. All titles are soon to be transferred to Library Catalogue.

Catalogue(s) available via the Internet: Details of all holdings are available via computer catalogues on the Internet.

Access: Prior permission necessary. Opening hours term time: Mon, Wed, Fri, 10.00–17.00; Tue, Thu, 10.00–20.00. Other times: Mon-Fri, 10.00–17.00.

Access to researchers from outside: Yes by appointment only and on written application.

Viewing and listening facilities: Six video playback machines.

Charges: No charge.

Copyright: ERA licence and Open University off-air recording scheme.

The LONDON INSTITUTE – CENTRAL ST MARTIN'S COLLEGE OF ART AND DESIGN, MUSEUM AND STUDY COLLECTION

Southampton Row
LONDON
WC1B 4AP
Tel: 020 7514 7146
Fax: 020 7514 7146

Contact: Ms Sylvia Backemeyer, Head. Lucy Rushin Museum & Study Collection.

Posters holdings: 37 German UFA posters from the 1920s conserved; 18 unconserved. Book of the 1999 exhibition *The Silent Screen*, edited by Sylvia Backemeyer.

Computerised database: Microsoft Access.

Catalogue(s) available via the Internet: In the year 2000.

Digitised collection: Yes.

Access to researchers from outside: Yes, by appointment during academic terms.

Charges: Various.

The LONDON INSTITUTE – CENTRAL ST MARTIN'S COLLEGE OF ART AND DESIGN LIBRARY

Southampton Row
LONDON
WC1B 4AP
Tel: 020 7514 8123
Fax: 020 7514 7033
Web: http://www.linst.ac.uk/library

Contact: Ms Joan Ingram, Media Librarian. Ms Joan Ingram, The Library.

E-mail: j.ingram@csm.linst.ac.uk

Video and film holdings: 2,500 videotapes.

Books holdings: 1,300 books.

Datasets holdings: *Film Index International* on CD-ROM.

Journals holdings: 10 titles.

Library OPACs with major holdings on moving image and radio: TALIS Library Catalogue.

Digitised collection: No.

Access: Library opening hours.

Access to researchers from outside: No.

Viewing and listening facilities: Yes.

Charges: None.

Copyright: No.

The LONDON INSTITUTE – LONDON COLLEGE OF FASHION

20 John Prince's Street
LONDON
W1G 0BJ
Tel: 020 7514 7454
Fax: 020 7514 7580

Contact: Ms Kate Purcell, Special Collections Librarian. Learning Resources.

E-mail: k.purcell@lcf.linst.ac.uk

The London College of Fashion Library holds a range of video recordings covering the subjects studied at the College. These include fashion, clothing and textile history and design, marketing and management, beauty therapy and health, hairstyling and make-up, cultural studies, art and design. The video collection consists of off-air recordings, commercially produced videos and College productions.

Video and film holdings: 1,754 videos.

Books holdings: Approx. 4,000 relating to film, television and radio out of total collection of 48,000.

Journals holdings: 2 relating to film, television and radio out of a total collection of 200.

Library OPACs with major holdings on moving image and radio: For all videos and books.

Websites relating to radio and moving images: http://www.linst.ac.uk/library

Digitised collection: No.

Access: Available to London Institute staff and students only during library opening hours.

Access to researchers from outside: External users may request an appointment to use the collection, although under the terms of the ERA licence off-air recordings cannot be used by visitors.

Viewing and listening facilities: 5 video presenters located in library.

Charges: None.

Copyright: ERA and OU licence held.

The LONDON INSTITUTE – LONDON COLLEGE OF PRINTING (LCP)

Media School
Back Hill
Clerkenwell Road
LONDON
EC1R 5EN
Tel: 020 7514 6875
Fax: 020 7514 6867
Web: http://www.linst.ac.uk/lcp

Contact: Mr Simon Lyes, Assistant Librarian, Library/Learning Resources.

E-mail: s.lyes@lcp.linst.ac.uk

A rapidly expanding collection of off-air and pre-recorded videotapes, covering a broad range of film styles and genres. Growing number of avant-garde and experimental films on video. NTSC playback material is acquired and held when no VHS PAL alternatives are available. All material held is in support of the undergraduate and postgraduate courses taught in the LCP Media School.

Video and film holdings: Approx. 2,500.

Masters holdings: No.

Books holdings: Varied collection in support of film, television and cultural studies.

Catalogue(s) available via the Internet: Yes. http://lib.linst.ac.uk:8001/www-bin/www_talis

Digitised collection: No.

Access to researchers from outside: Yes. Prior permission required. Apply in writing stating needs.

Viewing and listening facilities: VHS PAL/NTSC playback facilities in Library.

Charges: None.

Copyright: ERA licence.

LONDON JEWISH CULTURAL CENTRE FILM DEPARTMENT ARCHIVE

London Jewish Cultural Centre
The Old House
c/o King's College London
Kidderpore Avenue
LONDON
NW3 7SZ
Tel: 020 7431 0345
Fax: 020 7431 0361

Contact: Mr Stuart Libson, Archive Curator. Alex Gordon, Archive Curator.

The collection started in 1994 to fulfil the educational requirements of this Institute for the study of Jewish history and culture.

Video and film holdings: Video: 600 reels/cassettes. Documentary, feature films, news and current affairs.
Video components: VHS Video.
Film: 2 cans. Documentary.
Film components: 16mm.

Printed catalogue: Available, indexed.

Access: Access available. Mon-Fri 09.30–17.30. Access for disabled. Brochure available.

Viewing and listening facilities: Viewing on premises.

Charges: Charges for research for broadcast productions. Charges for facilities and handling. Charges for other services.

Copyright: Copyright held. Copyright advice available. Copyright adviser: Educational Recording Association.

LONDON NEWS NETWORK LIBRARY

London Television Centre
Upper Ground
LONDON
SE1 9LT
Tel: 020 7827 7784/5/6
Fax: 020 7827 7579
Web: http://www.londontonight.com

Contact: Mr David Waters, Librarian.

E-mail: library.sales@lnn-tv.co.uk

London News Network was established by Carlton and LWT in 1992 as a seven-day-a-week regional news, features and sport service for London. The Library holds transmitted stories and selected rushes/stock shots in a wide range of subject areas including the arts, crime, events, leisure, locations, social issues, and sport. The collection covers the period from autumn 1992 to date. Also some access to LWT news material 1990–1992. We also have an extensive collection of worldwide location footage e.g. Cuba, Jerusalem, Maldives and many others.

Video and film holdings: Video: 30,000 reels/cassettes. Mostly 30 minute and 90 minute tapes. News and current affairs, sport, news magazine features.
Video components: Beta/Beta-SP.

Storage: Store capacity for approximately 33,000 Betacam tapes on a mixture of mobile and static racks. Temperature controlled. Fast access as adjacent to librarians.

Computerised database: Available.

Cataloguing: Tapes are shotlisted onto the BASYS Archive II database. All terms input are indexed allowing for fast, flexible searches. Printouts can be made available.

Documentation: Programme scripts are held on the BASYS Newsroom system. Printouts can be made available.

Conservation policy: Transmitted stories, stock shot compilations and selected rushes tapes are kept in perpetuity. Rushes not selected for retention are wiped after one month.

Access: Limited access. By negotiation.

Viewing and listening facilities: Viewing on premises. Sales.

Charges: Charges for facilities and handling. Charges for research depend on how much work is involved.

Copyright: Copyright held. But some edited stories contain non LNN copyright material. Copyright advice available. Copyright adviser: Librarian.

LONDON WEEKEND TELEVISION – LWT IMAGES
---

see *Granada Media Clip Sales – London Weekend Television*

LONDON'S TRANSPORT MUSEUM
---

39 Wellington Street
LONDON
WC2E 7BB
Tel: 020 7379 6344
Fax: 020 7565 7252
Web: http://www.ltmuseum.co.uk

Contact: Mr Simon Murphy, Assistant Curator, Film & Photo Collections.

E-mail: simon@ltmuseum.co.uk

The collection includes films and videos made for/by London's public transport companies and their predecessors for a general audience and covering many aspects of London life, plus some more specialist training and instructional films. The earliest film is a Metropolitan Railway production of 1905. There are silent films of the 1920s and 1930s but the bulk of the collection today dates from the post-Second World War era up to the late 1960s – the heyday of Edgar Anstey's British Transport Films which are typically informative quality productions rich in social history and 'behind the scenes' detail. The Museum also holds for reference only a small selection of relevant off-air current affairs programmes, etc., and video copies of feature films featuring London Transport subjects.

Video and film holdings: Approx. 120 films available for viewing on video.

Masters holdings: Approx. 2,000 cans of film, 150 titles.

Card catalogue: No.

Printed catalogue: Alphabetical list with brief descriptions and tape references.

Computerised database: Detailed shotlists of most titles, staff access only at present.

Catalogue(s) available via the Internet: Possibly in future.

Digitised collection: 20% of 1-inch video masters transferred to DV Cam.

Access: By appointment. Mon-Tue only.

Access to researchers from outside: Yes.

Viewing and listening facilities: Material can be viewed on BITC videotapes.

Charges: Museum entrance fee: £5.50 plus £30.00 for VHS reference tape.

Copyright: Copyright held on core collection.

LUTON CENTRAL LIBRARY FILM AND SOUND ARCHIVE

Luton Central Library
St Georges Square
LUTON
LU1 2NG
Tel: 01582 547420
Fax: 01582 547450

Contact: Mr Mark Stubbs, Team Librarian/Information Services.

The Luton Central Library Film Archive consists of video copies of films donated by the Luton Borough Council archives and by individuals. The collection includes films of local interest, locally produced European travelogues from the 1960s and miscellaneous material. Much of the material was taken by amateurs. The originals are now located at the *East Anglian Film Archive* (q.v.).

Video and film holdings: Video components: VHS, U-matic.

Storage: AV storage cabinet. No special temperature or humidity controls.

Documentation: Background material to places and events in films available in Local History Library.

Conservation policy: None.

Access: Access available. By arrangement only. Access for disabled.

Viewing and listening facilities: Videos may be borrowed by arrangement.

Copyright: Copyright not held or not known for most of the collection.

LUX DISTRIBUTION

The Lux Centre
2–4 Hoxton Square
LONDON
N1 6NU
Tel: 020 7684 2844
Fax: 020 7684 2222
Web: http://www.lux.org.uk

Contact: Ms Josie Cadoret, Co-ordinator.

E-mail: dist@lux.org.uk

Lux Distribution is Europe's largest distributor of artists' film and video, with an expanding collection of over 3,500 titles. Alongside the large collection of British works are key pieces from the United States, Continent of Europe, Latin America, Japan and Australia. The collection is continually updated to include the best new contemporary work, while providing a key archive of historically important work dating back to the 1920s. All works in the catalogue are available for hire to museums, galleries, cinemas and colleges worldwide, and Lux can offer curatorial support and educational advice for those seeking access to the collection. Much of the collection is available for purchase by museums and educational institutions, and Lux operates as a sales agent for broadcast, Internet and video publishing. Works are available as individual titles and compiled in thematic and curated programmes. Formats include 16mm, 35mm and video, while a selection of artists' anthologies are available as retail videos.

Video and film holdings: Video: 450 hours. Video Art. Video components: Masters on U-matic, Beta-SP, DigiBeta.
Film: Approx. 500 hours.
Film components: 16mm, 35mm.

Storage: Shelf storage, temperature controlled.

Printed catalogue: Available on request.

Computerised database: Available.

Documentation: Additional information, stills, etc. available on request.

Conservation policy: Lux Distribution is currently working on several restoration projects.

Access: Access available. By arrangement only.

Viewing and listening facilities: Viewing on premises. Sales. Hires.

Charges: £5.00 per hour for use of viewing room. See http://www.lux.org.uk for hires and sales.

Copyright: Copyright resides with the artists, but Lux holds distribution rights for the films and videos it distributes.

MAGIC 105.4 FM

The Network Building
97 Tottenham Court Road
LONDON
W1P 9HF
Tel: 020 7504 7000
Fax: 020 7504 78001

Contact: Mr Richard Porter, Deputy Programmer.

The Magic radio stations, owned by EMAP Radio Ltd, share large private music collections.

MAGIC 1152 MW

NEWCASTLE UPON TYNE
NE99 1BB
Tel: 0191 420 3040
Fax: 0191 488 9222

Contact: Mr Tony McKenzie, Programme Director.

The radio station holds 42 days' output only to meet legal requirement. The Magic stations, owned by EMAP Radio Ltd, share large private music collections.

MAGIC 1161 AM

Commercial Road
HULL
Yorkshire
HU1 2SG

Tel: 01482 325141
Fax: 08546 382967
Web: http://www.magic1161.co.uk
Contact: Mr Stuart Baldwin, Programme Director.

The radio station holds 42 days' output only to meet legal requirement. The Magic stations, owned by EMAP Radio Ltd, share large private music collections.

MAGIC 1170

Radio House
Yales Crescent
Thornaby
STOCKTON-ON-TEES
TS17 6AA
Tel: 01642 888222
Fax: 01642 868288
Web: http://www.magic1170.com
Contact: Mr David Tigee.

The radio station holds 42 days' output only to meet legal requirement. The Magic stations, owned by EMAP Radio Ltd, share large private music collections.

MAGIC 1548

St John's Beacon
1 Houghton Street
LIVERPOOL
L1 1RL
Tel: 0151 472 6800
Fax: 0151 472 6801
Contact: Mr Richard Maddock, Programme Director.

The radio station holds 42 days' output only to meet legal requirement. The Magic stations, owned by EMAP Radio Ltd, share large private music collections.

MAGIC 828

51 Burley Road
LEEDS
LS3 1LR
Tel: 0113 283 5500
Fax: 0113 283 5501
Contact: Mr Adam Woodgate, Programme Controller.

The radio station holds 42 days' output only to meet legal requirement. The Magic stations, owned by EMAP Radio Ltd, share large private music collections.

MAGIC 999

PO Box 999
PRESTON
Lancashire
PR1 1XR

Tel: 01772 556301
Fax: 01772 201917
Contact: Mr Mike Bawden, Programme Director.

The radio station holds 42 days' output only to meet legal requirement. The Magic stations, owned by EMAP Radio Ltd, share large private music collections.

MAGIC AM

Radio House
900 Herries Road
SHEFFIELD
South Yorkshire
S6 1RH
Tel: 0114 285 2121
Fax: 0114 285 3159
Web: http://www.magicam.co.uk
Contact: Mr Anthony Gay, Programme Director.

The radio station holds 42 days' output only to meet legal requirement. The Magic stations, owned by EMAP Radio Ltd, share large private music collections.

MANCHESTER ARTS LIBRARY

Central Library
St Peter's Square
MANCHESTER
M2 5PD
Tel: 0161 234 1974
Fax: 0161 234 1961
Web: http://www.manchester.gov.uk/libraries

Arts Library.

E-mail: artcount@libraries.manchester.gov.uk

Video and film holdings: 300 (also some in other departments).

Music holdings: Some in other departments.

Sound holdings: Some in other departments.

Books holdings: Yes.

Journals holdings: Yes.

Newspapers holdings: Yes.

Card catalogue: Yes.

Library OPACs with major holdings on moving image and radio: Yes.

Digitised collection: No.

Access: Open access.

Access to researchers from outside: Yes.

Charges: For lending to non-Manchester borrowers.

MANCHESTER'S MAGIC 1152

Castle Quay
Castlefield
MANCHESTER
M15 4PR
Tel: 0161 288 5000
Fax: 0161 288 5001

Contact: Mr Andrew Robson, Programme Director.

The radio station holds 42 days' output only to meet legal requirement. The Magic stations, owned by EMAP Radio Ltd, share large private music collections.

MANX NATIONAL HERITAGE

Manx National Heritage Library
Kingswood Grove
DOUGLAS
IM1 3LY
Tel: 01624 648000
Fax: 01624 648001

Contact: Mr R M C Sims, Archivist. Wendy Thirkettle, Assistant Archivist.

E-mail: library@mnh.gov.im

The collection was begun in the late 1980s to provide a home for film and video material relating to the Isle of Man.

Video and film holdings: Video: 700 hours. 320 hours of unedited tapes of the island's scenery not used in complete documentaries. Advertising, amateur, documentary, news and current affairs, science and education, unedited documentary material.
Video components: VHS Video, hi-band U-matic, lo-band U-matic, Beta/Beta-SP.
Film: 85,000 feet. 70% colour film, 30% black and white film. Advertising, amateur, documentary.
Film components: 8mm, Super 8mm, 9.5mm, 16mm, 35mm, positive film, negative film, fine grain print, final mix.

Storage: Stored in archive stack; temperature and humidity controlled environment.

Cataloguing: Cataloguing has been started using FIAF cataloguing rules; an in-house catalogue will be available for researchers. No date available regarding its estimated completion.

Conservation policy: Once accessioned, film and videotape is permanently kept.

Access: Access available. Mon-Sat 10.00–17.00. Access for disabled.

Viewing and listening facilities: Viewing on premises.

Material which has been transferred to video may be viewed in the library, by appointment.

Copyright: Copyright not held. Copyright holders unknown in many cases. Copyright advice available. Copyright adviser: Wendy Thirkettle.

MARCHER GOLD

The Studios
Mold Road
WREXHAM
Wales
LL11 4AF
Tel: 01978 752202
Fax: 01978 759701
Web: http://www.marchergold.co.uk

Contact: Mr Terry Underhill, Programme Director.

The radio station holds 42 days' output only to meet legal requirement.

MARYLEBONE CRICKET CLUB (MCC) LIBRARY

Lord's Ground
LONDON
NW8 8QN
Tel: 020 7289 1611
Fax: 020 7289 9100

Contact: Mr Stephen Green, Curator.

Video and film holdings: Film: A small collection of cricket films and videos.

Access: Limited access. MCC gives access in special cases but does not have the facilities at the moment to make the collection readily available.

MASSEY FERGUSON, AUDIO VISUAL SERVICES

Massey Ferguson Ltd
Audio Visual Services. B8
Banner Lane
COVENTRY
Warwickshire
CV4 9FG
Tel: 024 7669 4400
Fax: 024 7685 1182

Contact: Mr Ivor L Clarke, Audio-visual Specialist.

The film library holds 16mm films, dating from 1945 to 1985, most of which are from Massey-Harris-Ferguson, with many on the original Ferguson TE20 tractor and implements. The video library holds U-matic and Betacam-SP video, from 1984 to the present, on all of the company's products.

Video and film holdings: Video: 300 reels/cassettes, 75 hours. Advertising, news and current affairs, science and education, sales and product features.
Video components: Lo-Band U-matic, Beta/Beta-SP.
Film: 130 cans, 50 hours. 30% colour film, 70% black and white film. Advertising, documentary, feature films, news and current affairs, science and education.
Film components: 16mm, positive film, negative film, effects mix.

Storage: Stored in filing cabinet.

Printed catalogue: Available, indexed.

Cataloguing: Only for video listing.

Documentation: List of 16mm films.

Conservation policy: To keep master set of old material only.

Access: Limited access. By arrangement only.

Viewing and listening facilities: Viewing on premises. Viewing off premises. Duplicating. Duplicating for video only.

Charges: Charges for facilities and handling. Price list for video available.

Copyright: Copyright held.

MAVERICK ENTERPRISES

31 Dobree Avenue
LONDON
NW10 2AD
Tel: 020 8459 3858
Fax: 020 8459 3895

Contact: Ms Ghizela Rowe, Director.

The collection was set up as a specialist music film library and concentrates on the 1960s extending to the late 1970s, with live concert and promo material on numerous British and American rock/pop/soul/punk acts. The 1960s' footage also covers a wide range of personalities of the era in interviews and at work, with many visual profiles on the leading pop artists such as Hockney, etc. Films on the Columbia state riots, and surfing and the Indyatlantic motor races, etc., all from the same area are also held. The collection includes all the material of the 1960s' filmmaker, Peter Whitehead, and Peter Clifton's pre-1978 material, before the demise of Notting Hill Studios, an active London-based production company.

Video and film holdings: Video: 120,000 feet. 50 hours. 1960s' music, fashion, interviews and sports.
Video components: VHS Video.
Film: 250,000 feet, 1,000 cans, 100 hours. 75% colour film, 25% black and white film. Amateur, documentary, feature films, news and current affairs, 1960s music, fashion, interviews and sports.
Film components: 16mm, 35mm, positive film, negative film.

Storage: Purpose-built vault.

Computerised database: Available.

Documentation: Many original artists' contracts and documentation of the various consents required for the original shoot, but little publicity material from the period.

Access: Access available.

Viewing and listening facilities: Viewing on premises. Viewing off premises. Duplicating. Sales. VHS copies on site.

Charges: Charges for research for broadcast productions. Charges for facilities and handling. Charges for other services.

Copyright: Copyright held for the majority of the films. Copyright advice available. Copyright adviser: Ghizela Rowe.

MCKINNON FILMS LTD

205 Royal College Street
LONDON
NW1 0SG
Tel: 020 7267 5530
Fax: 020 7267 4322
Web: http://www.mckinnonfilms.com

Contact: Ms Anna James. Mr Michael McKinnon.

E-mail: mckinnonfilms@dial.pipex.com

McKinnon Films Library holds material filmed in the Middle East over the last twenty years. It contains a large collection of natural history, environmental and cultural footage of the Arabian peninsula, Red Sea and Arabian Gulf. Most animals, birds and marine life from these locations are included in the collection. The archive also includes a limited amount of material originally shot for corporate programmes, of new Gulf cities and oil industry.

Video and film holdings: Video holdings: 50 hours of material transferred to video of which 30 hours (including final programmes and rushes) are from 16mm film, and 20 hours of rushes (underwater) originated on Beta SP. All of which is transferred to Beta SP and most is also on Digital Beta.
Film holdings: 120,000 feet of negative trims available but not transferred to video.

Storage: Tapes are stored on site. Negative and print off site.

Card catalogue: Card indexes for trims negative and printed logs for most programmes.

Computerised database: Microsoft Access database established recently for the video collection, cataloguing ongoing.

Access: Prior permission.

Access to researchers from outside: Yes.

Viewing and listening facilities: By appointment.

Charges: Ratecard on request.

Copyright: All copyright held.

MEDI SCENE

Medi Cine International plc
32–38 Osnaburgh Street
LONDON
NW1 3ND
Tel: 020 7387 3606
Fax: 020 7387 9693
Web: http://www.medi-cine.com

Contact: Mr Kevin Heath, Director/Producer.

E-mail: kheath@medi-cine.com

Medi Scene is the stock shot library of Medi Cine International. The company, which specialises in medical filmmaking, houses an extensive and varied collection of material on film and video going back over 30 years.

Video and film holdings: Video: 800 hours. Science and education.
Video components: VHS Video, lo-band U-matic, Beta/Beta-SP, 1-inch Video, DigiBeta.
Film: 1,000 cans. The library focuses on state-of-the-art scientific/medical footage. This comprehensive collection also includes extensive specialist sections on gastro-enterology, rheumatology, cardiology, laboratories and hospitals. 100% colour film. Science and education.
Film components: 16mm, 35mm, negative film.

Storage: All material is stored in secure vaults on site.

Computerised database: Available.

Cataloguing: DBase IV. All shots dating from 1988 are catalogued by cross-referenced subject on a quick-access computer database. This holds full time-coded log sheets for all productions. Video masters are also indexed with colour video prints to allow spot checks of scene compositions while running database searches.

Conservation policy: All video components retained, film trims pre-1988 junked, all negative retained.

Access: Access available. By arrangement only.

Viewing and listening facilities: Viewing on premises.

Charges: Charges for research for broadcast productions. Charges for research for academic purposes. Charges for facilities and handling. A price list is available upon request.

Copyright: Copyright held.

The MEDIA AND COMMUNICATION RESEARCH ARCHIVE (MACRA)

Loughborough University
Ashby Road
LOUGHBOROUGH
Leicestershire
LE11 3TU
Tel: 01509 223676
Fax: 01509 223944
Web: http://www.lboro.ac.uk/departments/ss

Contact: Dr Katie MacMillan, Media Archivist. Social Services.

E-mail: k.macmillan@lboro.ac.uk

The purpose of MACRA is to resource research and teaching in the mass media. The main holding within MACRA is an extensive newspaper archive, consisting of the national broadsheets from 1998 to date, and the national tabloids from 1992 to date. It also houses a special collection of Historic Newspapers. Its digital collection of media materials consists of all broadsheet newspapers (plus *Daily Mail/Mail on Sunday)* on CD-ROM from 1992 to date. Special collections of media broadcast materials include political media coverage 1992–1993; and broadcast news coverage on BBC 1, ITV and Channel 4 1996–1998.

Video and film holdings: Database currently being developed.

Sound holdings: MACRA's Sound Archive consists mainly of television and radio output. It has currently (October 2000) documented approximately 400 items on its computerised database, including news, film, documentaries, soaps and advertisements. Documentation of the actual collection, however, continues to expand the database at regular intervals.

Journals holdings: Broadcast, from 1995 to date.

Newspapers holdings: See description above.

Computerised database: Microsoft Access database.

Digitised collection: This is one of MACRA's aims but it has not begun to carry out this project yet.

Access: Prior permission.

Access to researchers from outside: Also with prior permission.

Viewing and listening facilities: Limited viewing facilities at present.

Charges: Contact Archivist for these.

Copyright: Holds usual university copyright.

MEDIA ARCHIVE FOR CENTRAL ENGLAND (MACE)

Institute of Film Studies, School of American and Canadian Studies
University of Nottingham
NOTTINGHAM
NG7 2RD
Tel: 0115 846 6448

Contact: Mr James Patterson, Director.

E-mail: james.patterson@nottingham.ac.uk

The Media Archive for Central England is being established as the public regional film archive for the East and West Midlands. At present (October 2000) employing only a Director to develop and establish the archive, MACE is currently not holding a film collection. Once established MACE will have, as its core collection, the local and regional output of ATV, Central Television and Carlton Television in the region. It is developing a strategy for the establishment of permanent, purpose-built facilities for this collection and for other material that it seeks to acquire as part of a major structured film search across the region. MACE's activity will be guided by the Film Archive Forum (FAF) statement of principles published in the document *Moving History; Toward a Policy for the UK Moving Image Archives* (1999), ISBN 0 952 5857 4 X. The Archive is committed to providing the widest possible access to the collection is develops over the coming years.

MERIDIAN BROADCASTING LTD

Television Centre
Northam
SOUTHAMPTON
SO14 0P2
Tel: 023 8071 2052/3
Fax: 023 8071 2311
Web: http://www.meridiantv.com

Contact: Mr Paul Johnson.

E-mail: johnsonp@meridiantv.com

Meridian took over the ITV franchise of the South and South East of England from Television South in 1993. The franchise holder before Television South was Southern Television. The collection includes many of the regional programmes made by Television South between 1982 and 1992, and the news/magazine programmes back to 1970. See also entry for *UTN: The*

Stockshot Agency, which is also operated by Meridian Broadcasting Ltd.

Video and film holdings: Video: 10,000 reels/cassettes. Documentary, news and current affairs, stock shot rushes.
Video components: Hi-Band U-matic, lo-band U-matic, Beta/Beta-SP, 1-inch Video.
Film: 1,000 cans. 98% colour film, 2% black and white film. Documentary, news and current affairs.
Film components: 16mm, positive film, negative film, effects mix, final mix.

Storage: Two separate archives on the Southampton site.

Card catalogue: Available, indexed.

Computerised database: Available.

Conservation policy: To keep all material transmitted as well as stock shot footage.

Access: Access available. By arrangement only.

Viewing and listening facilities: Viewing on premises.

Charges: Charges for research for broadcast productions. Charges for facilities and handling. A price list is available upon request.

Copyright: Copyright held. Copyright advice available.

MERIDIAN BROADCASTING LTD (NEWBURY SITE)

Unit 1–3 Brookway
Hambridge Lane
NEWBURY
Berkshire
RG14 5UZ
Tel: 01635 522322
Fax: 01635 30922
Web: http://www.meridiantv.com

Contact: Mr Gary Billingham, Librarian. Ms Stephanie Wilson, Librarian.

E-mail: newbury.library@meridiantv.co.uk

Meridian took over the ITV franchise of the South and South East of England from Television South (TVS) in 1993. The library generally holds material from that date. Newbury produces the local ITV news for the Thames Valley and North Hampshire. The collection is strong on transport, especially Heathrow, M3, M4 and M25 (West) motorways, Newbury bypass, various regional railway companies, e.g. South West Trains, Thames Trains, Great Western and Connex South Central.

Video and film holdings: Video: 2,400 reels/cassettes, 1400 hours. Material relating to transport by road, railway and air. News and current affairs.
Video components: Beta/Beta-SP.

Storage: All edited stories and an extensive collection of rushes are stored on site.

Computerised database: Available.

Cataloguing: Kept rushes (1993–99) currently being computer catalogued.

Conservation policy: All edited stories are kept, as well as selected rushes. In addition off-airs of the 6p.m. main evening regional news are kept from May 1993 onwards.

Access: Access available. By arrangement only. Access for disabled.

Viewing and listening facilities: Viewing on premises. Viewing off premises. Duplicating. VHS copies are available.

Charges: Charges for research for broadcast productions. Charges for facilities and handling. Charges for other services. A price list is available upon request. There is a charge for duplicating.

Copyright: Copyright held. Copyright advice available.

MERIDIAN BROADCASTING NEWS LIBRARY

West Point
NEW HYTHE
Kent
ME20 6XX
Tel: 01622 714055
Fax: 01622 714000
Web: http://www.meridiantv.co.uk

Contact: Ms Rosalyn Connors, News Librarian.

E-mail: connorsr@meridian.co.uk

Meridian News holds all edited items transmitted by former company (TVS) between 1982–1992, and by Meridian from 1993 to the present. This includes selected rushes and stock shots from stories relating to Kent, Sussex and parts of Essex. Separate news centres at Southampton and Newbury store material relating to the South and Thames Valley areas of the Meridian region.

Video and film holdings: Video: 10,000 reels/cassettes. Several thousand hours. Documentary, news and current affairs.
Video components: Hi-Band U-matic, Beta/Beta-SP.
Film: 100% colour film. Documentary, news and current affairs.
Film components: 16mm, positive film, negative film, effects mix, final mix.

Storage: One single storage room that can hold tens of thousands of small format video cassettes. At present only one third full. This is not humidity controlled. All film is stored separately on our Southampton site.

Card catalogue: Available, indexed.

Computerised database: Available.

Cataloguing: Database is Basys Archive 2. Holding information on material from 1991 to present. Print-outs are available on request.

Conservation policy: To hold all cut items of news but not the news programme itself. Rushes are junked and tapes recycled after one month unless otherwise advised.

Access: Access available. By arrangement only. Staff are available to assist. Access for disabled.

Viewing and listening facilities: Viewing on premises. Duplicating. VHS viewing copies can be made.

Charges: Charges for research for broadcast productions. Charges for research for academic purposes. Charges for facilities and handling. A price list is available upon request. A fee is charged for VHS viewing copies.

Copyright: Copyright held. Clearance must be obtained by researcher. Copyright advice available. Copyright adviser: Rosalyn Connors.

METHODIST CHURCH – METHODIST MISSIONARY SOCIETY

Note: *This collection is now housed at the National Film and Television Archive.*

METRO RADIO

NEWCASTLE UPON TYNE
NE99 1BB
Tel: 0191 420 0971
Fax: 0191 488 9222
Web: http://www.metrofm.co.uk

Contact: Mr Tony McKenzie, Programme Director.

E-mail: enquiries@metrofm.co.uk

The radio station holds 42 days' output to meet legal requirement. Local news items and recent interviews are kept on minidisc for one year.

MFM 103.4

The Studio
Mold Road
Gwersyllt
nr. WREXHAM
Clwyd
LL11 4AF
Tel: 01978 752202
Fax: 01978 759701
Web: http://www.mfmradio.co.uk

Contact: Mr Graham Ledger, Programme Controller.

E-mail: info@nfnradio.co.uk61

The radio station holds 42 days' output only to meet legal requirement.

MICHAEL ESSEX-LOPRESTI

14 Oakwood Park Road
Southgate
LONDON
N14 6QG
Tel: 020 8882 1337

Contact: Dr Michael Essex-Lopresti.

The collection holds approximately 150 titles of mainly medical films dating from 1897 to 1970, from silent black and white to colour sound. Approximately 150 titles. Also included are some semi-professional and amateur sound films made by the South London Film Society.

Video and film holdings: Video: No video holdings.
Film: About 150 films are held at the Archive. 60% colour film, 40% black and white film.
Film components: 16mm, 35mm, positive film, negative film.

Storage: Controlled environment.

Cataloguing: Personal listing on computerised database.

Access: Access to the collection is via Huntley Film Archives (q.v.).

Viewing and listening facilities: Private viewing for bona fide researchers can be arranged.

MIGRANT MEDIA ARCHIVE

Migrant Media
90 De Beauvoir Road
LONDON
N1 4EN
Tel: 020 7254 9701
Fax: 020 7241 2387
Web: http://www.homepages.poptel.org.uk/migrantmedia

Contact: Mr Ken Fero, Coordinator.

E-mail: migrantmedia@pop3.poptel.org.uk

Note: *Migrant Media Archive has two addresses. The second one is: 26 Shacklewell Lane, London E8 2EZ (same telephone and fax numbers).*

Since 1985 documenting experiences of migrant refugee and black communities in the UK and Europe. Focus on issues of self-defence, racist attacks, labour struggle and state human rights violations.

Video and film holdings: Video: 300 reels/cassettes, 150 hours. Documentary, news and current affairs. Video components: Hi-8 Video, Beta/Beta-SP.

Storage: Controlled environment.

Printed catalogue: Available, indexed.

Conservation policy: Material is never discarded.

Access: Access available. By arrangement.

Viewing and listening facilities: Viewing on premises.

Charges: Charges for research for broadcast productions. Charges for facilities and handling. Student access available with negotiable fees.

Copyright: Copyright held. Copyright advice available. Copyright adviser: Ken Fero.

MINSTER FM

PO Box 123
DUNNINGTON
York
YO1 5ZX
Tel: 01904 488888
Fax: 01904 481088
Web: http://www.minsterfm.co.uk

Contact: Mr John McCray, Station Manager.

E-mail: general@minsterfm.co.uk

The radio station holds 42 days' output to meet legal requirement only.

MORAY COLLEGE

Moray Street
ELGIN
Moray
IV30 1JJ
Tel: 01343 576000
Fax: 01343 576001
Web: http://www.moray.ac.uk

Contact: Mrs A Mackenzie, Librarian. Central Academic Services.

E-mail: angie.mackenzie@moray.uhi.ac.uk

A collection of books and videos to support college courses; video production, audio-visual presentation, photography.

Video and film holdings: 500.

Books holdings: 100 titles.

Printed catalogue: Yes. Arranged by in-house classification.

Digitised collection: No.

Access: During Library opening hours only.

Access to researchers from outside: Yes, for reference only.

Viewing and listening facilities: Available in Library.

Charges: External membership, £10 p.a. plus £5 per hour to use facilities.

MORAY FIRTH RADIO

Scorguie Place
INVERNESS
Scotland
IV3 8UJ
Tel: 01463 224433
Fax: 01463 243224
Web: http://www.morayfirth.co.uk

Contact: Mr Thomas Prague, Programme Controller.

E-mail: morayfirth@mfr.co.uk

From 1982 material of local history value has been archived, e.g. weekly interview series with local celebrities (on reel-to-reel and cassette), and also, from recent years, major news series and documentaries which will be available for researchers. Scripts are kept for about 2 years by the radio station.

MOSAIC

Second Floor
8–12 Broadwick Street
LONDON
W1V 1FH
Tel: 020 7437 6514
Fax: 020 7494 0595

Contact: Mr Adam Alexander. Helen Molchanoff.

E-mail: 75337.1233@compuserve.com

Mosaic has been producing documentaries all over the world for the past 20 years. The collection is made up of rushes from these productions. The library comprises international general views which are constantly being up-dated and is particularly strong on Russia.

Video and film holdings: Video: Documentary, news and current affairs.
Video components: Hi-8 Video, Beta/Beta-SP, DV.
Film: Documentary, news and current affairs.
Film components: 16mm.

Storage: The collection is kept at Mosaic's Gloucestershire office: The Old Butcher's Shop, St Briavels, Gloucestershire, GL15 6TA, tel: 01594-530708, fax: 01594-530094, e-mail: 100430.3545@compuserve.com.

Computerised database: Available.

Cataloguing: A catalogue of the collection is to be found on the website at http://www.mosaicfilms.com

Documentation: Everything is kept.

Access: Limited access.

Viewing and listening facilities: Viewing on premises. Viewing off premises. Duplicating. Viewing facilities can be organised by prior arrangement. Mosaic has its own in-house facilities for tape duplication.

Charges: Charges for research for broadcast productions. Charges for research for academic purposes. Charges for facilities and handling. Prices depend on the nature of the request.

Copyright: Copyright held.

MOVING IMAGE COMMUNICATIONS

61 Great Titchfield Street
LONDON
W1P 7FL
Tel: 020 7580 3300
Fax: 020 7580 2242
Web: http://www.milibrary.com

Contact: Mr Michael Maloney, Director.

E-mail: mail@milibrary.com

Established in 1994, Moving Image offers an extensive clip footage service, Staff are experienced at copyright clearance for all media, including multimedia. The collection holds a comprehensive range of archive and contemporary stock footage dating from the beginning of the century. Moving Image represents numerous independent producers and national organisations. In addition to general images, there are many specialist collections. Moving Image is constantly acquiring new collections.

The following collections are held:
Royal Society for the Protection of Birds (RSPB) Film Library.
Images of Britain 1925–1996, collection includes films made by the British Tourist Authority to promote travel in the UK and consists of current and historical images of the British Isles.
Tida Film – 27 verité documentary classics (some attributed to Grierson), shown on 35mm by the predecessor of the BTA to promote trade and industry between the two world wars. The collection provides a social historical portrait of British life in the thirties.
TV-am 1983–92 – over 7,000 hours of features from Britain's first breakfast television programme Good Morning Britain.
Time-Lapse – this collection features modern high quality scenes from San Francisco and New York including night traffic, daytime city scenes and activities; plus nature material.

Vintage Slapstick – humorous and quirky slapstick and melodrama from the silent era.
Freud Home Movies – rare home movies shot on 16mm by the Freud family between 1930–1939. A portrait of the founder of psychoanalysis, his family, friends and colleagues.
The Cuban Archive – this collection provides a portrait of the country before, during and after the Revolution.
Universal News – black and white American newsreels of 1950s and 1960s.
Wild Islands – Over 150 hours of material shot on Super 16mm of the animals and habitat of the British Isles.

Other collections include material on medical technology, NASA, classic travelogues, world destinations; landscapes and seascapes, developing world, business and industry, subaqua films and documentary shorts.

Video and film holdings: Video: Most film has been transferred to video masters. Documentary, news and current affairs, science and education.
Video components: VHS Video, hi-8, lo-band U-matic, Beta/Beta-SP, 1-inch Video.
Film: 25,000,000 feet, 11,000 hours. 80% colour film, 20% black and white film. Documentary, feature films, science and education.
Film components: 9.5mm, 16mm, 35mm, positive film, negative film.

Storage: Majority of footage is stored on site. However, the remainder is stored in facilities near our office for immediate access.

Printed catalogue: Available, indexed.

Computerised database: Available.

Cataloguing: All footage has been logged shot by shot on the computer. Online database of the moving image collections available soon.

Access: Access available. 09.00–18.00. Staff are available to assist with viewings. Footage enquiries are serviced by in-house researchers using a sophisticated computer database. All footage has been logged in detail so searching is fast and flexible. An online text database of Moving Image footage is available, with access to over 2,500 hours of archive and contemporary images.

Viewing and listening facilities: Viewing on premises. Viewing off premises. Moving Image will compile a preview cassette tailored to the enquiry brief. Alternatively, viewing can take place on the premises.

Charges: Charges for research for broadcast productions. Charges for facilities and handling. A price list is available upon request. Master footage can be provided quickly and efficiently. The master material is transferred within a day of ordering the clips.

Copyright: Copyright held for most of the material. Some uses need referrals. When copyright is not held, staff will clear copyright. Copyright advice available. Copyright adviser: In-house.

MUSEUM OF WELSH LIFE

St Fagans
CARDIFF
CF5 6XB
Tel: 029 573427
Fax: 029 573490

Contact: Ms Meinwen Ruddock, Assistant Curator, Audio-visual Collections.

A collection of films from various sources, some dating from the 1930s, but mainly fieldwork recordings dating from the 1960s dealing with various aspects of the folk life of Wales. The rate of acquisition is slow. Also a small collection of off-air video recordings of broadcasts relating to Welsh life.

Video and film holdings: Video: 270 reels/cassettes. Documentary.
Video components: VHS Video, lo-band U-matic, Beta/Beta-SP.
Film: 250 cans. 60% colour film, 40% black and white film. Documentary.
Film components: 16mm.

Storage: Special room, temperature and humidity controlled.

Cataloguing: Chronological register. Computerised database (in Welsh and English).

Conservation policy: The Museum's 16mm film collection has now been copied to Beta and VHS video.

Access: Access available. By prior appointment. Staff are available to assist. Most of the material is accessible to bona fide researchers by prior appointment.

Viewing and listening facilities: Viewing on premises.

Charges: Charges for research for broadcast productions.

Copyright: Copyright held for part of the collection. Copyright advice available. Copyright adviser: Beth Thomas/Meinwen Ruddock.

The MUSIC PERFORMANCE RESEARCH CENTRE

Barbican Music Library
Barbican Centre
Silk Street
LONDON
EC2Y 8DS

Tel: 01730 895052
Fax: 01730 895052
Web: http://www.musicpreserved.org

Contact: Mr Tim Appleyard.

E-mail: timapple@dial.pipex.com

The MPRC was set up to preserve sound documents of public performances for future generations, and to preserve, as far as possible, the integrity of the performances. It holds over 1,500 archive recordings of live performances, interviews both audio and video, from the 1930s to the present day, available at the Barbican Centre, London, or elsewhere by arrangement. There are on-site archive recordings made by the MPRC at concert halls and opera houses, such as the Barbican Centre, Symphony Hall Birmingham, Royal Festival Hall and the Royal Opera House. Off-air recordings of public performances, donated to the MPRC, dating from 1934 to the present day. The MPRC archive includes historic archive recordings that to the best of the MPRc's knowledge cannot be heard elsewhere. It holds recorded conversations with international conductors, soloists, singers and orchestral musicians and video archive recordings made from 1951 onwards, including a collection provided by the BBC Libraries and Archives Division.

Access: Mon, Wed, Thu, Fri, 09.30–17.30; Tue, 09.30–19.30; Sat, 09.30–12.30.

Access to researchers from outside: Yes. No need to book. Just arrive to hear or see the recordings of your choice.

Viewing and listening facilities: Individual listening booths.

Charges: No charges.

NAPIER UNIVERSITY LEARNING INFORMATION SERVICES

Sighthill Court
EDINBURGH
EH11 4BN
Tel: 0131 455 3558
Fax: 0131 455 3566
Web: http://www.napier.ac.uk

Contact: Mr Graeme Forbes, Head of Resource Management & Development. Learning Information Services.

E-mail: g.forbes@napier.ac.uk

The Head of Resource Management & Development also manages seven other learning centres in Edinburgh, Livingston and Melrose.

Video and film holdings: Approx. 4,000.

Books holdings: Approx. 5,000.

Journals holdings: Approx. 20.

Library OPACs with major holdings on moving image and radio: Dynix 'classic' and WebPAC.

Catalogue(s) available via the Internet: Yes.

Digitised collection: No.

Access to researchers from outside: Yes, by arrangement.

Viewing and listening facilities: VCRs in all learning centres.

NAPIER UNIVERSITY MERCHISTON LEARNING CENTRE

10 Colinton Road
EDINBURGH
Tel: 0131 455 3469
Fax: 0131 455 3428
Web: http://www.napier.ac.uk/depts/library/homepage.htm

Contact: Ms Marian Kirton, Subject Librarian. Learning Information Services.

E-mail: m.kirton@napier.ac.uk

Off-air collection of videos covers all subjects taught at the University. Amongst these are approximately 2500 titles relating to motion pictures, television and radio, of which a handful are commercial recordings rather than off-air. Most of these are simply cassettes containing two motion pictures.

Video and film holdings: 350 titles.

Books holdings: Approx. 1,000 items.

Journals holdings: Approx. 12 titles.

Library OPACs with major holdings on moving image and radio: Not major holdings.

Catalogue(s) available via the Internet: http://webpac.napier.ac.uk

Digitised collection: No. No plans to do so.

Access: Consultation open to all.

Access to researchers from outside: Yes.

Viewing and listening facilities: Video players.

Charges: For lending services.

NATIONAL ARCHIVE FOR THE HISTORY OF COMPUTING

Centre for the History of Science, Technology and Medicine
Manchester University
Maths Tower
Oxford Road
MANCHESTER
M13 9PL

Tel: 0161 275 5845
Fax: 0161 275 5699

Contact: Mr Jon Agar, Associate Director.

E-mail: agar@fs4.ma.mon.ac.uk

The National Archive for the History of Computing was created in 1987 to collect, preserve and make accessible to historians documents relating to the history of computing. The films and videos are part of the National Archive for the History of Computing collection.

Video and film holdings: Video: 10 reels/cassettes.
Video components: VHS Video, hi-band U-matic.
Film: 61 cans. 50% colour film, 50% black and white film.
Film components: 16mm.

Printed catalogue: Available.

Computerised database: Available.

Cataloguing: www page: http://www.man.ac.uk/
Science_Engineering/CHSTM/nahc.htm

Access: Access available. By arrangement.

Viewing and listening facilities: Duplicating. Viewing facilities only for VHS.

Charges: Charges for research for broadcast productions. Charges for facilities and handling.

Copyright: Some copyright held, but not all.

The NATIONAL ARMY MUSEUM

Royal Hospital Road
Chelsea
LONDON
SW3 4HT
Tel: 020 7730 0717 ext 2241/2214
Fax: 020 7823 6573
Web: http://www.national-army-museum.ac.uk

Contact: Dr A W Massie, Head of Archives, Photographs, Film and Sound.

E-mail: info@national-army-museum.ac.ik

The Museum has acquired film on a piecemeal basis since the 1960s but has recently begun to collect more actively, particularly amateur footage of the British and Indian armies in the 1930s and 1940s. The films show almost every aspect of army life at that time, including the introduction of mechanisation, training, engineering work, social life, and sports. In some cases they carry a soundtrack added by the original cameraman when the film was copied. Film collections of the Middlesex Regiment and Women's Royal Army Corps museums have recently been acquired, as have a number of Ministry of Defence recruiting and information films.

Video and film holdings: Video: 280 reels/cassettes.
Amateur, documentary, official.
Video components: VHS Video, lo-band U-matic.
Film: 265 cans. 15% colour film, 85% black and white film.
Amateur, documentary.
Film components: 8mm, 16mm, positive film.

Storage: Within photograph storage area in steel cupboards.

Computerised database: Available.

Cataloguing: A handlist is available for consultation in the reading room; access to holders of reader's tickets only.

Conservation policy: Film is copied onto video to facilitate its long-term preservation. Nitrate film is copied and disposed of for safety reasons.

Access: Access available. By prior appointment, preferably on Mondays. Access for disabled.

Viewing and listening facilities: Viewing on premises. Duplicating. Copies of some material can be supplied.

Charges: Charges for other services. There is a charge for copies of videos.

Copyright: Copyright not held. Copyright advice available. Copyright adviser: Dr A W Massie.

NATIONAL CENTRE FOR ENGLISH CULTURAL TRADITION

University of Sheffield
9 Shearwood Road
SHEFFIELD
S10 2TN
Tel: 0114 222 0195

Contact: Mr Robin Wiltshire, Archivist.

E-mail: r.h.wiltshire@sheffield.ac.uk

The video collection is held in the Archives of Cultural Tradition, established in 1964 to preserve material collected through the Centre's ongoing survey of language and folklore. The core of the collection comprises original field recordings of traditional customary events, made in the 1970s and early 1980s in and around the Yorkshire region. New accessions are now mainly fieldwork recordings submitted by students to accompany under- and postgraduate research projects in folklore studies.

Video and film holdings: Video: 165 reels/cassettes, 144 hours. Amateur, documentary, feature films, education, folklore.
Video components: VHS Video, lo-band U-matic, Sony V60H 1/2-inch tape.

Storage: Three-drawer lockable storage cabinet for U-matic; seven-drawer lockable storage cabinet for VHS.

Stored in main archive room where temperature and humidity levels are kept at as appropriate levels as possible. No air-conditioning. A flat roof and brick walls make the maintenance of constant levels very difficult to achieve.

Card catalogue: Available, indexed.

Cataloguing: Card catalogue is organised in terms of collector, informant and location indexes. There is also a very general subject index. Indexes cover the whole of the archival holding.

Documentation: Some shooting scripts and accompanying promotional material (printed).

Conservation policy: Resources currently not available to enable a programme of preservation copying to be undertaken.

Access: Given the lack of any working copy tapes access to the collection is severely limited.

Viewing and listening facilities: Viewing facilities at the Centre are available, although the VTR and monitor are situated in a communal reference area. Viewing must be by prior arrangement (minimum two weeks notice).

Charges: There is no charge for the viewing service.

Copyright: The situation regarding copyright is vague and inconsistent. In the past some depositors' contracts have been completed and access arrangements agreed. However, until recently, a lack of any archival staff has meant that much material has accumulated without any such depositors' agreements being confirmed. It would be a lengthy process to trace depositors for copyright clearance. Commercial recordings (and copies) in the collection will already have copyright agreements.

NATIONAL CO-OPERATIVE FILM ARCHIVE

The International Co-operative College
Stanford Hall
LOUGHBOROUGH
LE12 5QR
Tel: 01509 852333
Fax: 01509 856500

Contact: Mr A G Burton, Consultant.

The Archive was established in 1992 to coordinate information regarding the films of the British Consumer Cooperative Movement. Films are not stored at the Archive, but where possible video copies are.

Video and film holdings: Video: Advertising, amateur, documentary, feature films.
Video components: VHS Video, lo-band U-matic, Beta/Beta-SP.

Storage: There are no purpose-built storage facilities. Tapes are stored in conventional office conditions.

London Cooperative Society Film Unit van, c.1930s? (photo courtesy of National Co-Operative Film Archive)

Cataloguing: A complete historical catalogue by Alan Burton is available from Flicks Books (1997).

Documentation: A historical survey of the Co-operative Movement's use of film, *The People's Cinema: Film and the Co-operative Movement* (by Alan Burton, BFI, 1994).

Conservation policy: No material is junked. Acquired films are passed on to a relevant film archive.

Access: Limited access. By prior arrangement only. Access for disabled.

Viewing and listening facilities: Viewing on premises.

Charges: Charges for research for broadcast productions. Charges for facilities and handling. Charges for other services. A price list is available upon request.

Copyright: Copyright held. Copyright advice available. Copyright adviser: A G Burton.

NATIONAL EDUCATIONAL VIDEO LIBRARY

Arfon House
Bontnewydd
Siliwen Road
CAERNARFON
Gwynedd
LL54 7UN
Tel: 01286 676001. Mobile: 0468 105467.
Fax: 01286 676001
Web: http://www.madasafish.com/~nevl

Contact: Mr John Lovell, Head of Library.

E-mail: nevl@madasafish.com

16mm films and videotapes produced by the Educational Foundation for Visual Aids between 1950 and 1978.

Video and film holdings: Video: 283 reels/cassettes. Science and education.

Video components: VHS Video, hi-band U-matic, lo-band U-matic.

Film: 676 cans. 60% colour film, 40% black and white film, 5% nitrate film. Science and education.

Film components: 16mm, 35mm, positive film, negative film, fine grain print.

Card catalogue: Available, indexed.

Cataloguing: Catalogue on a loosely based Dewey system. Lists can be provided.

Documentation: For some of the titles a printed explanatory book is available.

Conservation policy: If material deteriorates it is scrapped; material kept until it deteriorates.

Access: Access available. Mon-Fri 09.00–17.00.

Viewing and listening facilities: Viewing off premises. Sales. Subject to availability.

Copyright: Copyright held. Copyright advice available. Copyright adviser: J Lovell.

NATIONAL FAIRGROUND ARCHIVE

The Library
University of Sheffield
SHEFFIELD
S10 2TN
Tel: 0114 222 7231
Fax: 0114 222 7290
Web: http://www.sheffield.ac.uk/uni/projects.nfa

Contact: Ms Vanessa Toulmin, Archivist.

E-mail: fairground@sheffield.ac.uk

The NFA is a unique collection of photographic, printed, manuscript, fairground ephemera and audio-visual material covering all aspects of the culture of travelling showpeople in the United Kingdom, their organisation as a community, their social history and everyday life and the artefacts and machinery of fairgrounds. Its collections continue to grow, with some 60,000 images now in the photographic collection. Over 1,000 images and associated archival documents relate to Nottingham Goose Fair and a further 4,000 relate to fairs in the Midlands from the 1930s onwards. 1,000 images of travelling cinematograph shows and family information and details of films shown are also included in the database. From Easter to October over 200 fairs are held weekly in the UK and the holdings present a comprehensive record of these events from the 1890s onwards.

In the past two years the NFA has doubled its photographic holdings with the donation of major image-based collections, including the Dick Price material (10,000 photographs), Lionel Bathe Collection (6,000 negatives), Bernard Fielding (5,000 images), Harry Lee

(1,000 items) and other related showland family albums. Additional collections include the Showmen's Guild Records and the Malcolm Airey Circus and Theatre Collection (20,000 items) with many items of interest to people studying the transition of music hall artistes to film actors. Materials in the NFA now cover all main formats – printed books, photographs, posters, business records, autobiographical manuscripts and posters.

The Development of the NFA Digital Collections. In 1998 the NFA received a grant of £88,700 from the Heritage Lottery Fund to digitise and catalogue 30,000 photographs in the collection – this task has now been completed. The NFA was the first University Library collection to receive HLF funding and now has the necessary experience and expertise in the management and organisation of this type of project. The Research Director and founder of the National Fairground Archive is co-editor of *Living Pictures: the Journal of the Popular and Projected Image to 1920* and has written various articles and books on all aspects of popular entertainment.

Masters holdings: All original material deposited at the National Film and Television Archive. Video copies only held.

Sound holdings: 300 hours of transcripts/audio cassette.

Stills holdings: 60,000 images; 1,000 early cinema related travelling shows to cinema.

Books holdings: Only early cinema, pre-1914, popular entertainment, magic lantern – 1,500 titles.

Manuscripts holdings: Tom Norman (ghost show, early cinema pioneer).

Theses holdings: 2.

Journals holdings: *Film History, Kinetop, MIJ.*

Payne's Bioscope, Hull Pleasure Fair, 1906 (courtesy of National Fairground Archive)

Newspapers holdings: *The Showman (1900–1912). World's Fair 1904–.*

Posters holdings: Mostly Victorian/Edwardian fairs with incidental references to bioscope.

Printed catalogue: OPAC – Star – Printed Catalogue soon to be all on Access database for internal users only.

Digitised collection: 30,000 images have been digitised.

Access: Mon-Fri, 09.30–16.30. Prior appointment necessary.

Access to researchers from outside: Yes.

Viewing and listening facilities: Video, all formats.

Charges: Only for commercial reproduction rights.

Copyright: Photographic rights only.

NATIONAL FILM AND TELEVISION ARCHIVE

21 Stephen Street
LONDON
W1T 1LN
Tel: 020 7255 1444
Fax: 020 7580 7503
Web: http://www.bfi.org.uk

Contact: Ms Olwen Terris, Chief Cataloguer.

The National Film and Television Archive began its existence in May 1935 in fulfilment of one of the ten aims of the British Film Institute, to 'maintain a national repository of films of permanent value'. Its role is to select, acquire, preserve, document and make available for research, study and screening a collection of films and television programmes of all kinds, exhibited and transmitted in the UK, of both British and foreign origin. As no law of statutory deposit for film, television and video production yet exists in the UK, material is acquired primarily by voluntary donation. The Archive's main source of finance is from the BFI's annual government grant, although it also receives funding from the independent television companies for the preservation of ITV, Channel 4 and Channel 5 programmes.

Video and film holdings: Video: See film holdings. Advertising, amateur, documentary, feature films, news and current affairs, science and education.

Video components: VHS Video, S-VHS Video, 8mm Video, hi-8, hi-band U-matic, lo-band U-matic, Beta/Beta-SP, 1-inch Video, 2-inch Video.

Film: In July 2000 the Archive's total holdings were *c.*350,000 titles, comprising feature and fiction films, shorts, documentaries, television programmes, newsreels, animation and amateur films, on the full range of film gauges and videotape formats and spanning the period from 1895 to the present day. Specialist collections such as sport, advertising films, political propaganda and material from industrial companies such as Courtaulds, British Steel, National Coal Board and British Transport form an important element of the Archive's collection. The National Film and Television Archive also has official responsibility for acquiring selected public record films made by governmental organisations and is now the permanent repository for all videotaped Parliamentary proceedings. Advertising, amateur, documentary, feature films, news and current affairs, science and education.

Film components: The Archive holds 90% of all formats, e.g. 8mm, Super 8mm, 9.5mm, 16mm, Super 16, 35mm, positive film, negative film, fine grain print, effects mix, final mix, etc.

Storage: All material is stored and cared for at the Archive's two out-of-London sites. In 1987 the J Paul Getty, Jnr, Conservation Centre opened at Ernest Lindgren House, Berkhamsted, Hertfordshire. The entire preservation operation takes place at the Centre, which includes a film laboratory, video unit, photographic studio, paper store and offices. Safety film (narrow gauges and most 35mm films made after 1951) and videotapes are kept in air-conditioned stores on this site. Nitrate film (most 35mm films made before 1951), because it is inflammable and subject to irreversible chemical deterioration, is stored in 216 specially constructed vaults at a remote site at Gaydon, Warwickshire.

Card catalogue: Available, indexed.

Printed catalogue: Printed catalogue for parts of the collection only, i.e. there is no complete printed catalogue of the Archive's holdings.

Computerised database: Available. Since January 1999 a computerised subject indexing system has been implemented, gradually replacing the card indexes.

Cataloguing: Cataloguing information (with the exception of the majority of newsfilm) is entered on SIFT, the BFI's database. Newsfilm information is still retained on card files. Shotlists (i.e. catalogue information on film and television programmes which have been viewed and described in detail) can be consulted on catalogue cards. They are listed by title, and in the case of newsfilm, by date. Computer listings of the collection by country of production and director are available for reference in the Cataloguing section. A subject index of over 20,000 headings refers the researcher to the classified section (UDC) of the card catalogues which collate material on related subjects with brief title, series and date information. Full details may then be obtained from SIFT. All catalogues can be consulted free of charge (preferably by appointment) on the Archive's premises at Stephen Street. There is an enquiry desk in the Section where cataloguers are able to give information on the collection and offer advice and guidance on the arrangement of the indexes. Enquiries by telephone or letter are also welcome. Catalogues listing the NFTVA's early television holdings up to and including 1979 and a viewing copy catalogue of its British film holdings are available. Smaller filmographies of the Archive's holdings (*The Spanish Civil War, Early Women Film-makers, Avant Garde, Irish History, Dennis Potter,* etc.) are also available for sale.

Documentation: The Archive also cares for the BFI's extensive collection of stills, posters and designs.

Conservation policy: To select, acquire, preserve, document and make available for research, study and screening a collection of films and television programmes of all kinds, exhibited and transmitted in the UK, of both British and foreign origin.

Access: Access available. Mon-Fri 10.00–17.30, by arrangement. Staff are available to assist. Access for disabled. Lift in the building. Disabled toilet. Three sections – Research Viewing Service, BFI Films, Donor Access – handle access to the holdings. In all cases access can only be provided subject to the Archive's preservation rules being observed and any necessary copyright clearance being obtained in advance.
1. Research Viewing Service: The Research Viewing Service caters for private viewings by bona fide researchers and students on the Archive's premises for which a handling fee is charged. The Archive's viewing print collection is by no means complete, but a continuous, systematic copying programme ensures that most actual and potential demands are met. The Viewings Supervisor, who arranges access to the Archive's film and television collections, is available for consultation at 21 Stephen Street, London W1P 1LP, Monday to Friday, between 10.30 and 17.30.
2. BFI Films: This service supplies extracts from the Archive's collection to film and television programme-makers for use in new productions when no other source exists. Enquiries should be made to the Archival Footage Sales Officer at 21 Stephen Street, who will arrange catalogue consultation, viewing, marking up and processing and provide a full scale of charges on request.
3. Donor Access: This section handles requests from donors for access to their own material and from copyright holders and authorised third parties wishing to purchase copies of films preserved in the Archive. Enquiries should be addressed to the Donor Access Officer at 21 Stephen Street.

Viewing and listening facilities: Viewing on premises.

Charges: Charges for research for broadcast productions. Charges for facilities and handling. There is a charge for viewing. Handling fees vary according to the use of the material.

Copyright: Copyright not held. The Production Library can advise on copyright clearance when extracts from the Archive are being used in a production. The National Film and Television Archive does not operate a general copyright enquiry service.

NATIONAL LIBRARY OF WALES – SOUND AND MOVING IMAGE COLLECTION

see *Wales Film and Television Archive/Archif Ffilm a Theledu Cymru.*

NATIONAL MARITIME MUSEUM ARCHIVE

National Maritime Museum
Greenwich
LONDON
SE10 9NF
Tel: 020 8312 6645/6727/6710
Fax: 020 8312 6599/6533
Web: http://www.nmm.ac.uk

Contact: Ms Lucy Hillary, Filming & Film Archive Officer. Ms Jane Constantini, Deputy Head of Maritime Resources.

E-mail: lhillary@nmm.ac.uk

National archive built up over the past fifty years. The collection grew from education requirements and gifts of special material as well as the Museum's involvement with productions for broadcast television. Varied archive of maritime related film.

Video and film holdings: Video: 200 reels/cassettes. The collection comprises all facets of maritime heritage of Great Britain and the sea. Advertising, amateur, documentary, feature films, news and current affairs, science and education, maritime.
Video components: VHS Video, Beta/Beta-SP.
Film: 1,500 cans. The collection comprises all facets of maritime heritage of Great Britain and the sea. 30% colour film, 70% black and white film. Advertising, amateur, documentary, feature films, news and current affairs, science and education.
Film components: 16mm, positive film.

Storage: Film is stored off site.

Card catalogue: Available, indexed.

Printed catalogue: Available, indexed.

Computerised database: Available.

Cataloguing: Detailed catalogues and a summary catalogue are available. All films have been catalogued.

The ship-rigged yacht 'Joseph Conrad', 1882. (photo copyright of the National Maritime Museum, Greenwich /Alan Villiers Collection)

Conservation policy: Museum/BFI standards. No film is let out without National Maritime Museum control.

Access: Access available. Mon-Fri 10.00–17.00. By appointment.

Viewing and listening facilities: Viewing on premises. Films can be viewed with a minimum of 48 hours' notice. Some VHS copies are available on a hire basis. Viewing facilities: Steenbeck.

Charges: Charges for research for broadcast productions. Charges for research for academic purposes. Charges for other services. A price list is available upon request. There is a charge for viewing and processing reproductions.

Copyright: Copyright resides with 3rd-party in main but National Maritime Museum has permission of many copyright holders to release the material on their behalf. Copyright advice available.

NATIONAL MOTOR MUSEUM FILM & VIDEO LIBRARY

National Motor Museum
BEAULIEU
Hampshire
SO42 7ZN
Tel: 01590 614664
Fax: 01590 612655
Web: http://www.beaulieu.co.uk/main/index.htm
Contact: Mr J Stephen Vokins, Film and Video Librarian/Telecine Facilities Manager.

The film archive was created in 1976 by the Trustees of the National Motor Museum, and was formally established with the appointment of a Sound and Film Archivist in November 1979. Since the Montagu Motor Museum was established in 1952, a number of films have been donated to Beaulieu, mostly from industrial sources. This material is now being fully catalogued, along with newer additions to the archive. The Library is further enhanced by its own in-house broadcast standard telecine facilities and standards conversion, which it is also able to offer to outside users.

Video and film holdings: Video components: VHS Video, 8mm Video, hi-band U-matic, lo-band U-matic, Beta/Beta-SP, 1-inch Video.
Film: The collection concentrates on motoring matters. It extends from the beginning of the century up to the present day, and efforts are made to keep up to date with current material. Areas of particular strength are Ford, Vauxhall, Rootes, Peugeot Talbot, Dunlop, AA, RAC, Metropolitan Police, the land-speed record and motor sport. There is also a sizable collection of classic cars of all ages shot more recently on videotape. Small amounts of nitrate are also held. The collection is still growing, especially the video content.
Film components: 8mm, Super 8mm, 9.5mm, 16mm, 35mm, positive film, negative film, fine grain print, final mix.

Storage: All material is stored on open shelves, with limited atmospheric conditions control. Nitrate storage facilities also exist.

Card catalogue: Available.

Computerised database: Available.

Access: Limited access. By appointment only.

Viewing and listening facilities: Viewing on premises. Duplicating. Telecine facilities to make viewing copies for those not able to visit in person.

Charges: Charges for research for broadcast productions. Charges for facilities and handling. Charges for other services.

Copyright: Copyright held. Apart from own material, other material is held on an agency basis. Copyright advice available. Copyright adviser: J Stephen Vokins.

NATIONAL MUSEUM OF PHOTOGRAPHY, FILM & TELEVISION

Pictureville
BRADFORD
West Yorkshire
BD1 1NQ
Tel: 01274 202030 Direct line: 01274 203381
Fax: 01274 723155
Web: http://www.nmpft.org.uk

Contact: Ms Mary Murphy, Head of Collections Group. Mr Paul Goodman, Registrar, or Mr Brian Liddy, Curator (Collections Access) Collections.

E-mail: m.murphy@nmsi.ac.uk

Founded in 1983, the National Museum of Photography, Film & Television quickly became the most visited national museum outside London. Its collections include more than three million items of historical, social and cultural value. The Museum aims to help the public understand and enjoy the history and contemporary practice of photography, film and television. It houses five collections – Photographs, Cinematography, Television, Photographic Technology, and Printed Materials and Ephemera. The growth and development of each collection are regulated by comprehensive acquisition and dispersal policies which are subject to regular review and update. The Photographs Collection holds an estimated three million photographs. Some special collections are: the W F Talbot Collection comprising 5,000 photographic prints, manuscripts and related material; the Science Museum Collection which contains 30,000 items; the Kodak Museum includes 50,000 photographs; the Howard and Jane Ricketts Collection is a large and important collection of 19th-century photograph albums and photographically illustrated books; the *Daily Herald* Photographic Archive contains some three million prints and 58,000 negatives spanning the period from the 1920s to the late 1960s. These and other collections illustrate the work of key photographers such as Zoltan Glass, Julia Margaret Cameron, Bert Hardy, Man Ray, Eamon McCabe, Dorothea Lange and many others. The Photographic Technology Collection is concerned with equipment associated with the production of still photographic images from the earliest period, e.g. the Kodak Museum Collection holds over 10,000 items of equipment. The Cinematography Collection houses material relevant to the filmmaking processes, the historical development of its technology and its 'delivery' methods. It contains around 13,000 objects, e.g. all formats of cine cameras, cine projectors, sound apparatus and associated equipment. Early camera technology is strongly represented. The Television Collection represents the evolution of the technological means of generating, storing and displaying moving images by electro-mechanical means from the late 19th century until the present. It comprises around 19,000 items of equipment and artefacts from cameras to viewing machines and iconic software and ephemera. The printed Materials and Ephemera Collection records and illustrates the development of photography, film and television and is helps to interpret the relationship between the visual media. In June 1999 the Museum opened its doors following a period of major refurbishment to its galleries and public facilities. Linked to this project are unrivalled, state-of-the-art, purpose-built research facilities which will deliver the highest quality of care and management of the Museum's Collections and service the access and research needs of its diverse range of audiences. This facility – Insight – The Research Centre – is scheduled to open during 2001.

The Research Centre will provide facilities in a research environment for the care and management of all the Museum's collections, and provide the infrastructure (both intellectual and physical) to enable staff, the general public, specialist researchers and the educational sector to use and understand these collections. It will be the main focal point for research on the visual media and will include navigational tools and access to a range of paper and computer-based reference sources.

For the first time in the Museum's history, the majority of its collections will be housed under one roof. The Centre has been specifically designed to facilitate and encourage public access to these original photographs and artefacts. Whilst totally committed to ease of access, every element of its design is geared towards providing appropriate levels of professional care and stewardship of multi-format collections. As a result of this innovative approach the Museum is now recognised as a 'centre of excellence' in this area. Facilities include: a suite of research rooms, two print archives, a custom-built viewing room, two large archives of artefacts, and a printed materials archive.

Journals holdings: *Picture Post, Lilliput,* (weekly) *Illustrated*, etc. An almost complete set of the *British Journal of Photography Almanac* (housed in the Printed Materials and Ephemera Collection).

Posters holdings: Small collection of Ealing and Bollywood film posters, plus an expanding collection of posters printed by W E Berry.

Equipment holdings: 13,000 objects of film, television and sound and associated equipment.

Printed catalogue: No.

Computerised database: Currently under construction.

Catalogue(s) available via the Internet: None at present but currently under development.

Digitised collection: The Museum has begun a project to catalogue and provide digital access to its most significant material.

Access: Open every day except Monday.

Access to researchers from outside: Yes. See final two paragraphs of description of Collection.

Charges: None.

NATIONAL MUSEUM OF PHOTOGRAPHY, FILM & TELEVISION (TELEVISION COMMERCIALS COLLECTION)

Pictureville
BRADFORD
West Yorkshire
BD1 1NQ
Tel: 01274 773399
Fax: 01274 723155
Web: http://nmpft.org.uk

Contact: Mr Ian Potter, TV Heaven Curator. Michael Harvey, Curator of Cinematography. Ms Sheena Vigors, TV Heaven Curator.

The film library comprises two collections: 1) Television Commercials Collection and 2) Film Samples Collection.
1) The collection originally belonged to the BBTA (British Bureau of Television Advertising). The BBTA's function was to demonstrate the advantages of television advertising to manufacturers who had not previously used this media. When the BBTA closed down in 1975 the library was taken over by the ITCA (now the ITV Association) which continued to add to the collection. In 1993 the collection was taken over by the National Museum of Photography, Film & Television.
2) The collection consists of about 200 frame samples illustrating film formats and processes from 1896 onwards, compiled since the 1930s by the Science Museum and the Kodak Museum, and now part of the National Museum of Photography, Film & Television.

Video and film holdings: Video: 5,000 items. Films are being transferred to Beta-SP as funding allows. This will enable easier access to the material. Advertising.
Video components: Lo-Band U-matic, Beta/Beta-SP, 1-inch Video, 2-inch Video.
Film: 15,000 cans. The collection contains a wide range of material (more than 20,000 items), from Gibbs SR *Ice Mountain* (the first ad) to some of the most recent. Over 4,600 different UK brands are represented. The strongest period in the collection is 1960–90. The collection is particularly strong on adverts produced by the agencies Young & Rubicam and JWT. Proctor and Gamble's products (e.g. Daz, Fairy Liquid) are very well represented. There is very little duplication within the collection, probably fewer than 250 items. Approximately 1,000 items are added each year.
There are a few examples of admags (though unfortunately not the most famous of these *Jim's Inn*). There are also examples of commercials from other countries. News and current affairs material consists of trims only. 80% colour film, 20% black and white film. Advertising, news and current affairs, frame samples.

Film components: 16mm, 35mm, positive film, negative film, final mix, frame samples: 9.5mm, 16mm, 17.5mm, 28mm, 35mm, 60mm, 70mm.

Storage: 1) Open shelving in partly air-conditioned store. 2) Science store within the archive.

Printed catalogue: Available.

Computerised database: Available.

Cataloguing: The printed catalogue is over 1,000 pages long. The collection is catalogued on a computerised database, which allows searches by product, date, agency or personality. Tailor-made printouts can be made. No shotlisting has been undertaken.

Documentation: Photocopies of relevant section of listing available on request.

Conservation policy: Material is never discarded.

Access: Access available. By arrangement only. No wheelchair access. Access available to television companies, freelance television researchers, academic researchers, educational establishments.

A major development programme took place at the Museum during the period 1997–2000. The aim of this programme was to improve access to all Museum collections. See previous entry for latest information.

Viewing and listening facilities: Viewing on premises. Sales.

Charges: Charges for research for broadcast productions. Charges for research for academic purposes. Charges for facilities and handling. Charges for other services. A price list is available upon request. Charges for telecine and broadcast standard copies.

Copyright: Copyright not held. Copyright held by individual product manufacturers. Copyright advice available. Copyright adviser: Lorna Mills.

NATIONAL RESOURCE CENTRE FOR DANCE (NRCD)

University of Surrey
GUILDFORD
GU2 5XH
Tel: 01483 879316
Fax: 01483 879500
Web: http://www.surrey.ac.uk/NRCD

Contact: Miss Helen Roberts, Manager. Mr Chris Jones, Archive Officer.

E-mail: NRCD@surrey.ac.uk

The Centre was established in 1982 with initial funding from the Calouste Gulbenkian Foundation to provide support services for dance research and education and as part of a major development in dance studies at the

University of Surrey and throughout the UK. The National Resource Centre for Dance is the sole national archive for dance and movement in the UK. The NRCD's 36 special collections and substantial core collection contain a variety of materials, including film/video, sound recordings, personal papers, photographs, books, periodicals, artwork, notation/music scores, programmes, posters, cuttings, and other ephemera. The special collections represent the life and work of dance companies, organisations, choreographers, movement theorists, educationalists, and critics. The Centre also provides a publishing programme, short courses, a summer school, and an information and bibliographic service.

Video and film holdings: Approx. 600 in the reference only collection of viewing copies.

Masters holdings: The special collections contain around 250 masters (mostly video, some film) across several collections. The off-air broadcast collection contains around 200 masters. The NRCD publications collection contains around 50 masters.

Music holdings: For some special collections the Centre has master tapes of the music/soundscape used during performance, which may have been filmed and are represented in the masters above.

Sound holdings: Approx. 300 sound recordings, mostly radio programmes taped from broadcasts; some oral history tapes.

Stills holdings: Some company collections have photographs of dances that may have been filmed and are represented in the masters above. The Fernau Hall Archive has photographs of television broadcasts of dance (particularly South Asian). The Rosemary Butcher Archive has stills of a dance work made for film.

Books holdings: Around 25 books about dance on screen, including directories of dance films/videos.

Manuscripts holdings: The Fernau Hall Archive has material concerning television broadcasts of dance, as Hall worked for Rediffusion Television. Company collections have material pertaining to the filming of their dances.

Theses holdings: Around 5 relating to dance on screen.

Datasets holdings: The Centre's own electronic database of dance-related television/film/radio programmes broadcast since 1996 (2,000+ entries).

Journals holdings: Collection of 11,000+ dance periodicals which may contain articles/reviews of dance on screen/radio. Plus the odd media-specific journal.

Newspapers holdings: In the general holdings, two files of cuttings about dance on screen and three files of television/radio listings of dance-related programmes from 1987 to the present. In the David Henshaw Collection, 10 ring binders of television/radio listings of dance-related programmes from 1981 to 1993.

Posters holdings: Approx. 12.

Ephemera holdings: Approx. 12 programmes pertaining to dance films and movie musicals. Company collections have programmes on dances that may have been filmed. Publicity materials about dance on screen.

Equipment holdings: Muray Superette Interchangeable 8/Super 8 projector; Eumig Mark 501 8/Super 8 projector; Prinz Magnon LV Super 8 projector; Gaf 64 handheld camera; two Muray film viewers; Premier film winding system; LPL 3-way cement splicer #702.

Card catalogue: For some collections.

Printed catalogue: Computer printout catalogues for most collections, particularly film/video/audio.

Computerised database: Own MS Access database, at present available only to NRCD staff. Soon updating to professional archive database (CALM 2000).

Access: Appointment required.

Access to researchers from outside: Yes.

Viewing and listening facilities: 1 television/video unit in the study room.

Charges: No charge for University of Surrey students. Others: £7.50 students, £10 for students using special collections, £15 other researchers for a day's use of the study room.

Copyright: ERA licence. Copyright held on some videos published by the NRCD and some in special collections.

NATIONAL TRAMWAY MUSEUM

The Tramway Museum Society
Crich
MATLOCK
Derbyshire
DE4 5DP
Tel: 01773 852565
Fax: 01773 852326
Web: http://www.tramway.co.uk

Contact: Mr Roger Benton, Member of the Board of Management.

British tramway history began *c.*1860 with horse tramways. Steam and cable trams followed and the development of the electric tramcar commenced in 1885. The modes overlapped, with the earlier propulsion systems being phased out mainly by about 1920, leaving electric tramcars dominant. Nevertheless the earlier systems survived long enough to have been captured by early cinematographers and many examples have survived.

Film collecting began in 1973, sources being varied and often obscure. The earliest film dates from 1896.

Video and film holdings: Video: 129 reels/cassettes. Advertising, documentary, feature films, news and current affairs, commercially produced and retailed but using material mainly shot by amateurs.

Video components: VHS Video, S-VHS Video, hi-band U-matic, Beta/Beta-SP, 2-inch Video.

Film: 90,000 feet. Some 450 titles showing trams from the earliest days through all aspects of development to the present day light rapid transport systems. 28% colour film, 72% black and white film. Advertising, amateur, documentary, feature films, news and current affairs, local authority and corporate visual records.

Film components: 8mm, Super 8mm, 9.5mm, 16mm, 35mm, positive film, negative film.

Storage: Contained within purpose-built library and archive complex which is air-conditioned, the main part being staffed by full-time employees of the Museum. The film collection is administered on a voluntary basis. Films stored in steel cupboards. Masters stored in another part of the complex.

Card catalogue: Available, indexed.

Documentation: New index being compiled of all known tramway footage shot, whether or not the material has in fact survived. Compiled from early filmmakers' catalogues, newsreel issue sheets and other notes received from individuals spotting items in film or television programmes. Card index in title order. Detail sheets in date order.

Conservation policy: Policy to offer any unwanted material to other interested bodies.

Access: Access available. 09.00–17.00, by arrangement only.

Viewing and listening facilities: Viewing on premises. Steenbeck viewing table available. Viewing copies of most titles on 16mm.

Charges: Charges for research for broadcast productions. Prices are subject to negotiation.

Copyright: Copyright resides, in most cases, with original photographer or owner.

NATIONAL VIDEO ARCHIVE OF STAGE PERFORMANCE

Theatre Museum
1E Tavistock Street
LONDON
WC2E 7PA
Tel: 020 7836 7891
Fax: 020 7836 5148
Web: http://www.theatremuseum.org

Henry Goodman as Shylock in Trevor Nunn's Royal National Theatre production of 'The Merchant of Venice', 2000. (photo courtesy of the National Video Archive of Stage Performance)

Contact: Ms Claire Hudson, Head of Library and Information Services.

E-mail: c.hudson@vam.ac.uk

The collection started in 1992 with trial recordings to establish best techniques and formats for recording live performance in front of an audience. There are now over 100 recordings, largely drama and some opera, musical theatre and pantomime.

Video and film holdings: Video: 200 hours. Live performance.

Video components: VHS Video, S-VHS Video, Beta/Beta-SP, DigiBeta.

Storage: Sub-masters and viewing copies stored on site. Masters preserved at the Victoria and Albert Museum store in Hammersmith.

Printed catalogue: Available, indexed.

Cataloguing: List of recordings can be sent to enquirers or seen on website.

Conservation policy: Submasters and viewing copies made. Then masters stored at Victoria and Albert Museum store.

Access: Access available. Tue-Fri 10.30–16.30, by arrangement only. All researchers are welcome to watch the recordings and look at associated materials. A list of the recordings is available.

Viewing and listening facilities: Viewing on premises.

Charges: There is a charge for specially arranged group viewings.

Copyright: Copyright in the performance remains with artists and copyright holders. Copyright in the recording resides with our institution and the Federation of Entertainment Unions. Copyright advice available. Copyright adviser: Jill Evans.

NESCOT – NORTH EAST SURREY COLLEGE OF TECHNOLOGY

Reigate Road
Ewell
EPSOM
Surrey
KT17 3DS
Tel: 020 8394 3174
Fax: 020 8394 3030

Contact: Mr Graeme Hodge, Library Services Manager.

E-mail: g.hodge@nescot.ac.uk

Video and film holdings: 3,000+ videos, purchased and off-air.

Masters holdings: None.

Music holdings: Very small CD collection, mainly classical or dance music.

Sound holdings: None.

Catalogue(s) available via the Internet: Available from 2000.

Digitised collection: No. No plans to do so.

Access: Hours as advertised.

Access to researchers from outside: Yes.

Viewing and listening facilities: 5 video playback stations.

Charges: None.

Copyright: None.

NEVIS RADIO

Inverlochy
FORT WILLIAM
Inverness-shire
PH33 6LU
Tel: 01397 700007
Fax: 01397 701007
Web: http://www.nevisradio.co.uk

Contact: Mr Iain Ferguson, Director of Programming.

Nevis Radio does not maintain an archive. Its website won the Radio Academy Award for technical innovation in 1999.

NEW COLLEGE, NOTTINGHAM

Stoney Street
The Lace Market
NOTTINGHAM
NG1 1NG
Tel: 0115 910 4549
Web: http://www.ncn.ac.uk

Contact: Mr Paul Kiddey, Media Programme Manager. above Communications Technology.

E-mail: paul.kiddey@ncn.ac.uk

The Nottingham Film Archive at New College Nottingham comprises approximately 100 cans of 16mm film and about 400 transparencies recording the events of the past 100 years in Nottingham and the surrounding area. It was bequeathed to the College three years ago on the death of the last remaining member of a local film/history group on the understanding that the College would eventually make it available for research purposes. The College is currently seeking funds/sponsorship/assistance to catalogue, archive and transfer the material to video.

Masters holdings: Approx. 100 cans of 16mm film. (Some of this material is now on Betacam.)

Stills holdings: Approx. 400 transparencies relating to 'Old Nottingham'.

Digitised collection: No. Not at the moment but if funds were available the College would consider it.

Access to researchers from outside: It could be – by negotiation. Currently not open for public viewing but the College is working on it.

Viewing and listening facilities: None yet.

NEW HALL

Huntingdon Road
CAMBRIDGE
Cambridgeshire
CB3 0DF
Tel: 01223 762202

Contact: Ms Alison Wilson, Librarian. Rosemary Murray Library.

E-mail: library@newhall.cam.ac.uk

New Hall has recently begun a video archive, planning to interview members of the College from its foundation in 1954 onwards. Eight people have been interviewed so far. There is film of the building of the College in 1964 (now a listed building) and a programme made for BBC East's *Matter of Fact* series about women's education. A CD-ROM was made for graduates of 1999 and there is a graduation video of the sixties. Funding is being sought for cataloguing.

Video and film holdings: About 10 videos of the history of the College and its art collection.

Masters holdings: About 8 digital films. One CD-ROM.

Books holdings: About 80 titles.

Computerised database: Access database of archival material.

Library OPACs with major holdings on moving image and radio: No.

Catalogue(s) available via the Internet: No.

Websites relating to radio and moving images: No.

Digitised collection: We would like to digitise. Recent film is digital.

Access: Not normally open to non-members.

Access to researchers from outside: Yes, by arrangement.

Copyright: Copyright in several college videos (ongoing).

NEWHAM ARCHIVES AND LOCAL STUDIES LIBRARY

Stratford Library
3 The Grove
Stratford
LONDON
E15 3EL
Tel: 020 8557 6881
Web: http://www.newham.gov.uk

Contact: Ms Sarah Harding, Assistant Archives and Local Records Advisor. Mr Richard Durack.

E-mail: sarah.harding@newham.gov.uk or richard.durack@newham.gov.uk

The Local Studies Library collects material relating to the London Borough, the former County Boroughs of East and West Ham, and Essex and London materials where relevant. The Library was opened in Stratford Reference Library in 1978.

Video and film holdings: Video: 50 reels/cassettes. Films transferred from film to video, e.g. *Torchlight Triumphant* (1940), a locally made film about the local area and school life during the Second World War. Approximately 50 videos, including material produced by the London Docklands Development Corporation,

and local organisations, including *The Trader's Tale* (1990) which portrays life at Stratford Wholesale Fruit and Vegetable Market before its move in 1991. Amateur, documentary.

Video components: VHS Video.

Film: 7 cans. The collection of films includes *Building of Plashet School* (1952); *West Ham United Football Club at First Cup Final at Wembley* (1923).

Film components: 9.5mm, 16mm, positive film, negative film.

Storage: Cabinet.

Cataloguing: *East End on Screen: a Catalogue of East London Film and Video*, Tower Hamlets Arts Project, 1985, contains details of the films. Listing in progress.

Conservation policy: A number of films have been transferred from nitrate stock onto video in recent years.

Access: Access available. By arrangement. Access for disabled.

Viewing and listening facilities: Films are not accessible for viewing at present, nor available for loan.

Charges: Charges for research for broadcast productions.

Copyright: Copyright not held. Copyright advice available.

NORTH WEST FILM ARCHIVE

Manchester Metropolitan University
Minshull House
47–49 Chorlton Street
MANCHESTER
M1 3EU
Tel: 0161 247 3097
Fax: 0161 247 3098
Web: http://www.nwfa.mmu.ac.uk

Contact: Ms Jo Abley, Collections Assistant. Geoff Senior, Collections Assistant.

E-mail: n.w.filmarchive@mmu.ac.uk

The North West Film Archive (NFWA), established in 1977, is a public regional collection holding material from early 'animated' pictures to contemporary productions. The experiences and interests of North West people are captured in both professional and amateur footage – a record of modern urban society in moving pictures. The collection dates from 1897 and includes cinema newsreels, documentaries, educational and training films, travelogues, advertising and promotional material, corporate videos and regional television programmes. A wide range of subject matter is represented: work and local industry, sport and leisure, holidays, local traditions and celebrations, transport, housing, healthcare and wartime experiences. The Archive's collection of amateur films is particularly extensive and includes family home movies. The North West Film Archive is structured within the Library Service of the Manchester Metropolitan University and is a registered charity (No. 1030912). The Archive is supported by North West Arts Board, the Heritage Lottery Fund, Granada Television, Lancashire and Cheshire County Councils, the Association of Greater Manchester Authorities and the Higher Education Funding Council for England. The NFWA proactively seeks opportunities to widen access to the collection for all the region's people – this has included pioneering action research led by people with visual or hearing impairments. The North West Film Archive became a member of the International Federation of Film Archives (FIAF) in 1994.

Video and film holdings: Over 25,000 items of film and video (master holdings) plus 5,500 items on videotape and film print for viewing.
Video components: DigiBeta, Beta/Beta SP, VHS, S-VHS, 8mm, hi-8, hi-band U-matic, lo-band U-matic, 1-inch video, Philips, 1/2-inch reel to reel.
Film components: 8mm, Super 8mm, 9.5mm, 16mm, 35mm (positive, negative and track).
Television holdings: regional news and current affairs programmes on colour film (1970s/1980s).
Complementary collections: Whilst moving images are the NWFA's primary concern, complementary collections of still photographs, oral history recordings, books and journals, posters and ephemera are held relating to the film and cinema industry of the North West of England. Over 16,000 items in total.

Whitwalker girls, 1966 (photo courtesy of the North West Film Archive)

Storage: NFWA's purpose-designed accommodation incorporates four temperature and humidity controlled vaults for colour film, black and white film, magnetic media and complementary collections. Separate storage and inspection facilities for vinegar-syndrome infected material. Inergen gas drenching system installed.

Computerised database: Searchable online Film & Video Catalogue available on the NFWA website. In-house computerised catalogues relating to complementary photograph and documentation collections.

Conservation policy: Material not relevant to this collection is re-directed to the most appropriate home. Nitrate films are also offered to the National Film and Television Archive for selection. Preservation priority is afforded to titles on chemically unstable stock.

Access: Access Mon-Fri 09.00–17.00. User search of online Film & Video Catalogue recommended in advance; assistance available.

Viewing and listening facilities: Viewings at NWFA by appointment only and subject to preservation requirements. In-house copying available, including amateur gauges to broadcast standard.

Charges: Research and reference on premises usually free to public and academic users. Rate card available for commercial users.

Copyright: Copyright not held by NWFA – information and assistance on request. Material must be cleared before supply.

NORTH WEST SOUND ARCHIVE

Clitheroe Castle
CLITHEROE
Lancashire
BB7 1AZ
Tel: 01200 427897
Fax: 01200 427897
Web: http://www.nw-soundarchive.co.uk

Contact: Mr Andrew Schofield, Sound Archive Officer.

E-mail: nswa@ed.lancscc.gov.uk

The collection holds *c.*40,000 radio broadcasts from BBC Radio Blackburn, BBC Radio Manchester & GMR and Radio Piccadilly from the establishment of the stations in 1988. The recordings cover all aspects of the stations' output, including news reports, local history series, music programmes, sports reports and programmes, and 'celebrity' interviews.

Music holdings: Music contained within programmes – *c.*5,000.

Sound holdings: *c.*40,000.

Computerised database: Yes.

Digitised collection: No. No plans to do so.

Access: Mon-Fri, 09.00–17.00.

Access to researchers from outside: Yes.

Charges: Cassette copies may be loaned.

NORTHAMPTONSHIRE LIBRARIES & INFORMATION SERVICE, NORTHAMPTONSHIRE STUDIES COLLECTION

Northamptonshire Central Library
Abington Street
NORTHAMPTON
NN1 2BA
Tel: 01604 462040
Fax: 01604 462055

Contact: Ms Janet Walls, Local History Librarian.

Video and film holdings: Film: 14 cans. The collection comprises items of local interest including Hamtune (Northampton Film Society 1952), Coronation celebrations 1953, *Focus on Northampton* (Anglia Television 1965). 4 cans colour, 10 cans black and white. Amateur, documentary.
Film components: 16mm, positive film.
Video: *c*.100 videos (mainly VHS).

Storage: Strong room, temperature and humidity controlled.

Sound holdings: *c*.200 cassette tapes relating to interviews and programmes broadcast by BBC Northampton Radio.

Access: No access. Access only available on written application to the Local Studies Librarian.

Viewing and listening facilities: No viewing copies or facilities available.

Copyright: Films made by outside bodies – copyright rests with them. Addresses can be provided in some cases.

NORTHAMPTONSHIRE RECORD OFFICE

Wootton Hall Park
NORTHAMPTON
NN4 8BQ
Tel: 01604 762129
Fax: 01604 767562

Contact: Ms Rachel Watson, Archivist. Ms Sue Groves, Deputy County Archivist.

E-mail: archivist@nro.northamptonshire.gov.uk

Small collection, which dates from 1954 to 1969, deposited by Anglia Television in 1974. It includes local

items on Oakham's Horseshoes, development scheme for Corby, etc., as well as home movies, mainly for the parishes of Moulton and Byfield *c*.1950s and 1960s, and the Ismay of Haselbech Collection, including visits to Africa and United States from 1930s to *c*.1950s. Amateur film, documentary. Police, Home Guard.

Video and film holdings: Video: 5 reels/cassettes. Amateur, documentary.
Film: 200 cans. 25% colour film, 75% black and white film.
Film components: 16mm, positive film, negative film, fine grain print.

Card catalogue: Available, indexed.

Conservation policy: Concerned to preserve information about and reflections on Northamptonshire life. Specialist advice taken when it is considered necessary by office conservators.

Access: Access available. By arrangement. Access for disabled. Anglia Television films cannot be used for commercial purposes without consent.

Viewing and listening facilities: Viewing by arrangement only.

Charges: Charges for other services. There is a charge for copying if required.

Copyright: Copyright advice available. Copyright adviser: Archivist.

NORTHANTS 96

19–21 St Edmund's Road
NORTHAMPTON
NN1 5DY
Tel: 01604 795600
Fax: 01604 795601

Contact: Mr Mark Jeeves, Programme Controller.

E-mail: reception@northants96.musicradio.com

The radio station holds 42 days' output to meet legal requirement.

NORTHERN COLLEGE OF EDUCATION

Aberdeen Campus
Hilton Place
ABERDEEN
AB24 4FA
Tel: 01224 283569
Fax: 01224 283655
Web: http://www.norcol.ac.uk

Contact: Mr Les McMorran, Senior Librarian.

E-mail: r.l.mcmorran@norcol.ac.uk

The collection comprises mainly off-air recordings of educational television broadcasts.

Video and film holdings: 1,700 items on VHS.

Library OPACs with major holdings on moving image and radio: DYNIX.

Catalogue(s) available via the Internet: via telnet – library.norcol.ac.uk

Digitised collection: No. No plans to do so.

Access to researchers from outside: Yes, for reference only.

Viewing and listening facilities: Yes.

Charges: No.

NORTHERN IRELAND DIGITAL FILM ARCHIVE

For details see under *Ulster Folk and Transport Museum.*

NORTHERN REGION FILM & TELEVISION ARCHIVE

Blandford House
Blandford Square
NEWCASTLE UPON TYNE
NE1 4JA
Tel: 0191 232 6789 ext 456
Fax: 0191 230 2614

Contact: Ms Liz Rees, Chief Archivist. Tyne and Wear Archives Service.

E-mail: twas@dial.pipex.com

In 1998 the University of Teesside, Gateshead Metropolitan Council, Tyne & Wear Archives and Trade Films, established the Northern Region Film and Television Archive which is held at Tyne & Wear Archives Newcastle and at the University of Teesside, Middlesbrough. In 1999 the Northern Film & Television Archive based at Gateshead was physically moved to the Tyne & Wear Archives at Blandford House, Blandford Square, Newcastle upon Tyne NE1 4JA. All correspondence about the Archive should be addressed to Chris Galloway at this address. The collection housed at Teesside University comprises news items from the BBC *Look North* programme, dating largely from the 1960s to the 1980s, with a small number of earlier items, and documentaries, dramas, children's programmes and popular culture programmes from Tyne Tees Television. It also houses a small private collection of home movies dating from 1928 to 1965 and film produced by local industry in the 1930s. The collection is particularly useful in the subject areas of local history, politics, social and industrial history. Tyne & Wear Archives houses the Turners Film Collection, material from Border Television, and substantial deposits of material from independent film and television companies and amateur filmmakers.

Masters holdings: 20,000 film and related sound reels (mainly 16mm, some 35mm and 9.5mm).

Music holdings: None.

Sound holdings: Some pre-production material and scripts.

Stills holdings: Slides relating to some programmes.

Equipment holdings: None.

Card catalogue: No.

Printed catalogue: Partial printed catalogue available.

Computerised database: Access 2 database with partial catalogue. New catalogue under development.

Catalogue(s) available via the Internet: Currently under development.

Digitised collection: By agreement with the BBC, the Archive will digitise one hundred hours of their material.

Access: Mon-Fri, 09.00–16.00. By appointment.

Access to researchers from outside: Yes.

Viewing and listening facilities: Video and 16mm flat bed projection facilities available.

Charges: None for research and viewing. Transfer and copyright charges apply.

Copyright: Copyright held by the original donors of films.

NORTHSOUND ONE

45 Kings Gate
ABERDEEN
AB15 4EL
Tel: 01224 337000
Fax: 01224 400003
Web: http://www.northsound.co.uk

Contact: Mr Rod Webster, Managing Director. Ms Fiona Stalker, News Director.

E-mail: northsound1@srh.co.uk

The radio station maintains on disc a news archive of major local and national news items. Everything else is held to meet legal requirement only (in English, not Scottish).

NORTHUMBERLAND COUNTY LIBRARY

County Central Library
The Willows
MORPETH
NE61 1TA
Tel: 01670 534524
Fax: 01670 534513

Contact: Ms Pat Hallam, Adult Services Librarian, County Library.

E-mail: phallam@northumberland.co.uk

The Film Collection is housed in the County Central Library in Morpeth. It comprises over 3,000 books and an archive of periodicals on all aspects of the cinema; actors, directors, production, scripts, social and political history, world cinema, genres, theory and criticism. Some screen plays are also acquired. The collection provides an opportunity to read in depth about film. As far as can be ascertained there is no other public collection like the Teesside Film Collection in the UK (the British Film Institute considers it has no parallel elsewhere in Britain). Its scope includes all significant work published in the UK. The collection is divided into 10 areas and has its own classification scheme to make it more user friendly.

Books holdings: 3,000 books.

Datasets holdings: *Film Index International* on CD-ROM.

Card catalogue: Yes.

Digitised collection: No, Under consideration.

Access: Library opening hours.

Access to researchers from outside: Yes.

Viewing and listening facilities: Public Internet access.

OBAN FM

132 George Street
OBAN
Argyll
PA34 5NT
Tel: 01631 570057
Fax: 01631 570530

Contact: Mr Ian Mackay, Station Manager. Mr George Berry, Programme Director.

E-mail: us@oban.fm.freeserve.co.uk

The radio station holds 42 days' output to meet legal requirement.

OLYMPIC TELEVISION ARCHIVE BUREAU

Axis Centre
Burlington Lane
LONDON
W4 2TH
Tel: 020 8233 5353
Fax: 020 8233 5354
Web: http://www.otab.com

Contact: Ms Julia Veng Sieck, Sales Manager.

E-mail: jsieck@imgworld.com

Management of the International Olympic Committee's 'one stop shop' Archive of Moving Imagery, involving administration of licensing procedures, tape duplication and delivery of material. This also includes administration of OTAB's website.

Video and film holdings: Over 20,000 hours of film, television and newsreel material from the first modern Games in Athens, 1896 to the present day.

OPEN UNIVERSITY LIBRARY

Interactive Open Learning Centre & Media Archive
Walton Hall
MILTON KEYNES
MK7 6AA
Tel: 01908 652366
Fax: 01908 653571
Web: http://oulib1.open.ac.uk/wh/teaching/index.htm

Contact: Ms Liz Mallett, Manager, Interactive Open Learning Centre and Media Archive.

E-mail: library-IOLCMA-helpdesk@open.ac.uk

The Interactive Open Learning Centre & Media Archive holds a wide range of OU teaching materials, including audio-visual resources, printed course materials, multimedia resources and digital video. The audio-visual resources include OU television and radio programmes from 1971; OU audio cassettes from 1978 and video cassettes; CDs and CD-ROMs; production transcripts and programme synopses, a slide collection; and the Training and Development Resource for staff development. Programme material covers the Faculties of Arts, Social Sciences, Mathematics, and Computing, Science, Technology, Education and Language Studies, Law, the Business School and School of Health and Social Welfare. Also, information about the Open University. These resources can be used in the Library which has a specialised viewing area. Information on most of the resources is available through the Library catalogue. A help desk is available for further information.

Video and film holdings: Video: Over 10,000 reels/ cassettes. Television and non-broadcast materials. Expansion rate of 200 programmes per year.
Video components: VHS Video, lo-band U-matic, Beta.
Film: 1,000,000 feet. Early Open University television programmes.

Storage: Open shelves for recent reference material. Other material, including master tapes, stored in air-conditioned area.

Sound holdings: Over 6,000 programmes. Open University only, from the early 1970s onwards.

Stills holdings: Slide collection.

Computerised database: Available.

Catalogue(s) available via the Internet: Yes, available via the web page at http://oulib1.open.ac.uk/

Cataloguing: From 1984 material transferred to computer database. Text searching on subject terms possible.

Documentation: Transcripts, synopses.

Digitised collection: Partially. 80 hours digitised video using Informedia system. A project (DIVA) is underway to further digitise the video collection.

Conservation policy: Endeavour to maintain one master copy of each OU television and radio programme, and the video and audio cassettes which are an integral part of many courses.

Access: Access available. By arrangement only. Material available for reference and use in the University Library. Current video material (on VHS), comprising 1,400 programmes, is available for loan to Library members.

Charges: Note: No sale of material from the OU Library. All requests for hire and purchase to be directed to Open University Worldwide, the Berrill Building, Walton Hall, Milton Keynes, MK7 6AA, Internet: http://www.ouw.co.uk

OPEN UNIVERSITY WORLDWIDE LTD

The Berrill Building
Walton Hall
MILTON KEYNES
MK7 6AA
Tel: 01908 858745
Fax: 01908 858787
Web: http://www.ouw.co.uk

Contact: Mrs Sue Hitchen, Commercial Operations Manager. Carol Langham.

E-mail: s.e.hitchen@open.ac.uk

Video and film holdings: 1,000 thirty-minute programmes approx.

Printed catalogue: Open University Worldwide Catalogues of Learning Resources.

Websites relating to radio and moving images: http://www.ouw.co.uk

Digitised collection: No. There are plans but no time-scale.

Access: Prior permission.

Access to researchers from outside: Yes. By special arrangement.

Viewing and listening facilities: By arrangement only.

Charges: None.

OVERSEAS FILM AND TELEVISION CENTRE

4th Floor
184–192 Drummond Street
LONDON
NW1 3HP
Tel: 020 7383 2288
Fax: 020 7384 2333
Web: http://www.film-images.com

Contact: Mr James Kearney, Film Researcher, Research Department.

E-mail: research@film-images.com

The Overseas Film and Television Centre (OFTVC) is a collection of some of the most historically meaningful films still in existence showing Britain's former colonies, mainly Africa and the Caribbean. Its main purpose was to promote economic and social development in the colonies and for all the colonial countries to obtain their own independent film units with technical help from the organisation in Britain. Also incorporated in the collection are a number of films from other clients, including Milk Marketing Board, Gullick (mining equipment manufacturer), RSPCA, Young's Brewery, Castrol Oil, Crawfords Advertising Agency, Conservative Party, and the British Travel Association. There are also commercials made by the OFTVC for clients such as Ovaltine, Barclays Bank and Guinness.

Video and film holdings: Film: Over 1,400 titles.
Film components: 16mm/35mm black and white and OCN.
Video components: Beta SP. U-matic, hi/lo band.

Storage: Custom-made temperature-controlled vaults off-site in London.

Haile Selassie from 'ACCRA Conference' 1965 (photo courtesy of Film Images [London] Ltd)

Catalogue(s) available via the Internet: Available online at http://www.film-images.com. A separate part of the site gives the researcher access to the OFTVC database and shotlist.

Access: Access available (appointments necessary). Access for disabled. Research can be carried out on behalf of customers.

Viewing and listening facilities: In-house viewing facilities available from VHS PAL reference library, and 16mm/35mm Steenbecks available to view from film. Tailor-made VHS or U-matic cassettes can be made for preview purposes (a fee is payable for this). Showreels are available upon request.

Charges: Fees are charged for research, licence fees and transfers/delivery. All fees are clearly outlined in advance, dependent on the project.

Copyright: Copyright is managed by Film Images on behalf of the owners/originators of the footage.

OXFAM FILM ARCHIVE

Oxfam – Information Services
274 Banbury Road
OXFORD
OX2 7DZ
Tel: 01865 313764
Fax: 01865 313770
Web: http://www.oxfam.org.uk

Contact: Ms Chrissie Webb, Archivist. Ms Rosie Dodd.

E-mail: cwebb@oxfam.org.uk or rdodd@oxfam.org.uk

The collection comprises films – documentary, educational and promotional – from about 1958 to1990, relating to Oxfam's work, made by or on behalf of Oxfam. It holds copies of television programmes and other films about Oxfam or on subjects closely related to its interests.

Video and film holdings: Video: 80 hours. Documentary.
Video components: VHS Video, S-VHS Video, hi-8, hi-band U-matic, lo-band U-matic, Beta/Beta-SP, 1-inch Video.
Film: 90 cans, 35 hours. Educational and promotional documentaries. Documentary.
Film components: 16mm, positive film, negative film.

Storage: Secure storage as part of Oxfam Archive.

Computerised database: Available.

Cataloguing: Database on Blackwell's Idealist. Relates to positives only. Negatives still in process of being sorted and documented. Video catalogue is available.

Documentation: Some film catalogues, 1970s-1980s, distributed by Oxfam and others.

Conservation policy: Material to be permanently preserved.

Access: Access available. By arrangement only. Staff are available to assist. Access for disabled.

Viewing and listening facilities: Viewing on premises.

Charges: There are no charges at present.

Copyright: Copyright held. Copyright held for 43% of holdings only. 41% is non-Oxfam copyright and copyright of remainder is unclear at present.

OXFORD BROOKES UNIVERSITY AND ROYAL COLLEGE OF PHYSICIANS MEDICAL SCIENCES VIDEO ARCHIVE

Headington
OXFORD
OX3 0BP
Tel: 01865 483146
Fax: 01865 483998
Web: http://www.brookes.ac.uk/schools/bms/medical

Contact: Ms Katie Hambrook, Audio-visual Librarian. Donald Marshall, The Library.

E-mail: khambrook@brookes.ac.uk

The Archive was founded in 1984 by Sir Gordon Wolstenholme and Dr Max Blythe, on behalf of the Royal College of Physicians and Oxford Polytechnic, now Oxford Brookes University. Funded by Oxford Brookes University until 1992. Small initial grant from the Wellcome Trust, later further support from the Trust (1995–1998) to increase the number of interviews undertaken and the facilities of the Oxford Brookes University TV recording studio. Support has also come from the Nuffield Trust (1993–1994) for a specific project on epidemiology. At the beginning of 1999 187 major interviews had been completed and edited. Transcripts have slightly lagged behind with about ninety now completed. International developments have involved a collaboration with the Australasian Academy of Science which arranged a first short series of television broadcasts in 1998, based on interviews conducted in Australia. The Oxford Brookes University and Royal College of Physicians Medical Science Video Archive resources are held by the University and are available for viewing by researchers, by appointment. Subsidiary collections of tapes are eventually to be held by the Royal College of Physicians, the Wellcome Trust, and Oxford Brookes University Library, where a special collection on medical biography is being developed.

Video and film holdings: Approx. 200 videos.

Catalogue(s) available via the Internet: http://www.brookes.ac.uk/schools/bms/medical

Access: Available for viewing by researchers by appointment.

Access to researchers from outside: Yes.

Viewing and listening facilities: Yes.

Charges: No.

Copyright: Rights owned by Oxford Brookes University.

OXFORD SCIENTIFIC FILMS LTD

Lower Road
LONG HANBOROUGH
Oxfordshire
OX8 8LL
Tel: 01993 881881
Fax: 01993 882808. Film Library Fax: 01993 883969
Web: http://www.osf.uk.com

Contact: Ms Jane Mulleneux, Film Library Collection Manager.

E-mail: film.library@osf.uk.com

Oxford Scientific Films has developed from origins as a natural history filmmaker with a world-wide reputation for award-winning programming. Its production business now encompasses peak-time broadcast series and television commercials for the international market in natural history, science, and special effects, while the company's specialist film and photo libraries have achieved a world-wide market for their image resources.

Video and film holdings: Video: Stockshots, commercial film, documentary, science and education.
Video components: DigiBeta, D1, Beta SP, 1-inch, U-matic, VHS.
Film: 2,000,000 feet. A wide range of stock footage covering natural history, science, world-wide locations, macro, micro, special effects, time-lapse and high-speed. Footage available from both the Oxford Scientific Films archive and represented collections. 100% colour film.
Film components: 16mm, Super 16mm, 35mm, positive film, negative film.

Storage: Print and viewing tapes are held in Oxford. Video masters are held in London for speedy transfers. Original negative also held in London.

Stills holdings: Photo Library held.

Card catalogue: Not available.

Printed catalogue: Available, indexed.

Computerised database: Available on site.

Cataloguing: Subject and species lists and showreels available.

Conservation policy: Transfer to DigiBeta, D1 and Beta-SP tape.

Access: By arrangement only.

Viewing and listening facilities: VHS preview tapes by post. Viewing on site by appointment.

Charges: Research, transfer and licence fees payable. Quotations on request.

Copyright: OSF copyright footage and agent for non-OSF copyright material.

PARTRIDGE STOCK SHOT LIBRARY

Partridge Films
The Television Centre
Bath Road
BRISTOL
BS4 3HG
Tel: 0117 972 3777
Fax: 0117 971 9340

Contact: Ms Kate Edmundson, Library Manager.

E-mail: wildlife@partridge.co.uk

Wildlife film production company since 1970s. All productions shot on 16mm film and telecine mastered to Beta-SP and some DigiBeta.

Video and film holdings: Video: 4,000 hours. 3,000 hours from the 16mm film negatives have been mastered on Beta-SP videotape. Documentary.
Video components: VHS Video, Beta/Beta-SP, DigiBeta.
Film: 3,500 hours. 100% colour film. Documentary.
Film components: 16mm, negative film.

Computerised database: Available.

Conservation policy: No film material has been junked.

Access: Access available. 09.00–18.00, by arrangement. Staff are available to assist. Access for disabled.

Viewing and listening facilities: Viewing on premises.

Charges: Charges for research for broadcast productions. Charges for research for academic purposes. Charges for facilities and handling. Charges will be negotiated.

Copyright: Copyright held. Copyright advice available. Copyright adviser: Kate Edmundson.

PATRICK STANBURY COLLECTION

12 Laurel Crescent
Woodham Lane
WOKING
Surrey
GU21 5SS
Tel: 01932 345924

Contact: Mr Patrick Stanbury.

Extensive collection of silent features and short subjects (fiction and documentary), American and European, and animation material. Official representative for the Blackhawk Library, a long-established US-based 16mm collection of silent and early sound material, much of it rare and unobtainable elsewhere. The collection is expanding on a consistent basis.

Video and film holdings: Film: 1,000 cans.
Film components: 9.5mm, 16mm, 35mm.

Storage: Vaults.

Cataloguing: Available for Blackhawk Library only.

Access: Access available. Open to all researchers.

Viewing and listening facilities: Viewing on premises. Sales. Film viewing can be arranged by appointment. Prints from Blackhawk Library available for sale.

Charges: Fees dependent on use.

PHILOSOPHY LIBRARY, OXFORD UNIVERSITY

10 Merton Street
OXFORD
Oxfordshire
OX1 4JJ
Tel: 01865 276927
Fax: 01865 276932
Web: http://www.bodley.ox.ac.uk/boris/guides/philosophy

Contact: Miss Hilla Wait, Philosophy Librarian, Philosophy Library.

E-mail: hilla.wait@bodley.ox.ac.uk

The Philosophy Library is developing a collection of philosophy videos, with a preference for current philosophical debate rather than as standard lecture substitutes. It holds the set of *Philosophers in Conversation* (Donald Davidson, Willard Quine, Peter Strawson), and a video debate between Juergen Habermas and Richard Rorty. These were all obtained commercially. The Library has no unpublished material.

Video and film holdings: 30 videos.

Books holdings: Small section on philosophy of visual arts, including film.

Computerised database: Computerised catalogue.

Library OPACs with major holdings on moving image and radio: Cataloguing onto OLIS – Oxford University's online system (Z39.50 compliant) is in process.

Digitised collection: No.

Access to researchers from outside: Access generally is for university students. Other access is at Librarian's discretion.

Viewing and listening facilities: On-site television/video unit.

PHOTOPLAY PRODUCTIONS LTD

21 Princess Road
LONDON
NW1 8JR
Tel: 020 7722 2500
Fax: 020 7722 6662

Contact: Mr Patrick Stanbury. Kevin Brownlow.

Specialising in silent material, the company handles films from the private collections of its founders as well as material acquired in the course of making major television documentaries on silent film history.

Video and film holdings: Video: Tapes are available on some subjects.
Film: The collection comprises several thousand reels. There is also access to interview material specially shot for the Thames Television series: *Hollywood, Unknown Chaplin, Buster Keaton: A Hard Act to Follow, Harold Lloyd – The Third Genius* and *D.W. Griffith – Father on Film.*
Film components: 9.5mm, 16mm, 35mm.

Storage: All in vaults, some on site.

Documentation: No catalogue or lists – material too diverse. Requests are dealt with on an individual basis.

Conservation policy: Interview transcripts and substantial paper and stills archives.

Access: Access available. Research advice can be provided to aid locating material from other sources. Available to all researchers. All enquiries by telephone or letter in the first instance.

Viewing and listening facilities: Viewing on premises. Film viewing facilities available by appointment. Tape viewing copies can be arranged in most instances.

The PLANNED ENVIRONMENT THERAPY TRUST ARCHIVE AND STUDY CENTRE

Church Lane
TODDINGTON
Gloucestershire
GL54 5DQ
Tel: 01242 620125
Fax: 01242 620125
Web: http://www.pettarchive.org.uk

Contact: Dr Craig Fees, Archivist.

E-mail: archive@pettarchive.org.uk

The film/video collection forms part of the archive of The Planned Environment Therapy Trust. The Archive was founded in 1989 in order to gather and protect the papers of individuals and organisations involved in environment therapy, milieu therapy and therapeutic communities.

Video and film holdings: Video: 200 hours. Amateur, documentary, educational films, conference proceedings. Percentage of material in colour: 50%. Percentage of material in black and white: 50%.
Video components: VHS Video, S-VHS Video, hi-band U-matic, lo-band U-matic, Beta/Beta-SP, 1-inch Video, Hi 8.
Film: 55 hours. Amateur, documentary. No nitrate material held.
Film components: 8mm, 16mm, negative film.

Storage: Temperature and humidity controlled archive storage area.

Printed catalogue: Available.

Computerised database: Available.

Conservation policy: All material is kept indefinitely.

Access: Limited access. By arrangement only. Staff are available to assist. Access and facilities provided for disabled.

Viewing and listening facilities: Viewing on premises. Duplicating possible in exceptional circumstances.

Charges: Charges for research for broadcast productions.

Copyright: Copyright held for some of the collections. Copyright advice available. Copyright adviser: Craig Fees.

PLATO VIDEO

70 Richmond Hill
BOURNEMOUTH
Dorset
BH2 6JA
Tel: 01202 554382
Fax: 01202 761227
Web: http://www.plato-video.co.uk

Contact: Mr Lionel Fynn, Video Librarian.

E-mail: lionel@plato-video.co.uk

The collection is composed of 8mm, 9.5mm and 16mm film and video material from the 1920s to the present day. Completed programmes on transportation and other subjects are held together with stock footage on related subjects. Completed programmes on aviation, liquor licensing (public houses, etc.), rural and urban planning

'Waverley' moored at Swanage Pier (photo courtesy of Plato Video)

and design, and shipping interests. Shipping includes paddle steamers, cross channel ferries, excursion ships, hovercraft (including last day of cross-channel operation), liners (including pre-war cruise liner *Bremen*) and Southampton Docks in the 1930s, showing visiting liners and general dock workings. Aviation material includes early biplane airliner flight to Paris from Croydon Airport, air shows going back to the 1950s, flights in World War II aircraft and flights in Concorde and extensive footage of Concorde. Buildings include black and white 16mm film of London, Paris and River Thames in the late 1930s and video of rural and urban locations in the UK, Paris, Venice and the USA.

Stills holdings: There is also a library of 35mm and 2 1/2-inch square colour slides, and colour and black and white photos and postcards of railways, transportation, buildings and general scenes in the UK, Europe, Australia and the USA.

Access: Access available. By arrangement.

Viewing and listening facilities: Supply of viewing copies on VHS tapes. Sale and duplication of copyright held material.

Copyright: Copyright held for most of the material.

PLYMOUTH COLLEGE OF ART
AND DESIGN

Tavistock Place
PLYMOUTH
PL4 8AT
Tel: 01752 203412
Fax: 01752 203444

Contact: Ms Linda Harding, Librarian, The Library.

E-mail: lharding@pcad.plym.ac.uk

Small independent College of Art Library serving about 1800 students and 100 staff. Subject specialisation is in Fine Art, Interior Design, Graphic Design, Fashion, Photography, Film and Media. Courses range from ND level through to BA. Stock is mainly books, periodicals, videos and CD-ROMs. The Critical Studies Group of the College of which the Librarian is Chair has produced a useful student study guide which includes advice on referencing and compiling a bibliography for film and video material plus illustrations.

Video and film holdings: 350.

Books holdings: 600.

Datasets holdings: *Film Index International.*

Journals holdings: Titles include *Sight & Sound* and *Screen International.*

Catalogue(s) available via the Internet: http://141.163.172.100/

Digitised collection: No.

Access to researchers from outside: Yes. members of the public are welcome to use the Library for reference purposes.

Viewing and listening facilities: 2 video machines.

PLYMOUTH LIBRARY SERVICE – LOCAL STUDIES AND NAVAL HISTORY LIBRARY

Plymouth Central
PLYMOUTH
PL4 8AL
Tel: 01752 305909
Fax: 01752 305905

Contact: Ms Joyce Brown, Local Studies and Naval History Librarian.

The collection comprises videos of local events, areas and people, mostly of historic nature as well as videos of naval information concerning training, recruitment and commercials.

Video and film holdings: Video: 100 reels/cassettes. The collection is growing. Advertising, amateur, documentary.
Video components: VHS Video.
Film: The film material has been deposited at the TSW Film Archive at Derry's Cross, Plymouth.

Storage: Material is stored on shelves.

Computerised database: Available.

Access: No access.

Viewing and listening facilities: Video monitor available but booking essential.

Copyright: Copyright held for some of the material.

POLYGRAM TELEVISION INTERNATIONAL

Note: *Polygram and Universal TV merged in 1999. All ATV/ITC catalogue was sold to Carlton International in July 1999.*

PORT OF LONDON AUTHORITY FILM COLLECTION, MUSEUM IN DOCKLANDS

Unit C14
Poplar Business Park
10 Prestons Road
LONDON
E14 9RL
Tel: 020 7515 1162
Fax: 020 7538 0209

Contact: Mr R R Aspinall, Museum in Docklands Librarian and Archivist.

E-mail: raspinall@museumofdocklands.org.uk

The Port of London Authority was set up in 1909. Since that date, it has been responsible for the management and administration of the River Thames from Teddington to the Nore, and for the operation of the enclosed dock systems. The first PLA film was made around 1921. Films were made at regular intervals. Probably the best-known films relating to the Port of London, *City of Ships* and *Waters of Time,* are in the collection. However, all the early nitrate stock, as well as the masters for the later films, are held by the National Film and Television Archive. The collection spans roughly sixty years (1920–1980). A number of recent films about modern cargo handling facilities at Tilbury Docks are held. It is likely that further films will be added as they are made by the PLA. In 1986, responsibility for the collection was passed to the Museum of London and now forms part of the Docklands Project.

Video and film holdings: Video: 1.25 hours. The Archive holds a handful of films on video. Documentary. Video components: VHS Video, Beta/Beta-SP.
Film: 300 cans. There are about 90 different films in the archive. Principal subjects covered include docks and all the various activities associated with docks, cargoes, the River Thames and pollution. 5% colour film, 95% black and white film. Documentary, engineering work in progress, construction, pollution.
Film components: Positive Film.

Storage: Racking along one of the units. The films are stored with the rest of the PLA archive. Two humidifiers have been installed and a constant temperature is maintained within the unit.

Cataloguing: None at present. The collection is in the process of being catalogued on a computer, along with the rest of the PLA archive. For the early films a detailed shot-by-shot catalogue is proposed.

Documentation: An important photographic collection is also conserved.

Access: Access available. By arrangement only. Access for disabled.

Viewing and listening facilities: Viewing on premises. Viewing off premises. The best of the early films have been transferred to Betacam-SP and video format to facilitate easy viewing by researchers. Videos can be viewed on premises. 16mm films have to be viewed off premises.

Charges: Charges for other services. Charge for hire, copyright and reproduction.

Copyright: Copyright held.

PORTSMOUTH CITY MUSEUM AND RECORDS OFFICE

Museum Road
PORTSMOUTH
PO1 2LJ
Tel: 023 9282 7261
Fax: 023 9287 5276
Web: http://www.portsmouthrecordsoffice.co.uk

Contact: Mr David Evans.

E-mail: devans@portsmouthcc.gov.uk

Items presented to the city from time to time by individual film companies.

Video and film holdings: Film: Mainly newsreel items of local interest, such as Winston Churchill receiving the Freedom of Portsmouth.
Film components: 16mm, 35mm, positive film.

Access: All film transferred to Wessex Film and Sound Archive, Winchester. Contact Hampshire Record Office.

POST OFFICE FILM AND VIDEO LIBRARY

PO Box 145
SITTINGBOURNE
Kent
ME10 1NH
Tel: 01795 426465
Fax: 01795 474871

Contact: Mr Barry Wiles, Manager.

The collection comprises classic material from the 1930s and current Post Office footage.

Video and film holdings: Video: Documentary.
Video components: VHS Video, hi-band U-matic, lo-band U-matic, Beta/Beta-SP, 1-inch Video, 2-inch Video.

Film: Documentary.
Film components: 16mm, positive film, final mix.

Printed catalogue: Available, indexed.

Viewing and listening facilities: Viewing off premises. Sales.

Charges: Charges for research for broadcast productions. Charges for facilities and handling. A price list is available upon request.

Copyright: Copyright held.

POWELL-COTTON MUSEUM

Quex Park
BIRCHINGTON
Kent
CT7 0BH
Tel: 01843 842168
Fax: 01843 846661

Contact: Mr John Harrison, Curator.

In the 1930s Major P H G Powell-Cotton and his daughter Dr Diana Powell-Cotton made several ethnographic films in Africa, chiefly in Italian Somaliland and southern Angola, and mostly illustrating local crafts. In the 1950s and 1960s other members of the family made ethnographic and wildlife films in Kenya and Uganda. The Museum has over thirty of these films, the earliest dating from 1922 and made in the Cameroons.

Video and film holdings: Video: 7 reels/cassettes. Small selection of copy videos (incomplete). Amateur.
Video components: VHS Video.
Film: Silent 16mm black and white film of various African tribes showing such skills as pot making, iron smelting, marriage ceremony and day-to-day life. Silent 16mm colour natural history material of African big game and birds. 50% colour film, 50% black and white film. Amateur, documentary. Mostly available on VHS.
Film components: 16mm, positive film.

Storage: Archive store.

Cataloguing: Typed lists.

Conservation policy: Some field notes available with films relating to tribes in Angola pre-World War II.

Access: Access available. By arrangement only. Films may occasionally be made available for television and commercial use; rates can be quoted on application.

Viewing and listening facilities: Films may be viewed at the museum, if three to four weeks notice is given, by parties, groups of bona fide students and researchers.

Charges: Charges for research for broadcast productions. Charges for facilities and handling.

Copyright: Copyright held. Copyright advice available.

The PRAXIS ARCHIVE

Praxis Films Ltd
PO Box 290
MARKET RASEN
Lincolnshire
LN3 6BB
Tel: 01472 399976
Fax: 01472 399976
Web: http://www.praxisfilms.com

Contact: Sue Waterfield, Archivist.

E-mail: archive@praxisfilms.com

Built up over 20 years through purchase and shooting own material in Eastern and Northern England. The collection began with a series of rural, sea-fishing and industrial films. Current affairs, documentary and educational films made in Northern England, throughout the UK and internationally are continually being added to the holdings.

Video and film holdings: Video: Regular additions. The Yellowbelly Collection (colour): over 70 hours of professionally shot broadcast images in Lincolnshire in the 1980s. The Fishing Collection: harbours, docks, fleets throughout this century comprises over 20 hours. Amateur, documentary.
Video components: Hi-Band U-matic, Beta/Beta-SP, 1-inch Video.
Film: 90% colour film, 10% black and white film. Amateur, documentary.
Film components: 16mm, positive film, negative film.

Storage: In secure vault.

Card catalogue: Available, indexed.

Computerised database: Available.

Farmers at cattle auction, 1980s (photo courtesy of the Praxis Archive)

Documentation: Shooting scripts and interview transcripts. Shot lists. Cutting script in most cases.

Conservation policy: Everything possible is preserved.

Access: All research done in-house. No external researchers.

Viewing and listening facilities: Viewing off premises. Normally arrange viewing in London or Leeds.

Charges: Charges for research for broadcast productions. Charges for facilities and handling. A price list is available upon request.

Copyright: Copyright held.

PRISM DIGITAL COMMUNICATIONS LTD

15 Marden Road
STAPLEHURST
Kent
TN12 0NF
Tel: 01580 891683
Fax: 01580 890143

Contact: Mr Steve Bergson, Director.

E-mail: stevebergson@cs.com

Mainly rushes from productions – broadcast, corporate, home video and multimedia.

Video and film holdings: Video: 2,000 hours. Documentary, news and current affairs, science and education.
Video components: Beta/Beta-SP, 1-inch Video.
Film: 20 hours. 80% colour film, 20% black and white film. Documentary.
Film components: 16mm, positive film, negative film.

Storage: Vault.

Computerised database: Available.

Conservation policy: Very little is thrown away.

Access: Limited access. By arrangement. Access for disabled.

Viewing and listening facilities: Viewing on premises. Viewing off premises. Viewing copies sent out preferably.

Charges: Charges for research for broadcast productions. Charges for research for academic purposes. Charges for facilities and handling. A price list is available upon request.

Copyright: Copyright held for the main part of the collection but some third-party clearances sometimes apply. Copyright advice available. Copyright adviser: Steve Bergson.

PUBLIC RECORD OFFICE OF NORTHERN IRELAND

66 Balmoral Avenue
BELFAST
Northern Ireland
BT9 6NY
Tel: 028 9025 1318
Fax: 028 9025 5999
Web: http://www.proni.nics.gov.uk/index.htm

Contact: V M E Adams, Principal Record Officer.

E-mail: proni@nics.gov.uk

A collection of about 200 films, the earliest dating from the 1920s, from private and official sources; contains documentary footage, some newsreels, tourist promotional films, and amateur footage.

Video and film holdings: Video: 19 reels/cassettes. Documentary, news and current affairs, science and education.
Film: 213 cans. The majority of the holdings are black and white. 5% nitrate film. Amateur, documentary, news and current affairs, science and education.
Film components: 8mm, Super 8mm, 9.5mm, 16mm, 35mm, positive film, negative film.

Storage: Purpose-built strong rooms (reinforced concrete windowless areas) with temperature and humidity control and automatic fire detection and extinguishing system in each room. No facilities for storing nitrate film – these are held by the National Film and Television Archive.

Printed catalogue: Available, indexed.

Cataloguing: A computerised database is under preparation.

Conservation policy: Almost all film material is kept, simply because so little appears to have survived.

Access: Access to film collection under review at present.

Charges: Charges for research for broadcast productions. A price list is available upon request.

Q102.9 FM

The Riverside Suite
Old Waterside Railway Station
Duke Street
LONDONDERRY
Northern Ireland
BT47 6DH
Tel: 028 7134 4449
Fax: 028 7131 1177
Web: http://www.q102-fm.com

Contact: Mr Frank McLaughlin, Managing Director.

E-mail: q102@iol.ie

The radio station holds 42 days' output to meet legal requirement. Special events programmes may be kept.

QUEEN MARGARET UNIVERSITY COLLEGE

Corstorphine Campus
Clerwood Terrace
EDINBURGH
EH12 8TS
Tel: 0131 317 3301/3303
Fax: 0131 339 7057
Web: http://www.qmced.ac.uk

Contact: Faculty Librarian (Arts).

Video and film holdings: 417 VHS videos; 284 C-60 videos. Only a couple on the subject of moving image.

Sound holdings: 151 audiotapes; 11 sound recordings; 42 sound disks; 275 tape-slide sets.

Stills holdings: 219 slide sets; 275 tape-slide sets. None relating to moving image.

Books holdings: 1,686 titles covering mass media, radio broadcasting, television broadcasting, motion pictures, radio and television.

Journals holdings: 8 titles.

Printed catalogue: Yes.

Catalogue(s) available via the Internet: Details of all video, book and journal titles are available for information on the Library's Web based catalogue, WebCat.

Websites relating to radio and moving images: http://unicorn.qmced.ac.uk/

Access: Open to the public for reference only.

Access to researchers from outside: Yes.

Viewing and listening facilities: Video playback facilities are available.

QUEEN'S UNIVERSITY OF BELFAST

Main Library
University Square
BELFAST
Northern Ireland
BT7 1LS
Tel: 028 9027 3831
Fax: 028 9032 3340
Web: http://www.qub.ac.uk/lib/

Contact: Mr Stuart Rawson, Head of Acquisitions and Cataloguing.

E-mail: s.rawson@qub.ac.uk

The moving image collection is mainly designed to support the Film Studies course.

Video and film holdings: 200 videos. 300 DVDs.

Books holdings: 1,000 books.

Theses holdings: 3 theses.

Journals holdings: 4 journals.

Library OPACs with major holdings on moving image and radio: Yes.

Catalogue(s) available via the Internet: http://library.qub.ac.uk/qcat

Digitised collection: No. No plans to do so.

Access: Many items for use in library only.

Access to researchers from outside: Yes.

Viewing and listening facilities: DVD and video.

Charges: None for library members.

Copyright: None.

The RADIO ACADEMY

5 Market Place
LONDON
W1N 7AH
Tel: 020 7255 2010
Web: http://www.radioacademy.org

Contact: Mr John Bradford, Director.

The Radio Academy is a forum for the British radio industry. Its website covers industry news, skills and studies in radio, marketing information, conference, festival and events information and the Sony Radio Awards. An A-Z Radio Stations Listing is included and details are given of a number of useful organisations in the field. Its Hall of Fame (still in development) is the Academy's tribute to those figures in the public eye who have made an outstanding contribution to the radio industry and radio in the UK.

The RADIO AUTHORITY

Holbrook House
14 Great Queen Street
Holborn
LONDON
WC2B 5DG
Web: http://www.radioauthority.org.uk

Contact: Ms Julia McCatty, Chief Press Officer.

The Radio Authority officially began its regulatory and licensing role on 1 January 1991. The Authority licenses and regulates all commercial radio services on both analogue and digital platforms. The Authority is responsible for monitoring the obligations on its licensees required by the Broadcasting Acts of 1990 and 1996. Its three main tasks are: to plan frequencies, to appoint licensees with a view to broadening listener choice, and to regulate programming and advertising. The annual *Radio Authority Pocket Book* is available from the Authority.

Access: The Radio Authority has a Reading Room in which applications for eight-year local analogue and digital radio licences may be read by appointment only. Open Mon-Fri, 09.00–17.00.

RADIO BORDERS

Tweedside Park
GALASHIELS
Scotland
TD1 3TD
Tel: 01896 759444
Fax: 01896 759494
Web: http://www.radioborders.co.uk

Contact: Mr Danny Gallagher, Programme Controller.

Radio station. Holds 42 days' output to meet legal requirement. Some sports broadcasts and special items may be kept.

RADIO CEREDIGION

Yr Hen Ysgol Gymraeg
Ffordd Alexandra
ABERYSTWYTH
Ceredigion
SY23 1LF
Tel: 01970 627999
Fax: 01970 627206

Contact: Mr Dan Griffiths. Library.

Radio station. Regional news programmes kept. Notable events are stored at the National Library of Wales (audio is stored on videotape). These include news bulletins for the past 8 years. Local programming is recorded every week. Recordings are largely in the Welsh language; some may be in English.

RADIO MALDWYN

The Studios
The Park
Newtown
POWYS
SY16 2NZ
Tel: 01686 623555
Fax: 01686 623666
Web: http://www.magic756.com

Contact: Mr Austin Powell, Programme Controller.

E-mail: radio.maldwyn@uk.online.co.uk

The radio station holds 42 days' output to meet legal requirement. A few scripts for news items are kept.

RADIO SOCIETY OF GREAT BRITAIN

Lambda House
Cranborne Road
POTTERS BAR
Hertfordshire
EN6 5HU
Tel: 01707 659015
Fax: 01707 645105
Web: http://www.rsgb.org.uk

Contact: Mr John Crabbe, Librarian/Museum Curator, AM Radio Department.

Video and film holdings: Videos. Some 9.5mm, 8mm and 16mm films of amateur radio activities.

Sound holdings: Recordings of lectures, etc. of amateur radio-related topics.

Stills holdings: Archive photos of radio activities.

Books holdings: 600 books on amateur radio and related subjects.

Journals holdings: Amateur radio journals from worldwide societies.

Ephemera holdings: Amateur radio museum and archives.

Equipment holdings: The Museum holds 150 radio exhibits.

Printed catalogue: Library list.

Digitised collection: No, not yet.

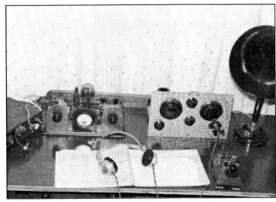

Amateur radio station, 1925. Shows l. to r. valve transmitter, valve receiver, horn, loudspeaker and Morse key (photo courtesy of Radio Society of Great Britain)

Access: Mon and Thu, 10.00–16.00, or with prior permission.

Access to researchers from outside: Yes.

RADIO XL 1296 AM

KMS House
Bradford Street
BIRMINGHAM
B12 0JD
Tel: 0121 753 5353
Fax: 0121 753 3111

Contact: Mr Barry Curtis, Programme Controller.

Radio station. Holds 42 days' output to meet legal requirement. Maintains a private library of South Asian music on hard disc.

RAM FM

35–36 Irongate
DERBY
DE1 3GA
Tel: 01332 205599
Fax: 01332 851199

Contact: Mr Rob Wagstaff, Programme Controller.

E-mail: admin@ramfm.musicradio.com

The radio station holds 42 days' output to meet legal requirement. Special events, e.g. charity events and slices of *The Breakfast Show* are kept for a year.

RAMBERT DANCE COMPANY ARCHIVE

94 Chiswick High Road
LONDON
W4 1SH
Tel: 020 8995 4246

Contact: Ms Jane Pritchard, Archivist.

E-mail: jp@rambert.org.uk

Video and film holdings: Video: Videos documenting company's productions from 1970s onwards held in the company archive.
Film: Film material from 1930s to the 1960s deposited at National Film and Television Archive with copies held at the Dance Collection, New York Public Library.

Access: No access. Access restricted to company only.

RAY HOOLEY 'RUSTON' COLLECTION

16 Alexandra Avenue
North Hykeham
LINCOLN
LN6 8NR
Tel: 01522 682406 (evenings and weekends)
Fax: 01522 512929

Contact: Mr Ray Hooley.

E-mail: rayhooley@gofornet.co.uk

A small collection of 16mm and 35mm films of Ruston & Hornsby (Engineers) of Lincoln and Grantham (oldest film dated 1908).

Video and film holdings: Film: Approximately 50 films on internal combustion engines and their various applications are held. 30% colour film, 70% black and white film, 10% nitrate film.

Film components: 16mm, 35mm, positive film, negative film.

Storage: Shelf storage – part of a more comprehensive collection of Ruston & Hornsby archive material.

Documentation: An archive collection, including trade catalogues, photographs, drawings, periodicals, books and artifacts.

Access: Access available. By arrangement.

Viewing and listening facilities: Viewing on premises. Viewing off premises.

Copyright: Copyright not held. Copyright advice available.

RED DRAGON FM

Atlantic Wharf
Cardiff Bay
CARDIFF
Wales
CF10 5DJ
Tel: 029 2066 2066
Fax: 029 2066 2060
Web: http://www.RedDragonfm.co.uk

Contact: Mr Andy Johnson, Programme Controller.

E-mail: mail@RedDragonfm.co.uk

The radio station holds first broadcasts and maintains a news archive for each year for the past 15 years.

REID KERR COLLEGE

Renfrew Road
PAISLEY
Renfrewshire
PA3 4DR
Tel: 0141 581 2222
Fax: 0141 581 2204

Contact: Mr Stephen Grant, Librarian.

E-mail: stephenjgrant@yahoo.co.uk

Video and film holdings: 1,200.

Journals holdings: 2 journals.

Printed catalogue: Annual update.

Computerised database: Yes.

Digitised collection: No. No plans to do so.

Access: 09.00–17.00 term time.

Access to researchers from outside: No.

Viewing and listening facilities: Televideo.

Charges: None.

REUTERS TELEVISION LIBRARY

c/o ITN Archive
Independent Television News Ltd
200 Gray's Inn Road
LONDON
WC1X 8XZ
Tel: 020 7430 4480
Fax: 020 7430 4453
Web: http://www.itnarchive.com

Contact: Mr Alwyn Lindsey, Sales Director.

E-mail: archive.sales@itn.co.uk

Reuters Television, the international news agency, provides a daily syndicated news service to more than 400 broadcasters in 84 countries. The agency is jointly owned by Reuters, NBC and the BBC. A network of cameramen, staff and stringers, numbering approximately 400, works for Reuters Television throughout the world. In addition, Reuters Television has access to all news material shot by its owner-organisations. Special arrangements also exist for acquiring news material from television organisations in Africa, Eastern and Western Europe, South America, China, Japan and elsewhere. All this material, together with that from other sources, ultimately finds its way into the Reuters Television Library. In addition to its own archives, the Library holds several newsreel libraries and special interest collections.

Video and film holdings: Video: 60,000,000 feet. The total footage, film and video, is 60,000,000 feet. News and current affairs.

Video components: VHS Video, Beta/Beta-SP, 1-inch Video, BVU.

Film components: 16mm, 35mm.

Storage: Most of the Reuters Television collection is stored in the library on roller shelving in an open plan area. An exception is the nitrate material in the early newsreel libraries. Much of this film is now on 1-inch videotape with VHS copies being made available for viewing purposes at the library. All the nitrate material was deposited at the National Film and Television Archive and the Imperial War Museum. All the newsreel acetate film has been kept at the Reuters Television Library.

Card catalogue: Available, indexed.

Cataloguing: Computerised database since 1992.

Documentation: Production and issue sheets, some accession books, video selected list and video roll file.

Conservation policy: Items serviced to subscribers are never junked. Other non-serviced items are selected for retention. Records of junked material are kept. Material may be rejected because of poor physical quality or because the library already holds the same story from another source.

Access: Access available. 09.00–17.30. Staff are available to assist.

Viewing and listening facilities: Viewing on premises. Duplicating.

Charges: Charges for research for broadcast productions. Charges for research for academic purposes. Charges for facilities and handling. Charges for other services. A price list is available upon request.

Copyright: Copyright of most material is held. Copyright advice available. Copyright adviser: Alwyn Lindsey.

RHODES HOUSE LIBRARY

South Parks Road
OXFORD
Oxfordshire
OX1 3RG
Tel: 01865 270911
Fax: 01865 270912

Contact: Ms Amanda Hill, Archivist.

E-mail: rhodes-house-library@bodley.ox.ac.uk

Video and film holdings: *c.*10.

Sound holdings: *c.*100.

Card catalogue: Card catalogue to manuscripts with more detailed handlists of particular collections as appropriate.

Digitised collection: No.

Access: Bodley Library reader's ticket required.

Access to researchers from outside: Yes, subject to reader's ticket being obtained.

Viewing and listening facilities: Limited; special arrangements would have to be made.

Charges: There may be a fee for issue of reader's ticket if not a registered member of Oxford University.

ROLLS-ROYCE PLC, IMAGE RESOURCE DEPARTMENT, FILM AND VIDEO ARCHIVE

Rolls-Royce
PO Box 31
DERBY
DE24 8BJ
Tel: 01332 242424
Fax: 01332 249936

Contact: Mr Malcolm Thomas.

E-mail: malcolm.j.thomas@rolls-royce.com

The Rolls-Royce Image Resource film archive covers the 90 years of the company's involvement in aero-engine manufacture and the airframes and airlines associated with it. These include both military and civil applications in airframes, aviation, ships and shipping, transport, technology, energy, engineering, education. Recent footage includes the Allison aero-engine of the USA. Other footage includes the Rolls-Royce Industrial Power Group with subject matter including Diesel Engines and Power Generation Systems.

Video and film holdings: Video: 6,000 reels/cassettes. Advertising, documentary, news and current affairs, science and education, heritage (1914–1997).

Video components: Hi-Band U-matic, lo-band U-matic, Beta/Beta-SP.

Storage: All Betacam-SP tapes are stored together on purpose-built storage at room temperature.

Cataloguing: Individual log sheets and a computerised search can be given out on request of subject matter. All footage is logged on to a database and searches for material are made easily.

Conservation policy: Video tapes and original films are never discarded and are always available.

Access: No access.

Viewing and listening facilities: Viewing off premises. Sales.

Charges: Charges for research for broadcast productions. Charges for research for academic purposes. Charges for facilities and handling. A price list is available upon request. All footage is supplied on Beta-SP. Search material is offered on VHS.

Copyright: Copyright held.

The RONALD GRANT ARCHIVE

The Cinema Museum
The Master's House, The Old Lambeth Workhouse
2 Dugard Way
Kennington
LONDON
SE11 4TH

Tel: 020 7840 2200
Fax: 020 7840 2299

Contact: Mr Ronald Grant. Mr Martin Humphries.

E-mail: ronald@cinemamuseum.org.uk

The collection was started by Mr Grant as a schoolboy in the 1940s collecting small rolls of 35mm film. The Archive has grown from this modest beginning to be of interest now at international level. The collection embraces the important and early material collected by the late Graham Head between 1918 and 1980, and original camera negatives 1899–1906 of Mitchell and Kenyons fiction films.

Video and film holdings: Film: 17,000,000 feet. General fact and fiction material from 1895. Early films from 'The Brighton School', including work of G A Smith, James Williamson, William Friese-Greene, Esme Collings, Mitchell and Kenyon films (including fake Boer War films). Large collection of aviation material. Cinema (and television) advertisements from 1920s to date, coming attraction day-titles and announcements. Over 1,000 feature film trailers; 6,000,000 feet of feature film from 1920s on. Advertising, feature films.
Film components: 35mm, positive film, fine grain print, combined negatives.

Storage: Acetate film stored here. Nitrate stored off the premises, allow 48 hours for retrieval.

Equipment holdings: There are a great many other items concerning cinemas – silent and sound projectors, slide lanterns and other equipment, staff uniforms, carpet samples, light fittings, ticket machines, etc.

Card catalogue: Available.

Cataloguing: Film stock cataloguing incomplete but ongoing on card index. Computerising.

Documentation: Over 1,000,000 film stills, portraits, colour transparencies, lobby cards and posters. Also programmes, synopses and campaign books, film fan and trade periodicals, film reports, scripts, etc. Reference library of over 2,500 books. Many trade periodicals, including a complete run of *The Cinema News and Property Gazette* 1912–1975. There are files of letters, photos and sound tapes concerning 'Brighton School' pioneers. Photographs of cinemas.

Conservation policy: Only terminally unstable nitrate is junked.

Access: Access available. By arrangement. Applications from students and serious researchers are encouraged, but as the film collection is only one element of the Archive's wide collection of cinema history, the Archive is not sympathetic to poorly researched 'trawling' enquiries.

Viewing and listening facilities: Viewing on premises.

Charges: Charges for research for broadcast productions. Charges may be made for research for academic purposes. A price list is available upon request.

Copyright: Copyright held only for some of the material. Copyright advice available. Copyright adviser: Martin Humphries.

ROSE BRUFORD COLLEGE

Lamorbey Park Campus
Burnt Oak Lane
SIDCUP
DA15 9DF
Tel: 020 8308 2626
Fax: 020 8308 0542

Contact: Mr John Collis, College Librarian, The Library.

E-mail: john@bruford.ac.uk

The Rose Bruford College Library video collection is made up mainly of off-air recordings. Its particular subject strengths are films and plays, arts documentaries, opera, musicals and dance, and programmes about writers/dramatists.

Video and film holdings: c.8,000 titles.

Books holdings: c.320 titles.

Journals holdings: *Film Review* 1991–94; *Monthly Film Bulletin;* 1972–91; *Screen* 1979–89; *Screen Education* 1979–82; *Sight & Sound* 1966–.

Printed catalogue: Yes.

Digitised collection: No.

Access: Prior permission by phone.

Access to researchers from outside: Yes.

Viewing and listening facilities: Two video rooms, one on each college site.

ROTHAMSTED FILMS

British Universities Film & Video Council
77 Wells Street
LONDON
W1T 3QJ
Tel: 020 7393 1500
Fax: 020 7393 1555
Web: http://www.bufvc.ac.uk

Contact: Mr Geoffrey O'Brien, Assistant Director.

A small collection of material shot mainly by Chris Doncaster at the Rothamsted Experimental Station and passed to the BUFVC. The earliest material dates from 1959.

Video and film holdings: Video: 2 hours. Science and education.

Video components: VHS Video, S-VHS Video, lo-band U-matic.

Film: 2 hours. 60% colour film, 40% black and white film. Science and education.

Film components: 16mm, positive film, negative film.

Storage: No special temperature control.

Cataloguing: Most of the shots were meticulously listed immediately after shooting with details of the aperture, exposure and lighting used. The quality of the shot is often indicated.

Access: Access available. By arrangement.

Viewing and listening facilities: Viewing on premises. Sales.

Charges: A price list is available upon request.

Copyright: Copyright held. Copyright advice available. Copyright adviser: Geoffrey O'Brien.

ROTHERHAM METROPOLITAN BOROUGH COUNCIL

Brian O'Malley Central Library
ROTHERHAM
S65 1JH
Tel: 01709 823616
Fax: 01709 823650

Contact: A P Munford, Archivist.

E-mail: archives@rotherham.gov.uk

Acquired in a haphazard manner over the years, the collection comprises twenty films. It includes newsreel items of local events, civic films and some amateur footage.

Video and film holdings: Video: 51 reels/cassettes. 25 video newsreels of Rotherham news c.1974. Video of debate between S Crowther, MP and Arthur Scargill, 1981. Video from BBC TV programme *Comic Roots* on Paul Shane. Number of community-made videos. Advertising, amateur, documentary, news and current affairs.

Video components: VHS Video, lo-band U-matic.

Film: 20 films are held. Amateur, documentary, news and current affairs.

Film components: 8mm, 16mm, 35mm, positive film, negative film.

Storage: In the muniments room, which is temperature and humidity controlled.

Cataloguing: No catalogue available.

Conservation policy: Permanent retention.

Access: Access available. Tue, Wed, Fri 10.00–17.00; Thu 13.00–19.00; Sat 09.30–13.00; 14.00–16.00. Access for disabled.

Viewing and listening facilities: Viewing on premises. Arrangements for viewing must be made in advance.

Charges: Charges for research for broadcast productions. Charges for research for academic purposes. Charges for facilities and handling.

Copyright: Copyright held for some of the material.

ROYAL AIR FORCE MUSEUM FILM COLLECTION

Hendon
LONDON
NW9 5LL
Tel: 020 8205 2266
Fax: 020 8200 1751
Web: http://www.rafmuseum.org.uk/index_collections .cfm

The Royal Air Force Museum was established in 1963 to collect, preserve and display all forms of material recording the history of the Royal Flying Corps, the Royal Navy Air Service, the Royal Air Force and aviation generally. The Museum is the only national museum concerned solely with aviation. The Royal Air Force Museum Film Collection was formally established in April 1974 although the Museum did have a small number of films prior to this date. Since 1988 the collection has formed part of the Visual Arts Department of the Museum.

Video and film holdings: Film: 5,000,000 feet. RAF Museum accessioned material covers aviation generally and the RAF in particular. The RAF Museum also looks after the RAF/PR Library film covering the period 1950–1978.

Storage: All the film material is stored at the Museum's premises in Hendon.

Cataloguing: At this stage only accession lists have been completed; few films have been shotlisted and none indexed. This is due to the rapid growth of the collection.

Documentation: In some cases there are cameraman's dope sheets, transcripts, shooting scripts, press clippings etc., but these mainly belong to the RAF/PR Library.

Access: Limited access. A limited service is available at the present time due to the shortage of staff and of viewing equipment. The museum has given help and assistance to researchers working privately or for film and television companies and the RAF. The Visual Arts Department anticipates an increase in its public services in the future.

ROYAL ANTHROPOLOGICAL INSTITUTE

50 Fitzroy Street
LONDON
W1T 5BT
Tel: 020 7387 0455
Fax: 020 7383 4235
Web: http://www.therai.org.uk

Contact: Ms Gail S Thakur, Film Officer.

E-mail: film@therai.org.uk

The RAI's film library was set up in 1971. The major part of the collection is contemporary (i.e. 1960 until present). Most of Granada Television's *Disappearing World* series is held. **Note:** *The RAI sponsors an Ethnographic Film Festival every two years, which is held at different hosting institutions each time.*

Video and film holdings: More than 300 titles in Film & Video Library. Over 100 titles in Video Sales Collection.

Masters holdings: Approx. 100 masters.

Stills holdings: RAI has a Photo Archive which is completely separate from Film and Video Collections.

Books holdings: RAI has a book library which is housed with British Museum (Museum of Mankind before recent changes) which is completely separate from Film and Video collections.

Printed catalogue: *RAI Film Catalogue Vols. I and II,* plus additional leaflet for new acquisitions.

Catalogue(s) available via the Internet: Video sales list and *Film & Video Library Catalogues* (restricted use to UK).

Digitised collection: No. Ongoing debate.

Access: Hiring and Sale of films and videos for non-commercial educational purposes only.

Access to researchers from outside: Yes.

Viewing and listening facilities: None.

Copyright: RAI own copyright in limited cases.

ROYAL BALLET VIDEO ARCHIVE

Royal Ballet Company
Royal Opera House
Covent Garden
LONDON
WC2E 9DD
Tel: 020 7240 1200
Fax: 020 7212 9121
Web: http://www.royalballet.org.uk

Contact: Mr Robert Jude, Company Manager.

E-mail: robert.jude@roh.org.uk

A collection of rehearsals on stage of the repertoire of the Royal Ballet. Since 1956 all productions have been recorded. Recordings between 1956 and 1970 were made on 16mm film, now lodged with the British Film Institute, but video copies remain in the collection. Small amounts of in-house non-broadcast recordings of interviews and master classes, educational resources material, etc.

Video and film holdings: Video: 1,000 hours. Recordings of rehearsals on stage.

Video components: VHS Video, hi-8, lo-band U-matic. Beta.

Storage: Master tapes stored in temperature-controlled environment, viewing copies stored and viewed in different locations where the Royal Ballet Company rehearse.

Printed catalogue: Available, indexed.

Cataloguing:

Conservation policy: To ensure that the past repertoire of the Royal Ballet Company is available for study by the next generation of dancers and to assist in the reconstruction of ballets in the future. Generally no master tapes are ever erased.

Access: Limited access. Presently very limited access. Access based on individual application.

Viewing and listening facilities: Viewing on premises.

Charges: Charges for research for broadcast productions. Postgraduate research students may have free access to research.

Copyright: Copyright held. Copyright advice available. Copyright adviser: Robert Jude.

ROYAL FOREST OF DEAN COLLEGE

Five Acres Campus
Berry Hill
COLEFORD
Gloucestershire
GL16 7JT
Tel: 01594 833416
Fax: 01594 837497
Web: http://www.rfdc.ac.uk

Contact: Miss S J Evans, Librarian, Learning Resources.

RFDC is a further education college and does not specialise in the moving image. It records or purchases items appropriate to its courses.

Video and film holdings: 400.

Masters holdings: 100.

Books holdings: 50–100.

Computerised database: Heritage.

Digitised collection: No.

Access: Phone first.

Access to researchers from outside: Yes, if for study.

Viewing and listening facilities: 2 televideos.

Charges: None. (Must be associate member or member of the Gloucestershire Learning Network.)

ROYAL GEOGRAPHICAL SOCIETY PICTURE LIBRARY

1 Kensington Gore
LONDON
SW7 2AR
Tel: 020 7591 3060
Fax: 020 7591 3061
Web: http://www.rgs.org/picturelibrary

Contact: Ms Joanna Scadden, Picture Library Manager.

E-mail: pictures@rgs.org

The RGS Picture Library covers people and landscapes from around the globe. Photographs and artwork from the 1830s onwards include a variety of subjects such as anthropology, landscapes (e.g. polar regions and deserts) colonial empire, climbing, indigenous peoples, and remote destinations. The focus of the collection is not the generic stock shot, but the portrayal of humankind's resilience, adaptability and mobility in remote places of the world. Artwork includes a range of sketches, watercolours, pastels, portraits and oil paintings by both amateur and established artists. And 'the largest private map collection in the world'.

Stills holdings: Over 500,000 images.

Card catalogue: Yes.

Access: Mon-Fri by appointment.

Access to researchers from outside: Yes.

Viewing and listening facilities: Limited.

ROYAL HIGHLAND FUSILIERS REGIMENTAL MUSEUM

RHQ RHF
518 Sauchiehall Street
GLASGOW
Scotland
G2 3LW
Tel: 0141 332 0961
Fax: 0141 353 1493
Web: http://www.rhf.org.uk

Contact: Major W Shaw, Curator.

E-mail: assregsec@rhf.org.uk

This is a collection of films and videos ranging from 1915 to the present day. It covers various aspects of regimental life including parades, royal visits, war and training. The films form part of a larger collection of regimental property held at Regimental Headquarters and in the Regimental Museum.

Video and film holdings: Video components: VHS Video.
Film: Newsreel and other material featuring the regiment. Shots in Scotland and in Germany. Titles include *Free French Leader in Scotland, The Prince with His Fusiliers, British Movietone News issue number 752* and *Repatriation of PoWs at Leith.*
Film components: 16mm.

Storage: Museum storage, no special environmental monitoring at present.

Printed catalogue: Available, indexed.

Cataloguing: The Scottish Film Archive holds a copy of a list of RHF films. The material is classified in line with other items in the Museum collection.

Access: Access available. By arrangement only. The collection is accessible to researchers, students, etc. All enquiries should be sent to Major W Shaw.

Viewing and listening facilities: Viewing on premises. There are no viewing facilities at the Regimental Headquarters. The Imperial War Museum has copied/is copying onto videotape the titles mentioned above.

Copyright: Copyright held.

ROYAL HOLLOWAY LIBRARY

University of London
Egham Hill
EGHAM
TW20 0EX
Tel: 01784 444065
Fax: 01784 477670
Web: http://www.lb.rhbnc.ac.uk

Contact: Mr Graham Firth, Liaison Librarian. David Ward, The Library.

E-mail: g.firth@rhbnc.ac.uk

Video and film holdings: 2,000+.

Music holdings: 5,000 LPs and CDs, unknown number relating to films.

Books holdings: Several thousand.

Theses holdings: Yes, PhD and M. Phil.

Datasets holdings: FIAF, WOS, PCI, MLA.

Journals holdings: 30+ titles currently subscribed to.

Newspapers holdings: On CD-ROM.

Digitised collection: No. No immediate plans.

Access: See Web pages.

Access to researchers from outside: Yes.

Viewing and listening facilities: In all libraries.

ROYAL INSTITUTION

21 Albemarle Street
LONDON
W1X 4BS
Tel: 020 7670 2924
Fax: 020 7629 3559
Web: http://www.ri.ac.uk

Contact: Dr Frank James, Keeper of Collections.

E-mail: fjames@ri.ac.uk

Most of the moving image collection relates to videos of lectures held at the Royal Institution. There are two main subsets. Friday Evening Discourses are mostly scientific lectures. These are produced in-house and commence about 1970. Before that there are audiotapes going back to the 1950s. Christmas Lectures for Children are entirely on scientific subjects. These were first produced in 1966. Mostly they were made by the BBC but a few were produced by InCA in the late 1980s and early 1990s. The RI holds tapes of about 90% of the series. In addition there are a small number of miscellaneous films and tapes relating to various activities of the Royal Institution. Videos based on the RI's Mathematics and Science Masterclasses are available for sale direct from Dr Roger Bray.

Video and film holdings: Approx. 1,000 videotapes.

Sound holdings: Approx. 1,000 audiotapes.

Stills holdings: Large collection relating to the RI Lectures.

Books holdings: Books of Christmas Lectures.

Manuscripts holdings: Some material relating to Christmas Lectures.

Ephemera holdings: Some leaflets.

Computerised database: Yes.

Catalogue(s) available via the Internet: No.

Digitised collection: No. Yes in the medium term.

Access: By appointment only.

Access to researchers from outside: Yes.

Viewing and listening facilities: Video player.

Charges: For reproduction.

Copyright: Holds copyright on most RI films and videos.

The ROYAL LONDON HOSPITAL ARCHIVES AND MUSEUM

The Royal London Hospital
Whitechapel
LONDON
E1 1BB
Tel: 020 7377 7608
Fax: 020 7377 7413

Contact: Mr Jonathan Evans, Archivist.

Film collections have been built up since the 1930s by the Royal London Hospital for public information, recruitment and educational purposes. The Archives and Museum has brought collections together and deposited originals at National Film and Television Archive since 1988. The medical film unit was begun *c.*1950 at the London Hospital and produced approximately 100 films about surgery and medicine up to the 1970s. Films also made by London Hospital Dental Film Unit and London Hospital School of Nursing. Queen Elizabeth Hospital for Children films (1930s+) also held. Various scientific films, (USA, France, Germany, 1930s–1970s).

Video and film holdings: Video: 30 reels/cassettes. 60% of the material is documentaries, 40% relates to science and education. Documentary, science and education.

Video components: VHS Video, lo-band U-matic.

Film: 250 films are held, 10% of which are documentaries and 90% science and education. 50% colour film, 50% black and white film. Documentary, science and education.

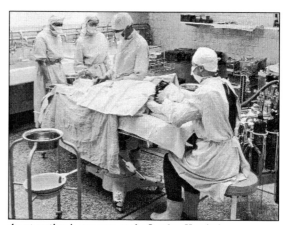

An operation in progress at the London Hospital, Whitechapel, c.1947 (photo courtesy of the Royal London Hospital Archives and Museum)

Storage: Storage of films is partly at the National Film and Television Archive and partly at the London Film Archive. Storage of videotape copies at The Royal London Hospital Archives and Museum, St Augustine with St Phillips Church, Newark Street, London E1 2AA where consultation is available on weekdays 10.00–16.00.

Card catalogue: Available.

Cataloguing: A printed catalogue is being prepared. The National Film and Television Archive has prepared viewing notes for numerous medical films transferred. The London Film Archive is preparing viewing notes for the 120 films transferred in February 2000. The Wellcome Trust Catalogue features details of some of the films held there in copy form.

Documentation: List of titles with brief details available from Royal London Hospital Archives.

Conservation policy: To transfer original film stock to National Film and Television Archive and London Film Archive for preservation.

Access: Access available. Mon-Fri 10.00–16.30. Staff are available to assist researchers. Access for disabled.

Viewing and listening facilities: Viewing on premises. Viewing off premises. Duplicating. Sales. Viewing off premises on payment of administration fee and on video only. Duplication of U-matic and VHS videos can be done on-site.

Charges: Charges for facilities and handling. A price list is available upon request.

Copyright: Copyright held. British Society for the Study of Orthodontic Films – copyright resides with the Hon Curator. Copyright advice available. Copyright adviser: Jonathan Evans.

ROYAL NATIONAL INSTITUTE FOR THE BLIND VOCATIONAL COLLEGE

RNIB
Radmoor Road
LOUGHBOROUGH
Leicestershire
LE11 3BS
Tel: 01509 611077
Fax: 01509 232013

Contact: Ms Susan Sutton, Learning Resource Centre Supervisor. Chris Michaelides, Technical and Information Services.

E-mail: lservice@rnib.org.uk

Sound holdings: Large collection of purchased audiotapes includes a number of RNIB productions.

Card catalogue: Each item card identified.

Computerised database: Access database (not Z39.50 compliant).

Websites relating to radio and moving images: RNIB HQ has a website at www.rnib.org.uk.

Digitised collection: No but RNIB has embarked on a digital access information system (DAISY).

Access: Opening hours: Mon-Fri, 09.00–17.00. Loan to members.

Access to researchers from outside: Yes, but for in-house use only.

Viewing and listening facilities: None. Portable television/video for classroom.

Charges: None.

Copyright: Copyright for transcription of texts sought on individual basis.

ROYAL NORTHERN COLLEGE OF MUSIC

124 Oxford Road
MANCHESTER
M13 9RD
Tel: 0161 907 5241
Fax: 0161 273 7611

Contact: Dr Rosemary Williamson, Librarian. Maureen Taylor.

E-mail: rosemary.williamson@rncm.ac.uk

The RNCM is a conservatoire which prepares gifted students of all backgrounds and nationalities for a professional career in music. The main emphasis is on preparation for a career in performance (including composition) but a balanced education in music is provided. The Library supports the teaching programme of the College and its collection of commercial videos and off-air recordings, which focuses on classical music, comprises the following: Operas – 71 off-air recordings, 42 commercial recordings; concerts/documentaries – 164 off-air recordings, 30 commercial recordings.

Video and film holdings: Approx. 300.

Card catalogue: Yes. By author, composer or performer.

Digitised collection: No.

Access: By appointment.

Access to researchers from outside: By appointment.

Viewing and listening facilities: 3 video/television players.

Charges: None.

The ROYAL PHOTOGRAPHIC SOCIETY

The Octagon
Milsom Street
BATH
BA1 1DN
Tel: 01225 462841
Fax: 01225 469880
Web: http://www.rps.org

Contact: Ms Claire Bertrand, Collection Manager.

E-mail: collection@collection.rps.org

The Photographic Collection, dating from 1827 to the present day, is one of the best in the world for 19th-century and early 20th-century photography, with an overwhelming emphasis on historical and technical development, art photography and aesthetics, pictorialism, cultural and social values and the evolution of photographic processes. It is unique in its breath, integration and great depth, where each part of it relates to each other part. The most important, best known, best researched and most seen collections are those of the major photographers, like Talbot, Hill & Adamson, Fenton, Cameron, Evans, and Coburn, and American Photo Secessionists such as Steichen, Stieglitz, White, Kasebier, etc., but there is an equal wealth of material amongst the lesser known items, such as early colour, large collections of hitherto unprinted glass negatives, albums, lantern slides, etc., which relate to and support the main bodies of work by putting them in context. There are also collections of more contemporary work by Karsh, Edward Weston, Albert Renger-Patzsch, Walter Poucher, Martin Parr and other present-day exhibitors.

Stills holdings: 250,000 prints.

Books holdings: 13,000 books. The Rare Book Collection comprises some 1,100 pre-1900 items, including foreign-language material. 2,000 pamphlets. 85 bound volumes of pamphlets, in English, French and German date from the 1850s and 1860s.

Manuscripts holdings: Fox Talbot Papers relating to the invention of photography, The Linked Ring Papers include several hundred letters, catalogues, notebooks and press cuttings relating to the period 1892–1910 of British secession photography. Hurter and Driffield Bequest papers on sensitometry. Walter Woodbury (inventor of the Woodburytype, used in 19th-century book illustration) Papers. There is an archive of approx. 5,000 letters to, from and about photographers.

Journals holdings: 120 current titles. 13,000 bound periodicals.

Newspapers holdings: The Linked Ring papers include press cuttings.

Equipment holdings: 6,000 cameras and other items of equipment.

Card catalogue: It is the RPS's increasing concern to catalogue, copy, make available, contextualise and explain what the Collection is all about.

Computerised database: The RPS has been awarded a Heritage Lottery Grant to document and catalogue part of its Photographic Collection on an electronic database.

Access: Membership is open to everyone with a real interest in photography. Gallery opening hours: Seven days a week, 09.30–17.30.

The ROYAL SOCIETY AUDIO-VISUAL ARCHIVE

6 Carlton House Terrace
LONDON
SW1Y 5AG
Tel: 020 7541 2605
Fax: 020 7930 2170
Web: http://www.royalsoc.ac.uk

Contact: Mrs Joanna M Corden, Archivist. Library and Information Service.

E-mail: joanna.corden@royalsoc.ac.uk

The Audio-visual Archive covers the period 1931 to the present and consists of audio-visual recordings by or about Fellows of the Royal Society. The bulk of the collection consists of audio material, in particular cassette recordings of the Society's named lectures which have been preserved in this manner since 1974. The remainder of the series has been acquired as supplementary material to the Personal Records, although there are a few items which predate those autobiographies. The series is arranged chronologically. Several items are dictabelts for which the Society has no suitable playback facilities. It is intended to reproduce these as standard cassettes.

Video and film holdings: 84 (Films – 6; videos – 29; television programmes – 36; records – 13).

Music holdings: One recording.

Sound holdings: 326.

Card catalogue: There is a handlist to the collection, updated as new lectures are recorded, and a small card catalogue appended to the General Card Catalogue which acts as an index to contributing Fellows and other scientists.

Computerised database: Yes.

Digitised collection: Not at present.

Access: By appointment during opening hours.

Access to researchers from outside: Yes. Open to all.

Viewing and listening facilities: By appointment.

Charges: Considered on individual basis.

Copyright: Copyright over own Royal Society material.

The ROYAL SOCIETY FOR THE PROTECTION OF BIRDS (RSPB) FILM LIBRARY

see *Moving Image Communications.*

ROYAL TELEVISION SOCIETY LIBRARY AND ARCHIVE

Holborn Hall
100 Gray's Inn Road
LONDON
WC1X 8AL
Web: http://www.rts.org.uk

Contact: Ms Clare Colvin, Archivist.

E-mail: info@rts.org.uk

Masters holdings: Of the RTS's events.

Music holdings: MSS of RTS events and early history of television.

Sound holdings: Items on RTS events and early history of television.

Stills holdings: 4,000 images.

Books holdings: 250 books and copies of RTS journals.

Manuscripts holdings: Sir Ambrose Fleming and John Logie Baird papers.

Journals holdings: *Royal Television Society Journal* and *Television.*

Newspapers holdings: Cuttings of the Society's events.

Computerised database: Yes, of the collection.

Digitised collection: No.

Access: Written application to the Archivist.

Access to researchers from outside: Yes.

The ROYAL VETERINARY COLLEGE HISTORICAL COLLECTIONS

Royal College Street
LONDON
NW1 0TU
Tel: 020 7468 5161
Web: http://www.rvc.ac.uk

Historical Collections.

Many reels of film of various sizes, unidentified and some damaged, are held in basement vault. Subjects include students' research trips to Africa, etc., and operations, veterinary procedures, etc.

Video and film holdings: 43 video; lots of film reels.

Masters holdings: Unknown.

Sound holdings: 8 cassettes; 1 reel.

Card catalogue: Handlists.

Computerised database: Microfilm reels 1–27 only, catalogued on Register of Preservation Microforms and on (RVC) Unicorn.

Digitised collection: No.

Access: By appointment only.

Viewing and listening facilities: None for archival cinefilm. VHS video machines and microfilm reader-printer in Library.

Copyright: Some RVC copyright.

RURAL HISTORY CENTRE, UNIVERSITY OF READING

University of Reading
Whiteknights
PO Box 229
READING
RG6 6AG
Tel: 0118 931 8668
Fax: 0118 975 1264
Web: http://www.ruralhistory.org

Contact: Dr J H Brown, Archivist. B Holden, Assistant Photo Librarian. Mr C Benson, Photographic Assistant.

E-mail: rhc@rdg.ac.uk

The Rural History Centre acts as the national information centre for rural and agriculture history. Film has been collected on a random basis, usually as part of larger archive collections. About half of the 1,000 original film reels are from the Ministry of Agriculture, the rest being primarily from agricultural engineering firms such as Ransomes, International Harvester and Ford New Holland. The earliest films are from the 1920s and show John Fowler ploughing engines at work, but the majority of material is from the post-1945 period. With the exception of the MAFF films, almost all items are listed, and catalogue records are available online for several collections. Particular subject strengths are tractors, harvesting machinery, dairying, agrochemicals and agricultural aviation. As well as advertisements, there are training films and general interest newsreels.

Video and film holdings: Video: 100 reels/cassettes. Information on the history of the countryside and its economic and social activities. Documentary.
Video components: VHS Video.
Film: Approximately 1,000 cans, chiefly technical subjects; government information and commercial production film; uncatalogued at present. Documentary.
Film components: 16mm, positive film, negative film.

197

Sound holdings: Small collection of oral history recordings. Sound recordings/some films on Library OLIB Catalogue.

Stills holdings: Photograph stills library of over one million items, documenting agricultural history and rural life since c.1850. The bulk of the collection is post-1914. Collected as part of total resources – books, archives, objects – of the Rural History Centre.

Card catalogue: Available, indexed.

Cataloguing: Card, handlist, some photographs are also on the online catalogue.

Conservation policy: To stabilise material, to store for as long as possible in containers, to copy fragile or degraded material. Fund-raising for new building.

Access: Access available. Mon-Fri 09.00–17.00, by appointment. Access for disabled.

Viewing and listening facilities: Steenbeck, VCR and audio facilities on site.

Charges: Charges for research for broadcast productions. Charges for facilities and handling. A price list is available upon request. Reprographic or other search and consultation fees.

Copyright: In most cases copyright is held by the Rural History Centre – or subject to a special agreement. Copyright advice available.

SAVE THE CHILDREN ARCHIVES

Mary Datchelor House
17 Grove Lane
Camberwell
LONDON
SE5 8RD
Tel: 020 7716 2269
Fax: 020 7708 2508
Web: http://www.savethechildren.org.uk

Contact: Ms Susan Sneddon, Archivist.

E-mail: s.sneddon@scfuk.org.uk

Save the Children has been using film as a resource for education and fundraising since 1921. In 1995 all the organisation's films were transferred to the National Film and Television Archive in London. No films have been produced since 1985.

Video and film holdings: Video: Copies of the above film holdings.
Video components: VHS Video.
Film: 16.5 hours. Films have mainly been produced for fund raising purposes. 56% colour film, 44% black and white film.
Film components: 16mm.

Storage: Films are stored at the National Film and Television Archive. Video cassettes are stored in Camberwell.

Printed catalogue: Available, indexed.

Computerised database: Available.

Cataloguing: Information about the holdings is also available on a localised 'Internet' type browser and may in future be available on the Internet.

Access: Access available by prior arrangement. Mon-Fri 10.00–17.30, Staff are available to assist.

Charges: There is a nominal cost for copying VHS cassettes.

Copyright: Copyright held.

SCIENCE FOOTAGE

Note: *This collection is now held by Film Images, q.v.*

SCOTTISH LIFE ARCHIVE – GORDON-MORE COLLECTION OF AGRICULTURAL FILMS

Royal Museum of Scotland
Chambers Street
EDINBURGH
EH1 1JF
Tel: 0131 225 7534 or Direct line: 0131 247 4076
Fax: 0131 2247 4312

Contact: Ms Dorothy Kidd. Elaine Edwards.

The collection comprises about 60 films made by the Edinburgh School of Architecture (c.1935–1950) which have all been copied onto U-matic and VHS tapes.

Video and film holdings: Video: All films have been copied onto video.
Video components: VHS Video, hi-band U-matic, lo-band U-matic.
Film: About 60 films.

Access: Access available. Mon-Fri, by appointment.

Viewing and listening facilities: Copies of films and videos can be purchased. A search fee may be charged.

Copyright: Copyright does not necessarily rest with this institution.

SCOTTISH SCREEN

249 West George Street
GLASGOW
Scotland
G2 4QE
Tel: 0141 302 1700/1730
Fax: 0141 302 1711
Web: http://www.scottishscreen.com

Contact: Ms Isabella Edgar, Information Officer. Information Department.

E-mail: info@scottishscreen.com

The Scottish Screen Information Service aims to provide for the information needs of organisations and individuals concerned with the moving image in Scotland. The Service is responsible for the annual publication of Scottish Screen Data and is currently developing the Scottish Screen website.

Video and film holdings: Lindsay Anderson VHS Collection – 2,100; EIFF VHS Collection – 700; Scottish Screen VHS Collection – 1006.

Stills holdings: Over 200 stills.

Books holdings: Over 1,000 books.

Manuscripts holdings: Shiach Script Library.

Journals holdings: Wide range of trade periodicals and trade directories taken. Runs of *Sight & Sound* and *Monthly Film Bulletin* from the 1930s.

Newspapers holdings: Daily newspaper cuttings.

Computerised database: Lindsay Anderson VHS Collection; EIFF VHS Donations; Scottish Screen VHS Collection; Scottish Films and Television Database; Newspaper Cuttings Database.

Catalogue(s) available via the Internet: For the future.

Websites relating to radio and moving images: http://www.scottishscreen.com

Digitised collection: Yes.

Access: Opening hours: Mon-Thu 10.00–17.00; Fri, 10.00–16.30.

Access to researchers from outside: Yes.

Viewing and listening facilities: Viewing rooms available.

Charges: For photocopying.

SCOTTISH SCREEN ARCHIVE

No. 1 Bowmont Gardens
GLASGOW
G12 9LR
Tel: 0141 337 7400
Fax: 0141 337 7413
Web: http://www.scottishscreen.com

Contact: Ms Annie Docherty, Admin and Enquiry Officer.

E-mail: archive@scottishscreen.com

The Scottish Screen Archive was established in November 1976. The film collection was inherited in part from its parent body, the Scottish Film Council, and has subsequently been enlarged through acquisitions from private and public sources in Scotland. The material dates from 1896 to the present day and concerns aspects of Scottish social, cultural and industrial history.

Video and film holdings: Video: Approx. 1,500 titles are available for viewing on videocassette. Gaelic language programmes: approx. 940 titles (1,530 hours) are available for viewing on videocassette.
Video components: S-VHS Video, hi-band U-matic, lo-band U-matic, Beta/Beta-SP, 1-inch Video, DigiBeta.
Film: 21,000 cans. Predominantly non-fiction material in excess of 20,000 cans, split 40/60 16mm to 35mm film. Also 8mm and 9.5mm amateur footage. Nitrate footage is transferred to safety stock as acquired. Within the collection, emphasis is on local cinema newsreels, advertising, industrial and promotional films, educational, documentary and amateur footage. Regional television news, documentary and some light entertainment programmes are held. Special collections include: *Upper Clyde Shipbuilders* 1926–71. Official records of launches and trials of vessels built by constituent companies. Films of Scotland. Documentary and sponsored film about Scotland in all aspects. 35mm prints, master and production material 1938–1982. Approximately 160 titles. *James S. Nairn.* Cinema manager. Local topical made for various cinemas, 1929–1959. 40% colour film, 60% black and white film. Advertising, amateur, documentary, news and current affairs, science and education, sports, promotional films.
Film components: 8mm, Super 8mm, 9.5mm, 16mm, 35mm, positive film, negative film, fine grain print, final mix, colour reversal.

Storage: Temperature and humidity controlled vaults for black and white and colour acetate masters. and for magnetic stocks. Storage: 2,500 square feet. Small nitrate store to rear of building used for temporary storage, pending duplication or disposal.

Stills holdings: Approx. 700 photographs relating to cinema buildings and film production in Scotland.

Manuscripts holdings: 50 special collections relating to film production, cinema exhibitors in Scotland, including the corporate papers of the Scottish Film Council 1934–1997, and the Films of Scotland Committee 1954–1982.

Card catalogue: Available, indexed.

Printed catalogue: Yes, and Films of Scotland monograph.

Computerised database: SSA records are held on a computer database.

Cataloguing: Films shotlisted, and database records containing the shotlist and technical information are filed by shotlist number. Personality, genre, location and subject indexes are compiled from the shotlists. Also series and production company indexes, and alphabetical titles and chronological indexes.

75% of total collection fully indexed, 20% partially catalogued by hand-list or summary listing (Aug. 2000). Anticipate 100% catalogued by 2002. Printed reference catalogue summarising 1,500 titles of general series (excluding television holdings) was published in 1995.

Special collections: *Films of Scotland Committee* 1938–1982: administrative and financial records, production files, scripts and stills, festival commendations and screenings. *Scottish Amateur Film Festival* 1933–1979: administrative records and festival programmes, including adjudicators' comments, press coverage, etc. *Edinburgh International Festival* 1947 to present day: programmes, press digests, etc. *Scottish Film Council* 1934–1975, 1990–1998: administrative and financial records, publications, including activities of various divisions of SFC, e.g. Scottish Central Film Library, Scottish Educational Film Association, Educational Films of Scotland. *James S Nairn:* cinema projectionist and manager. 1917–1974. Personal records of a lifetime in the industry, press cuttings, stills, souvenir programmes, oral history and memorabilia. *Donald Alexander Papers* 1935–1991, includes records relating to Data Film Unit, National Coal Board Film Unit and production files.

Documentation: Minimal documentation to complement small percentage of films, e.g. press cuttings, reviews, teaching notes, etc. Written archives, photographic and oral collections concerning cinema exhibition, film production and personal recollections of the trade in Scotland.

Publications available from the Scottish Screen Archive: *To Speak Its Pride – the work of the Films of Scotland Committee* 1938–1982, A Scottish Film Monograph by Jo Sherington, Scottish Film Archive. A historical account of the remit and achievement of Films of Scotland, including a comprehensive filmography, production company index, listing of unrealised projects and description of written sources.
Scottish Film Archive Catalogue, 1st edition. A reference catalogue of 3,000 non-fiction titles relating to Scottish life in the twentieth century.

Digitised collection: Selected elements of the collection are being digitised in extract form for the SCRAN (Scottish Cultural Resources Access Network) project. Text-based film records data are online at http://www.pads.ahds.ac.uk

Conservation policy: Relatively little footage is rejected. Anything totally unconnected with Scottish interests is offered to the Imperial War Museum or the National Film and Television Archive before junking, e.g.

newsreel material, feature films. The NFTVA has the option on preserving anything retained by the Scottish Screen Archive at its expense. Also informal contacts/exchanges with other specialist and regional film archives.

Access: Access available. Mon-Fri 09.00–12.30 and 14.00–17.00, by prior appointment, within the constraints of the preservation needs of the material and copyright considerations, for any bona fide academic, cultural or commercial purpose. The Archive offers a limited service to those producing programmes for commercial or broadcast use. Enquiries are welcomed and should be addressed to the Administrative & Enquiry Officer. Detailed conditions of access and relevant charges are available upon request. Selected titles are available by mail order on VHS; leaflet available.

Viewing and listening facilities: Viewing on premises. Viewing off premises. Some titles available as video viewing copies. Viewing copies are available for approximately 50% of the catalogued general collection. Viewings by appointment.

Charges: Charges for facilities and handling and usage for commercial purposes. A price list is available upon request.

Copyright: Copyright held by the Archive for specific collections, e.g. Films of Scotland 1938–1982, and for titles produced for Educational Films of Scotland and Scottish Educational Films Association. Otherwise, material is out of copyright or in active copyright to third party.

SCOTTISH TELEVISION FILM & VIDEOTAPE LIBRARY

Scottish TV
200 Renfield Street
GLASGOW
Scotland
G2 3PR
Tel: 0141 300 3000
Fax: 0141 300 3615
Web: http://www.scottishtv.co.uk

Contact: Ms Francesca Scott, Head of Library Sales.

E-mail: francesca.scott@smg.plc.uk

Scottish Television has held the ITV franchise for Central Scotland since 1957. The library is responsible for the storage and cataloguing of all programme output on film, videotape or videocassette and also maintains the company's advertising commercials library and acquired materials trafficking.

Video and film holdings: Video: 200,000 reels/cassettes.

Video components: VHS Video, hi-band U-matic, lo-band U-matic, Beta/Beta-SP, 1-inch Video, 2-inch Video, D2, DigiBeta.

Film: 4,000 cans. Transmission copies of all complete programmes. 90% colour film, 10% black and white film. Film components: 16mm, Super 16, 35mm, positive film, negative film, fine grain print, effects mix, final mix.

Storage: Air-conditioned temperature and humidity controlled storage area for film and videotape.

Card catalogue: Available, indexed.

Computerised database: Available.

Cataloguing: Bespoke computerised library information system allowing access via a variety of fixed fields or additionally via free-text retrieval using STRIX software. Camera original material is shotlisted in detail using time-code references.

Documentation: Printouts of shotlists from computerised database are available as part of our basic research facility.

Conservation policy: All complete programmes and selected camera original material retained.

Access: Limited access. By arrangement only. Access for disabled. Access to bona fide researchers only.

Viewing and listening facilities: Viewing on premises. Duplicating. Sales. 16mm and 35mm telecine and most video formats available. VHS standard conversion.

Charges: Charges for research for broadcast productions. Charges for research for academic purposes. Charges for facilities and handling. A price list is available upon request.

Copyright: Copyright held. Copyright advice available.

SELECT EFFECTS – STOX – THE MASTER SERIES – AEROSPACE

Arbory
Water Lane
Ospringe
FAVERSHAM
ME13 8TX
Tel: 01795 532228/9
Fax: 01795 530171

Contact: Ms Moira Maxwell.

E-mail: moiramaxwell@compuserve.com

The library comprises several collections. Select Effects is an animated and computer graphic library of over 14 hours of material. Stox is a predominantly British live-action library, including material from spiders in webs to industrial land fill sites. The Master Series has medical, scenery, aerial and wildlife titles. Aerospace is made up

of newsreel footage from Kennedy addressing Congress to NASA shots.

Video and film holdings: Video: Computer graphics, animations, animated graphics, live action and archive footage.

Video components: Beta/Beta-SP.

Printed catalogue: Available. Some collections indexed.

Viewing and listening facilities: Viewing off premises, VHS.

Charges: Charges for research for broadcast productions. Charges for facilities and handling. Charges for other services. A price list is available upon request.

Copyright: The copyright situation varies.

SHAKESPEARE CENTRE LIBRARY

The Shakespeare Birthplace Trust
Henley Street
STRATFORD-UPON-AVON
Warwickshire
CV37 6QW
Tel: 01789 201803
Fax: 01789 296083
Web: http://www.shakespeare.org.uk/library.htm

Contact: Dr Susan Brock, Senior Librarian.

The Shakespeare Birthplace Trust Library (founded 1862) and the Library of the Royal Shakespeare Theatre (founded 1880) were amalgamated in 1964. The Library is a research collection on Shakespeare's life, work and times, and on the stage history of his plays. Film and television materials have been added since the late 1970s. The Library purchases videos of Shakespeare films, television documentaries or productions relating to Shakespeare and to the Royal Shakespeare Company, as its budget allows. RSC archive includes production videos received on deposit since the 1980s.

Video and film holdings: Video: 1,505 reels/cassettes. The video archive grows at a rate of 30+ titles a year. Documentary, feature films, archive recordings of theatre performances.

Video components: VHS Video, hi-band U-matic.

Film: 20 cans. 20% colour film, 80% black and white film. Amateur, documentary, feature films.

Film components: 16mm, 35mm, positive film, negative film.

Storage: Custom-built basement audio-visual storage room temperature and humidity controlled, and air-conditioned.

Card catalogue: Available, indexed. (Videos are separately listed.)

Computerised database: Available, relating to RSC productions and personnel.

Cataloguing: Main catalogue was published on micro-fiche in 1990 as part 7 of *Shakespeare at Stratford-upon-Avon* (Emmet, 1990). RSC production database available for reference, and published by Greenwood as a supplement for 1978–90 to *Theatre at Stratford-upon-Avon: A Catalogue/Index,* by Michael Mullin (Greenwood 1978; supplement 1995).

Documentation: Press clippings of all Royal Shakespeare Company work including films and television productions are filed in the library's 'Theatre Records'. 'Theatre Records' published on microfiche for 1875–1975 as part 2 of *Shakespeare at Stratford-upon-Avon* (Emmet, 1990).

Access: Access available. Mon-Fri 10.00–17.00. Sat 09.30–12.30. Staff are available to assist. Access for disabled. Please telephone in advance.

Viewing and listening facilities: Viewing on premises. Viewing by arrangement in advance. RSC production videos may not be viewed by groups larger than six.

Charges: Staff time is not usually available to carry out research. No charge for literary use or viewing.

Copyright: Some copyright is held. Copyright advice available. Copyright adviser: Sylvia Morris.

SHAKESPEARE INSTITUTE LIBRARY

Information Services
University of Birmingham
Church Street
STRATFORD-UPON-AVON
Warwickshire
CV37 6HP
Tel: 01789 293384
Fax: 01789 292021
Web: http://www.is.bham.ac.uk/shakespeare

Contact: Mr James Shaw, Librarian.

E-mail: j.a.shaw@bham.ac.uk

The Shakespeare Institute Library aims to collect films and sound recordings relating to English Drama 1564–1642, particularly the works of William Shakespeare. Includes commercially available recordings and some recorded from television and radio.

Video and film holdings: 250 videos.

Music holdings: 100 CDs. 100 LPs. Film scripts.

Books holdings: *c.*1,000 (100,000 in total).

Theses holdings: *c.*30 (300 in total).

Journals holdings: Yes.

Newspapers holdings: 1964 to present.

Library OPACs with major holdings on moving image and radio: Yes.

Catalogue(s) available via the Internet: Yes.

Digitised collection: No.

Access: Limited opening hours.

Access to researchers from outside: Yes.

Viewing and listening facilities: 4 video recorders (PAL and NTSC).

Charges: None.

Copyright: For student productions recorded in videotape.

SHEFFIELD HALLAM UNIVERSITY

Learning Centre
Psalter Lane
SHEFFIELD
South Yorkshire
S11 8UZ
Tel: 0114 225 2721
Fax: 0114 225 2717
Web: http://www.shu.ac.uk/services/lc/people/psalter1.htm

Contact: Ms Claire Abson, Information Specialist, Learning Centre.

E-mail: c.abson@shu.ac.uk

The Learning Centre collection supports Sheffield Hallam University's undergraduate and postgraduate courses in film and media, which are primarily theoretical but also contain a production element. The collection also supports research in these areas within the University. It contains key reference books (e.g. *The Knowledge, Spotlight, AFI Catalog, BFI Handbook*) and the journals are a mixture of the popular (e.g. *Empire, Premiere*), critical (e.g. *Sight & Sound, Screen, Cahiers du Cinema*) and trade (e.g. *Variety, Broadcast*). A number of early journal titles (e.g. *The Bioscope, Kinematograph Weekly*) are also available on microfilm. Collection strengths include British cinema, biography, and broadcasting history and policy. There is a significant collection of approximately 200 items (including videocassettes of feature films) relating to Alfred Hitchcock.

Video and film holdings: *c.*8,000 videocassettes.

Masters holdings: Very small number.

Sound holdings: Very small number.

Books holdings: *c.*8,000 titles.

Manuscripts holdings: Archive of the IFVPA.

Theses holdings: *c.*20.

Datasets holdings: *Film Index International. International FilmArchive.* Access to SIFT, the BFI's film and television database.

Journals holdings: 27 titles.

Posters holdings: Small number of 1950s/1960s British film posters.

Computerised database: CD-ROMs.

Library OPACs with major holdings on moving image and radio: Yes.

Catalogue(s) available via the Internet: Yes (Z39.50 compliant). http:/opac.shu.ac.uk

Websites relating to radio and moving images: http://www.shu.ac.uk/srervices/lc/subjects/lcfilm1.html

Digitised collection: N/A.

Access: None. Mon-Thu, 08.45–21.00. Fri, 08.45–18.00. Sat, 10.00–17.00. Sun, 13.00–20.00. Reduced hours in vacations.

Access to researchers from outside: Yes, but visitors from outside the local area are advised to phone in advance (0114 225 2727) to check on the availability of specific materials.

Viewing and listening facilities: 140 reader spaces (16 for video viewing).

Charges: None.

Copyright: None.

SHEFFIELD LIBRARY AND INFORMATION SERVICES

Central Library
Surrey Street
SHEFFIELD
S1 1XZ
Tel: 0114 273 5067
Fax: 0114 273 5009

Contact: Mr D Hindmarch, Senior Local Studies Librarian.

E-mail: local.studies@dial.pipex.com

The Sheffield Libraries collection incorporates material held by the Local Studies Library, Sheffield Archives and the former South Yorkshire Record Office.

Video and film holdings: Video: 200 reels/cassettes. Videos including original productions, television programmes and film transfers.
Video components: VHS Video, hi-band U-matic, lo-band U-matic, Beta/Beta-SP.
Film: 500 cans. Items relating mainly to Sheffield, particularly the steel industry. No nitrate film. In 1961 all nitrate stock then held was transferred to the National Film and Television Archive. New nitrate acquisitions are offered to the national collections.

Film components: 9.5mm, 16mm, 35mm, positive film, negative film.

Storage: Film storage at Sheffield Archives. Temperature and humidity controlled with fire protection.

Cataloguing: No detailed shotlisting or indexing.

Documentation: Press cuttings, publicity brochures, stills etc. available for some films.

Conservation policy: No material will be discarded until there is an opportunity to make a full assessment.

Access: Access available. By arrangement. Access for disabled.

Viewing and listening facilities: Viewing on premises. Viewing off premises. Viewing on premises for VHS videos only.

Charges: Charges for facilities and handling. Prices by negotiation.

Copyright: Copyright held for some items. Copyright advice available. Copyright adviser: D Hindmarch.

SHELL FILM AND VIDEO UNIT

Shell International Ltd
Shell Centre
LONDON
SE1 7NA
Tel: 020 7934 3318
Fax: 020 7934 4918

Contact: Ms Jane Poynor, Archive Sales.

E-mail: jane.c.poynor@fi.shell.com

It contains almost all the films made by the Shell Film Unit since it was set up in 1934. It also contains copies of films made by and for Shell companies overseas, but these are not part of the main collection. Most of the films made during the war when the Shell Film Unit was working for the Ministry of Information are held by the Imperial War Museum. Since the collection is really only the work of the Shell Film and Video Unit it can only expand by taking in the new productions as they are made.

Video and film holdings: Video: 500 hours. Documentary, science and education, in-house productions not for general release.
Video components: VHS Video, hi-band U-matic, lo-band U-matic, Beta/Beta-SP, 1-inch Video, D2.
Film: 200 hours. 60% colour film, 40% black and white film. Documentary, science and education, in-house productions not for general release.
Film components: 16mm, 35mm, positive film, negative film, fine grain print, effects mix, final mix.

Storage: Purpose-built, temperature and humidity controlled vaults in sub-basement of Shell Centre. Videos only kept. All films material has been donated to the National Film and Television Archive.

Printed catalogue: Available, indexed.

Computerised database: Available.

Cataloguing: Computerised database for in-house use. Catalogue is only of current productions on release and is periodically updated – some titles added, some withdrawn. Some European operating companies issue their own catalogues.

Documentation: Post-production scripts of most of the films included are available.

Conservation policy: To keep most finished productions, and current rushes for unspecified time; then rushes are destroyed.

Access: Access available. Access for disabled. Disabled visitors have to be accompanied.

Viewing and listening facilities: No viewing facilities. VHS copies available on request.

Charges: Charges for research for broadcast productions. Charges for research for academic purposes. Charges for facilities and handling. Charges for other services. A price list is available upon request.

Copyright: Copyright held. Copyright advice available. Copyright adviser: Jane Poynor.

SKY NEWS LIBRARY

British Sky Broadcasting
6 Centaurs Business Park
Grant Way
ISLEWORTH
Middlesex
TW7 5QD
Tel: 020 7705 3132
Fax: 020 7705 3201
Web: http://www.sky.com/skynewslibsales

Contact: Mr Ben White, News Library Sales. Pauliina Porkka, Susannah Fritz.

E-mail: libsales@bskyb.com

Extensive coverage of world news and current affairs since 1989. Footage includes: the Gulf War, Balkans conflicts, South Africa, Russia and the British Royal Family, entertainment and showbiz. Detailed shotlists are available of all footage – both rushes and cut stories.

Storage: Everything stored on-site.

Computerised database: Computerised searchable database available.

Conservation policy: Material kept permanently.

Access: Access available. By appointment only. Access for disabled.

Viewing and listening facilities: Viewing on premises. Duplicating. Sales. Facility to cater for most broadcast formats. Viewing on premises by arrangement.

Charges: Charges for research for broadcast productions. Charges for research for academic purposes. Charges for facilities and handling. A price list is available upon request.

Copyright: Copyright advice available. Copyright advisers: Ben White, Pauliina Porkka and Susannah Fritz.

SOCIETY FOR CO-OPERATION IN RUSSIAN AND SOVIET STUDIES

320 Brixton Road
LONDON
SW9 6AB
Tel: 020 7274 2282
Fax: 0207274 3230

1934 film poster by I Bograd for the 1931 film 'Road to Life', directed by Nikolai Ekk (photo courtesy of the Society for Co-Operation in Russian and Soviet Studies)

Contact: Ms Jane Rosen.

Music holdings: Records, scores, 1,000 each; Russian and Soviet classical and folk music.

Stills holdings: 300 black and white stills of Soviet films. In total over 60,000 photographs, arts, crafts and realia cater for the picture researcher, set dresser, designer or student.

Books holdings: 500 books on Soviet films, including encyclopaedias, mainly in Russian.

Journals holdings: Some journals on Soviet film.

Newspapers holdings: Collection of cuttings, mainly English translations from Russian press.

Posters holdings: Posters and transparencies – film posters, political and historical.

Digitised collection: No.

Access: Mon-Fri, 10.00–13.00 and 14.00–18.00. Appointment necessary.

Access to researchers from outside: Yes.

Viewing and listening facilities: By appointment.

SOUTH EAST FILM & VIDEO ARCHIVE (SEFVA)

University of Brighton
Grand Parade
BRIGHTON
East Sussex
BN2 2JY
Tel: 01273 643213
Fax: 01273 643128
Web: Website to be launched in 2001.

Contact: Mr Frank Gray, Curator. Ine van Dooren, Archivist.

E-mail: sefva@bton.ac.uk

The South East Film & Video Archive (SEFVA), part of the University of Brighton, was established in 1992. The function of this regional archive is to locate, collect, preserve and promote films and videotapes made in the four counties of Kent, Surrey, East Sussex and West Sussex and the Unitary Authorities of Medway and Brighton & Hove. SEFVA is committed to the existence of a public collection of moving images for this region. The Archive is split between two sites. At the West Sussex Record Office in Chichester the master film material is inspected, catalogued and housed. At the University of Brighton the focus is on video production, website development, educational projects and research. The SEFVA collection now stands at over 2,000 items. This material has come from record offices, museums and private collections across the region. It includes newsreels, corporate documentaries, family and publicity material, features from the Progress Film Company in Shoreham (1919–1921), the work of the Bognor Regis Film Society in the 1930s and films by and on the Royal Sussex Regiment. The collection incorporates the material previously held by the Hastings Museum & Art Gallery and the West Sussex Record Office. SEFVA is very interested in forging partnerships with museums. It already has a special relationship with Hove Museum & Art Gallery in order to establish a museum-based collection on the film pioneers of the South East, in particular G A Smith and James Williamson. At the Elmbridge Museum at Weybridge, SEFVA is creating a Film Heritage Centre based on the work of Cecil Hepworth, R C Sherriff and local newsfilms. SEFVA is also interested in the many ways in which it can work with visual and performing artists on creative projects based on the Archive's collection. SEFVA is part of the Arts & Humanities Research Board's Centre for British Film & Television Studies.

Video and film holdings: Video: Video holdings are transfers from master film material held in the SEFVA collection.
Video components: VHS Video, S-VHS Video, hi-band U-matic, Beta/Beta-SPand DigiBeta.
Film: 2,000 cans. The collection comprises promotional and publicity films (20%), amateur footage (20%), documentaries (10%), short films and home cinema release (5%), news and current affairs (10%), educational films (5%), home movies and family films (30%). 30% colour film, 70% black and white film, 5% nitrate film.
Film components: 8mm, Super 8mm, 9.5mm, 16mm, 35mm, positive film, negative film.

Storage: Air-conditioned secure strong room.

Computerised database: Available.

Cataloguing: In development for an online use in museums, libraries, record offices and schools.

Conservation policy: Nitrate film housed at Wessex Film and Sound Archive. SEFVA is using Heritage Lottery Fund to produce new film negatives and prints from the master material.

Access: Limited access. By arrangement only. Access for disabled. Conservation Centre at the West Sussex Record Office: County Hall, Orchard Street, Chichester, West Sussex PO19 1RN, Tel: 01243 533911, Fax: 01243 533959.

Viewing and listening facilities: Viewing on premises.

Charges: Charges for research for broadcast productions. Charges for research for academic purposes. Charges for facilities and handling. A price list is available upon request.

Copyright: Copyright held in some cases. Copyright advice available.

SOUTH TYNESIDE COLLEGE

St George's Avenue
SOUTH SHIELDS
Tyne & Wear
NE34 6ET
Tel: 0191 427 3605
Fax: 0191 427 3643

Contact: Mrs P Robinson, Librarian. College Library.

E-mail: pam.robinson@stc.ac.uk

The Library has no particular strengths, mainly Shakespeare plays and films of classics.

Video and film holdings: 694 videos. 186 cassettes.

Journals holdings: *Sight & Sound* and *Empire.*

Computerised database: OPAC lists holdings.

Access: Mon-Fri, 08.45–20.00. No prior permission.

Access to researchers from outside: Anyone can use the Library for reference purposes.

Viewing and listening facilities: Video player in the Library.

Charges: None.

SOUTHAMPTON CITY ARCHIVES

Southampton City Archives Office
Southampton City Council
Civic Centre
SOUTHAMPTON
SO14 7LY
Tel: 023 8083 2251
Fax: 023 8083 2156

Contact: Mrs Sue Woolgar, Archives and Services Manager.

Collection of a few films which have been deposited in the City Archives Office (which deals primarily with written material) since 1954, by different depositors. There is no connection between them and there is no definite policy for collecting film material, but it is possible that additional items may be received occasionally.

Video and film holdings: Video components: VHS Video. Film: About 12 films deposited by own organisation and various depositors. The holdings include Pathé News items including the opening of the Municipal Building of the Civic Centre by the Duke of York 1932, the inauguration of the cheap airmail service by flying boat from Southampton to South Africa 1937 and miscellaneous events in Southampton 1936–39. *Southampton Gateway,* 1964. *Southampton Celebrates,* 1953 (covering events in Coronation Week). *Calling Blighty,* 1944 (Forces film with message from servicemen in India to families in Southampton area) *Inaugural Ball in the Guildhall,* 1937. *Beating the Bounds,* 1958. Film components: Positive Film.

Storage: All originals are now held by Wessex Film and Sound Archive, Hampshire Record Office, Sussex Street, Winchester – although we do hold a film print, video copies are held in a strong room.

Printed catalogue: Available.

Conservation policy: Through the Wessex Film and Sound Archive.

Access: Access available. By arrangement or via the Wessex Film and Sound Archive. Opening hours: Tue-Fri, 09.30–16.30 (one late evening per month by appointment).

Viewing and listening facilities: Arrangements for viewing film (after obtaining permission from the Record Office) should be made through the Wessex Film and Sound Archive. Videos can be seen at the Record Office, by arrangement.

Charges: Charges for other services. Use of copy film and copying.

Copyright: Some copyright is held. Copyright advice available. Copyright adviser: Mrs Woolgar.

SOUTHAMPTON INSTITUTE INTERNATIONAL ANIMATION RESEARCH ARCHIVE (SIIARA)

Research Office, Faculty of Media, Arts & Society
Southampton Institute
East Park Terrace
SOUTHAMPTON
SO14 0RF

Research Office, Faculty of Media, Arts & Society.

E-mail: eileen.watts@solent.ac.uk

Founded in 1996, SIIARA is not yet fully active. It will make available examples of animation from leading practitioners.

Video and film holdings: Video: 450 reels/cassettes. Documentary, feature films, science and education, short films, multi-part series.
Video components: VHS Video, hi-band U-matic, lo-band U-matic, Beta/Beta-SP, 1-inch Video, 2-inch Video.
Film: 3,000 cans. 95% colour film, 5% black and white film. Advertising, documentary, feature films, science and education, short films, multi-part series.
Film components: 8mm, Super 8mm, 16mm, 35mm, positive film, negative film, fine grain print, effects mix, final mix.

Storage: Plans are being made for newly-built storage facilities. At the moment film, and other materials are held in humidity controlled storage areas.

Cataloguing: No catalogues are yet available.

Documentation: Although varying from production to production, information held at SIIARA includes scripts, dope sheets, production letters, storyboards, press clippings and original promotional material.

Conservation policy: At this stage of the development of SIIARA nothing is discarded.

Access: Limited access. Consultative access only; fuller access will be made available in 1998.

Viewing and listening facilities: Viewing on premises.

Charges: Charges for research for broadcast productions. Charges for facilities and handling.

Copyright: Copyright not held.

SOUTHAMPTON INSTITUTE LIBRARY

East Park Terrace
SOUTHAMPTON
Hampshire
SO14 0YN
Tel: 023 8031 9248
Fax: 023 8031 9697
Web: http://www.solent.ac.uk

Contact: Mr John Moore, Head of Library. Helen Evans, Mountbatten Library.

E-mail: john.moore@solent.ac.uk

Video and film holdings: 9,000.

Music holdings: 10.

Sound holdings: 6.

Stills holdings: 200.

Books holdings: 4,000.

Manuscripts holdings: 20 (Ken Russell Collection).

Datasets holdings: *FIAF, Film Index International.*

Journals holdings: Approx. 100.

Computerised database: No (not of this particular collection).

Library OPACs with major holdings on moving image and radio: Yes.

Catalogue(s) available via the Internet: Yes.

Websites relating to radio and moving images: Yes.

Digitised collection: No. Possibly in the future.

Access: ERA membership of academic institution. Prior permission required.

Access to researchers from outside: Prior permission required.

Viewing and listening facilities: 24 monitors.

Charges: None.

Copyright: ERA licence held.

SOUTHERN CO-OPERATIVES LTD

44 High Street
FAREHAM
Hampshire
PO16 7BN
Tel: 01329 223000
Fax: 01329 223022

Contact: Mr Stephen McCloskey, Corporate Relations Department.

E-mail: link@southernco-op.co.uk

The collection is mainly made up of separate reels of 16mm black and white film (and a small quantity of early Agfa colour) produced during the period 1935–39. It is mainly concerned with recording the various commercial (retailing and productive) undertakings with which this Co-operative Society was then currently engaged. Apart from retailing operations there are short film sequences dealing with milk dairy processing; the bakery and a range of productive operations; building, coach building, sign writing; early motor transport, servicing, etc.

Huge crowds gathered for the Portsea Island Co-op's Radio Exhibition in 1935 (photo courtesy of Southern Co-operatives Ltd)

In addition there is some coverage of the social, recreational and leisure involvement with the Co-operative Membership as well as employee and staff welfare activities. Some interesting background material is recorded (city building, e.g. Portsmouth Guildhall – local parks and recreation areas) which were later damaged or destroyed as a result of enemy action during World War II.

Video and film holdings: Video: Much of the above material can now be borrowed on VHS video.
Film: The subject matter of this collection is mainly a record of the working of the Portsea Island Co-operative Society during the period 1935–1939. From film material provided, BBC South produced a short documentary film which was in one of the programmes in the series *Bioscope Days* in 1976. A copy of this film is held. Subsequently, a 16mm colour sound film was commissioned locally which showed how the Portsea Island Co-operative Society operated in 1977. The purpose was to compare and to contrast the present methods and activities (commercial and social/educational/recreational) in Royal Jubilee Year (some 40 years later) with those portrayed in the 1935–39 film.

Storage: *See Wessex Film Archive.*

Access: Access available. Access available to any reputable and recognised research body, educational/business organisation on the basis of free loan but payment of return postage/transport costs.

SOUTHWARK LOCAL STUDIES LIBRARY

211 Borough High Street
LONDON
SE1 1JA
Tel: 020 7403 3507
Fax: 020 7403 8633
Web: http://www.southwark.gov.uk

E-mail: local.studies.library@southwark.gov.uk

Inheritance from former Metropolitan Boroughs of Bermondsey, Southwark and Camberwell. Original material mostly held at the National Film and Television Archive; video copies are held at the Library. The collection comprises also copies from broadcasts, mainly news and documentaries regarding the area and copies of commercially produced videos on events, etc.

Video and film holdings: Video: 60 reels/cassettes. Feature films, news and current affairs.
Video components: VHS Video, Beta/Beta-SP.
Film: 16 cans. 100% black and white film. Feature films.
Film components: 16mm.

Cataloguing: A formal catalogue is incomplete. There is documentation in draft and note form. There is detailed synopsis of contents and copies of the National Film and Television Archive's catalogue cards for items deposited there.

Conservation policy: Stored in cool area. Access to originals under guidance: preventative rather than active.

Access: Access available. By arrangement only. Disabled access.

Viewing and listening facilities: Viewing on premises. Viewing by arrangement. Material can be duplicated at a bureau. There is a charge for copying material.

Copyright: Copyright held for all Authority produced material. Copyright advice available. Copyright adviser: the Librarian.

SPECTRUM INTERNATIONAL RADIO

International Radio Centre
204–206 Queenstown Road
Battersea
LONDON
SW8 3NR
Tel: 020 7627 4433
Fax: 020 7627 3409
Web: http://www.spectrum558am.co.uk

Contact: Mr Franco Baitwa, Production Manager.

E-mail: spectrum@apectrum558am.co.uk

Does not archive news items as it uses ITN. Rarely keeps interviews, e.g. with Jeffrey Archer, Michael Barrymore. Maintains a private music library of world music.

Computerised database: Maintains 8 weeks' back catalogue.

ST ANDREWS UNIVERSITY LIBRARY

North Street
ST ANDREWS
Fife
KY16 9TR
Tel: 01334 462281
Fax: 01334 462282

Contact: Ms J Young, Reference Staff.

E-mail: library@st-andrews.ac.uk

Journals holdings: 4 film/video titles currently purchased.

Library OPACs with major holdings on moving image and radio: Yes, but holdings are not major.

Catalogue(s) available via the Internet: Yes.

Websites relating to radio and moving images: No.

Access: No special restrictions when Library open.

Access to researchers from outside: Yes, if required.

Viewing and listening facilities: 3 VHS playback machines.

Charges: None in normal circumstances.

ST CATHARINE'S COLLEGE LIBRARY

CAMBRIDGE
CB2 1RL
Tel: 01223 338343
Fax: 01223 338340

Contact: Mrs S Griffiths, Assistant Librarian.

E-mail: sntg100@cam.ac.uk

The video collection comprises films of mainly foreign directors.

Video and film holdings: 90 videos.

Books holdings: c.40.

Computerised database: Collection listed on University of Cambridge union catalogue.

Digitised collection: No. No plans to do so.

Access: Current members of College only.

Access to researchers from outside: No.

Viewing and listening facilities: None. Undergraduates borrow VCR from JCR.

Charges: None.

ST GEORGE'S CHAPEL, WINDSOR CASTLE

St George's Chapel Archives
The Cloisters
Windsor Castle
WINDSOR
SL4 1NJ
Tel: 01753 865538
Fax: 01753 620165

Contact: Miss J Dicken, Archivist. Enid Davies, Assistant Archivist.

E-mail: archives@stgeorges-windsor.org

No collecting policy; donations or the result of special occasions.

Video and film holdings: Film: *Workings of Curfew Tower Clock*, 16mm c.1950; *London Cinema/TV News Service: The Quincentenary Exhibition*, 16mm, 1975. 100% black and white film.
Film components: 16mm.

Storage: In humidity controlled archive repository.

Cataloguing: Handwritten card catalogue, indexed.

Conservation policy: Conservation available if required.

Access: Access available. By arrangement only.

Viewing and listening facilities: Viewing off premises.

Charges: Charges for facilities and handling.

Copyright: Copyright held.

ST GEORGE'S HOSPITAL MEDICAL SCHOOL LIBRARY

AV Services
Hunter Wing
Cranmer Terrace
LONDON
SW17 0RE
Tel: 020 8725 3255
Fax: 020 8767 4696

Contact: Mrs Gillian Turner, Acquisitions Co-ordinator. AV Services.

E-mail: gturner@sghms.ac.uk

The reference collection covers medical, nursing and other health related subjects.

Video and film holdings: Over 540 off-air recordings. Commercially produced videos and media packs, as well as in-house productions, are also part of the collection.

Books holdings: Few books, as part of Staff Collection.

Journals holdings: *AV Librarian* 1990–1998.

Printed catalogue: Audio-visual subject list.

Computerised database: DB Textbooks in progress.

Library OPACs with major holdings on moving image and radio: Unicorn library system. Can be used to search for videos and other multimedia packs and CD-ROMs held in the Library.

Catalogue(s) available via the Internet: Webcat – Unicorn.

Websites relating to radio and moving images: http://www.sghms.ac.uk/depts/is/library/

Digitised collection: Yes.

Access: Opening hours: Term time: Mon-Fri, 08.00–22.00; Sat 09.00–17.00. Vacation: Mon-Fri, 09.00–21.00; Sat, closed.

Access to researchers from outside: The Service is free for members of the Library. Unauthorised users are not entitled to use the collection.

Viewing and listening facilities: 4 VHS machines in the Library Computer Resources Room.

Charges: None.

Copyright: Rights held for in-house productions made by the Audio-Visual Department of St George's Hospital Medical School. ERA and OU licences to record off-air.

STAFFORDSHIRE FILM ARCHIVE

Staffordshire University
Nelson Library
Beaconside
STAFFORD
ST18 0AD
Tel: 01785 353219
Fax: 01785 251058

Contact: Ms Sarah Glaccum. Ray Johnson, Coordinator Special Collections.

The collection began in 1980 as part of the documentary filmmaking activity of Ray Johnson, who had been incorporating industrial archive material in his films from 1973. Now housed at the Staffordshire University the Archive features Staffordshire industrial and social history. It comprises a collection of pottery-making archive film, the entire Rubery Owen Archive (including British racing motors 1950–64) and the entire British Commercial Vehicle Museum Archive (lorries and buses).

Video and film holdings: Video: 400 hours. Advertising, amateur, documentary, news and current affairs, science and education.
Video components: VHS Video, S-VHS Video, hi-band U-matic, lo-band U-matic, Beta/Beta-SP.
Film: 3,000 cans. Documentary films and archive compilations of the area made by Ray Johnson (1970 to present). Newsreels and documentaries of Stoke-on-Trent (1910–1934) from 35mm originals. Industrial 16mm promotional and documentary films made for specific pottery firms, notably Royal Doulton, Wedgwood, Spode, Twyfords and their subsidiary firms. 50% colour film, 50% black and white film, 5% nitrate film. Advertising, amateur, documentary, feature films, news and current affairs, science and education.
Film components: 8mm, Super 8mm, 9.5mm, 16mm, 35mm, positive film, negative film.

Storage: Temperature controlled basement store. Limited personnel access.

Printed catalogue: Available, indexed.

Cataloguing: A complete database should be available in 2002. Information can be supplied on individual items on request.

Documentation: References to pre-1930 material researched from microfilm of local press. Post-1930 research incorporates many personal interviews (on video).

Conservation policy: All material is being kept. Only badly degenerated nitrate stock has been junked to date; the rest is stored safely.

Access: Limited access. By arrangement. Staff are available to assist. Access for disabled.

Viewing and listening facilities: Viewing on premises. Duplicating. Access to Beta-SP and VHS edit suites and small duplicating bank.

Charges: Charges for research for broadcast productions. Charges for other services. There is a charge for telecine service.

Copyright: Copyright held for some of the material. Copyright advice available. Copyright adviser: Rod Pratt and Ray Johnson.

STAFFORDSHIRE UNIVERSITY

Thompson Library
College Road
STOKE-ON-TRENT
Staffordshire
ST4 2XS
Tel: 01782 294809
Fax: 01782 295799
Web: http://www.staffs.ac.uk/services

Contact: Ms Debbie Roberts, Senior Subject & Learning Support Librarian, Library and Learning Resources.

E-mail: d.e.roberts1@staffs.ac.uk

Video and film holdings: Approx. 3,000.

Music holdings: Not at present though the Library is in process of receiving the Favia Film Music Collection.

Books holdings: Approx. 4,000.

Datasets holdings: Only commercially produced CDs.

Journals holdings: Approx. 50 titles.

Catalogue(s) available via the Internet: Yes.

Digitised collection: No. Not in near future.

Access to researchers from outside: Yes, for reference only.

Viewing and listening facilities: Individual playback machines in Library.

STATES OF GUERNSEY FILM & SOUND ARCHIVE

Island Archives Service
29 Victoria Road
ST PETER PORT
Guernsey
Tel: 01481 724512
Fax: 01481 715814

Contact: Mr S A Lowe, Administrative Assistant.

Collection arising from: films of royal visits, etc., acquired from 1921; film deposits, 1915 onwards; films/ sound tapes prepared for the Education Department, 1970s; and the production of tapes (for sale) from collection of private films, 1930s onwards.

Video and film holdings: Video: 6 hours. 30+ video-tapes. Advertising, amateur, documentary.
Video components: VHS Video, Beta/Beta-SP.
Film: 6 hours. 90% black and white film. Advertising, amateur, documentary.
Film components: 35mm, positive film, negative film.

Storage: Cool area in main archive department.

Sound holdings: Sound Archives: Approx. 150 cassette tapes consisting of radio interviews, talks and lectures (historical and contemporary). Subjects include German occupation and wartime memoirs, the Liberation in May 1945, environmental issues, interviews with public figures, folk songs and tales.

Printed catalogue: Available.

Conservation policy: Re-making of old film (all nitrate film safely replaced).

Access: Access available. 09.30–16.30.

Viewing and listening facilities: Viewing on premises. Viewing off premises. Duplicating. Sales. Duplicating by special arrangement only.

Charges: Charges for research for broadcast productions. Charges for research for academic purposes. Charges for facilities and handling.

Copyright: Copyright held. No copyright held for Gaumont British.

STEVENSON COLLEGE

Bankhead Avenue
EDINBURGH
Lothian
EH11 4DE
Tel: 0131 535 4685
Fax: 0131 535 4666
Web: http://www.stevenson.ac.uk

Contact: Mr Alan MacCorquodale, Course Leader, Audio-visual Technology, TV & Film.

E-mail: a.mac@stevenson.ac.uk

Large college producing a continuous stream of student created moving image material, from drama to factual. College provides training in audio-visual technology, television operations and production and degree foundation film and television. The work is a microcosm of students' perceptions of life in its variegated forms as seen through the lens of student filmmakers. It ranges from documentary to location drama, from pop promos to sport. Many graduates work behind the camera in various capacities with BBC, ITV, Independents, and major film studios in the UK and abroad.

Video and film holdings: Yes.

Masters holdings: Showreels of student work plus individual pieces.

Music holdings: Continuous process of creation. MCPS member.

Sound holdings: Continuously created and disseminated.

Stills holdings: Photos, prints, transparencies, etc., from major Photographic Department.

Websites relating to radio and moving images: The College may put sample artefacts on site for moving and still images as appropriate.

Digitised collection: Will digitise as needed.

Access: College hours. By arrangement.

Access to researchers from outside: Yes.

Viewing and listening facilities: In-house.

Charges: By arrangement.

Copyright: College retains rights.

SUFFOLK RECORD OFFICE, BURY ST EDMUNDS BRANCH

77 Raingate Street
BURY ST EDMUNDS
IP33 2AR
Tel: 01284 352352
Fax: 01284 352355
Web: http://www.suffolkcc.gov.uk/libraries_and_heritage /sro

Contact: Mrs S Reed, Public Services Manager.

E-mail: bury.ro@suffolkcc.gov.uk

Cine-films deposited for preservation by private or institutional depositors. Future deposits, unless part of a larger archive, would probably be referred to the East Anglian Film Archive.

Video and film holdings: Film: 30 cans. Local interest material. Includes film of Cockfield Hall manor court leet 1955. 85% colour film, 15% black and white film. Amateur, documentary.
Film components: 8mm, 16mm, positive film, negative film.

Storage: Archive strong rooms.

Printed catalogue: Available.

Documentation: Manorial records of Cockfield Hall 19th-20th century.

Conservation policy: No conservation facility for film/video.

Access: Limited access. Access for disabled.

Viewing and listening facilities: No facilities for viewing.

Copyright: Copyright not held. Copyright advice available. Copyright adviser: Senior Archivist.

SUFFOLK RECORD OFFICE, IPSWICH BRANCH

Gatacre Road
IPSWICH
IP1 2LQ
Tel: 01473 584541
Fax: 01473 548533
Web: http://www.suffolkcc.gov.uk/libraries_and_heritage/sro

Contact: Mrs B Hanley, Public Service Manager.

E-mail: ipswich.ro@suffolkcc.gov.uk

Cine-films deposited for preservation by private or institutional depositors. Future deposits, unless part of a larger archive, would probably be referred to the East Anglian Film Archive.

Video and film holdings: Video: 2 reels/cassettes. Documentary.
Video components: VHS Video.
Film: 2 cans. Archives of Richard Garrett (Engineering) Ltd, Leiston – films of demonstration electric trolley buses 1928. 100% black and white film. Advertising.
Film components: 16mm, fine grain print.

Storage: Archive strong rooms.

Cataloguing: Typescript catalogues.

Documentation: Extensive archival records of electrical vehicles manufactured by Richard Garrett, Leiston.

Conservation policy: No conservation facility for film/video.

Access: Access available. By arrangement only. Access for disabled.

Viewing and listening facilities: No facilities for viewing.

Copyright: Copyright held for Garrett films only.

SUFFOLK RECORD OFFICE, LOWESTOFT BRANCH

Central Library
Clapham Road
LOWESTOFT
NR32 1DR

Tel: 01502 405357
Fax: 01502 405350
Web: http://www.suffolkcc.gov.uk/libraries_and_heritage/sro

Contact: Mrs L Clarke, Public Service Manager.

E-mail: lowestoft.ro@suffolkcc.gov.uk

Videos deposited for preservation by private or institutional depositors. Future deposits, unless part of a larger archive, would probably be referred to the East Anglian Film Archive.

Video and film holdings: Video: 3 hours. Two videos are held: *Eastern Coach Works, Serving the Community*, 1985; *Wrentham County Primary School, Fete*, 16 June 1984.
Video components: VHS Video.

Storage: Archive strong room.

Documentation: Archive of Eastern Coach Works, 1931–1986.

Conservation policy: No conservation facility for film/video.

Access: Limited access. Access for disabled.

Viewing and listening facilities: Viewing on premises. Viewing by prior appointment only.

Charges: A price list is available upon request. There is a charge for research conducted by own staff.

Copyright: Copyright not held. Copyright advice available. Copyright adviser: Senior Archivist.

SUNDERLAND CITY LIBRARY AND ARTS CENTRE

Fawcett Street
SUNDERLAND
Tyne and Wear
SR1 1RE
Tel: 0191 514 1235
Fax: 0191 514 8444
Web: http://www.sunderland.gov.uk

Contact: Mrs Jane F Hall, Head of Libraries, Arts and Information. Miss Vivienne Foster, Education and Community Services.

E-mail: jane.hall@edcom.sunderland.gov.uk

Books holdings: General collection relating to film, radio, television and new technologies.

Computerised database: Own in-house listings of items available.

Catalogue(s) available via the Internet: In process.

Websites relating to radio and moving images: None yet. In process.

SUNRISE RADIO

Sunrise House
Sunrise Road
SOUTHALL
Middlesex
UB2 4AU
Tel: 020 8574 6666
Fax: 020 8813 9800

Contact: Mr Ajmer Grewal, Production Manager.

E-mail: radio@sunriselondon.co.uk

Radio station. Holds 42 days' output to meet legal requirement. All commercials are archived. Maintains a large private collection of South Asian music.

SURF 107.2

PO Box 107
BRIGHTON
BN1 1QG
Tel: 01273 386107
Fax: 01273 273107
Web: http://www.surf107.co.uk

Contact: Mr Marcus Patrick, Programme Controller.

E-mail: info@surf107.co.uk

Radio station. Holds 42 days' output to meet legal requirement. Its news team keeps scripts for this period as well.

SURREY HISTORY CENTRE

130 Goldsworth Road
WOKING
Surrey
GU21 1ND
Tel: 01483 594594
Fax: 01483 594595

Contact: Dr D B Robinson, County Archivist.

Part of the Surrey Record Offices's collection of records and archives of all sorts relating to the County of Surrey. The first film was received *c.*1970, and the collection is ongoing. The office has no viewing facilities and therefore has to make special arrangements to identify film. There is a desire to see specialist facilities established and the office is participating in a project (led by Brighton University SE Arts) to establish a South East Film and Video Archive. **Note:** *All the Centre's films have now been transferred to the South East Film & Video Archive (q.v.), University of Brighton, BN2 2JY, Tel: 01273 643213. Contact: Frank Gray, Curator. The Centre has some video viewing copies but all enquiries should be directed to SEFVA which is responsible for administering copyright, etc.*

Video and film holdings: Video: Training films.
Video components: VHS Video.
Film: 49 cans. *Camp Schools,* a documentary film about the establishment of Camp Schools in 1939 and showing the facilities of Sheephatch School, Tilford, Farnham, probably 1950s. 15 films of Claygate Junior, later Middle School, 1968–75. Film and video used for the education of hearing-impaired pupils at Nutfield Priory School, 1960–70s. Thames TV film belonging to Mole Valley Conservative Association entitled *They Only Inherit.* Film of Imperial Airways HP42, Croydon Airport, *c.*1930s. 50% colour film, 50% black and white film. Advertising, amateur, documentary, business (vehicle tests), training.

Storage: In controlled archive store at constant 16°C (plus or minus 1°C) and relative humidity 54% (plus or minus 2%). Participating in current effort to establish South Eastern Film and Video Archive to improve storage facilities, especially for colour film.

Cataloguing: Typescript archive lists (generally including paper archive as well as film). Indexed by place in general archive index. Brief list of film holdings available.

Conservation policy: Effort to improve storage and to provide consultation copies.

Access: Limited access.

Viewing and listening facilities: Viewing off premises. Duplicating. No viewing facilities available at the Record Office. Special arrangements with South East Film and Video Archive by application to Surrey Record Office.

Charges: Charges for research for broadcast productions. Charges for research for academic purposes. Charges for facilities and handling. Charges for other services.

Copyright: Copyright not held. Copyright advice available. Copyright adviser: Michael Page.

SURVIVAL ANGLIA LTD

Anglia House
NORWICH
NR1 3JG
Tel: 01603 756923
Fax: 01603 765887
Web: http://www.surcat.com

Contact: Ms Margaret Bray, Library Manager.

E-mail: library@survival.co.uk

The Survival Unit has produced over 1,000 natural history documentaries for the ITV Network since 1961. The Library exists to service stock shot sales.

Video and film holdings: Video: 8,000 hours. Documentary.

Jaguar alert and watching intently, Amazonas, Brazil (Photo courtesy of Nick Gordon/Survival Anglia Ltd)

Video components: VHS Video, lo-band U-matic, DigiBeta master tapes.
Film: 14,000,000 feet. 100% colour film. Documentary.
Film components: 16mm, Super 16.

Storage: Material is housed in special temperature controlled storage at Norwich.

Computerised database: Available. All computerised.

Documentation: Shotlists detailing subject, camera shot, location and footage.

Conservation policy: All footage since its inception has been retained.

Access: Access available. 09.00–17.30. Staff are available to assist. Access for disabled.

Viewing and listening facilities: Viewing on premises. Viewing off premises by audition cassette.

Charges: Charges for research for broadcast productions. Charges for facilities and handling. A price list is available upon request.

Copyright: Copyright held.

SWANSEA CITY COUNCIL FILM ARCHIVE

see *West Glamorgan Archive Service*.

SWANSEA SOUND

PO Box 1170
Victoria Road
Gowerton
SWANSEA
Wales
SA4 3AB
Tel: 01792 511170
Fax: 01792 511171
Web: http://www.swanseasound.co.uk

Contact: Mr Andy Griffiths, Programme Director.

E-mail: info@swanseasound.co.uk

The radio station holds 42 days' output to meet legal requirement. Does not maintain an archive but holds a private music library.

TALK SPORT

18 Hatfields
Southwark
LONDON
SE1 8DG
Tel: 020 7959 7800
Fax: 020 7959 7804
Web: http://www.talksport.net

Contact: Mr Bill Ridley, Programme Director. Mr Jonathan Young, Creative Producer.

E-mail: s.woodward@talksport.co.uk (for general enquiries)

Formerly *Talk Radio*. The station holds 42 days' output to meet legal requirement. Retrieval of items within this period is possible. Recordings of major sports events, e.g. Euro 2000, are usually kept. Some *Talk Radio* recordings are held.

TATE GALLERY

Education Department
Tate Gallery
Millbank
LONDON
SW1 4RG
Tel: 020 7887 8000
Fax: 020 7887 8762
Web: http://www.tate.org.co.uk

Contact: Ms Deborah Robinson, Audio-visual and Film Manager.

E-mail: deborah.robinson@tate.org.uk

Collection began on an occasional basis from 1962, and then on a permanent basis from 1971.

Video and film holdings: Video: 300 reels/cassettes. Documentary.
Video components: VHS Video, hi-band U-matic, lo-band U-matic.
Film: The material includes film such as Arts Council films and artists working in film. 85% colour film, 15% black and white film. Documentary.
Film components: 8mm, 16mm, positive film.

Storage: Most material housed in room adjoining projection room – not temperature or humidity controlled. Small amount of material housed in vaults specially built for painting and sculpture, temperature and humidity controlled.

Printed catalogue: Available.

Cataloguing: A computerised database is under preparation.

Documentation: Advertising material and some press cuttings.

Access: Access available. Access for disabled. By written arrangement.

Viewing and listening facilities: Viewing on premises.

Charges: Charges for facilities and handling.

Copyright: Copyright not held.

TAY FM

6 North Isla Street
DUNDEE
Scotland
DD3 7JQ
Tel: 01382 200800
Fax: 01382 423252
Web: http://www.radiotay.co.uk

Contact: Mr Arthur Ballingall, Programme Director.

E-mail: tayfm@srh.co.uk

Radio station. A variety of programmes is kept from the last 20 years. In particular, programmes include interviews with local celebrities and community-based interviews and material. **Note:** *News items are not really archived.*

TCB RELEASING LTD

Note: *Changing economic circumstances have forced this specialist jazz library to close down. All films in the collection have been returned to the owners and original producers. Much of the material that was in the library is now available elsewhere.*

TEESSIDE ARCHIVES

Exchange House
6 Marton Road
MIDDLESBROUGH
TS1 1DB
Tel: 01642 248321

Contact: Mr David Tyrell, Archivist.

Formerly Cleveland Archives Department.

Video and film holdings: Video: 7 hours. Documentary, oral history interviews.
Video components: VHS Video.

Film: Four films are held. 1) Opening of Middlesbrough Transporter Bridge 1911, 60 ft. 2, 3, 4) Opening of Tees Bridge 1934, newsreel film, 969 ft. 100% black and white film.
Film components: 16mm, 35mm, positive film, negative film.

Storage: Archive storage rooms, temperature and humidity controlled and protected from fire by halon gas system.

Conservation policy: Material to be preserved indefinitely.

Access: Access available. Mon, Wed, Thu 09.00–17.00; Tue 09.00–21.00; Fri 09.00–16.30. Access for disabled. Wheelchair lift into building, and disabled toilets.

Viewing and listening facilities: Viewing off premises.

Copyright: Copyright not held.

THAMES VALLEY UNIVERSITY

Walpole House
18–22 Bond Street
Ealing
LONDON
W5 5AA
Tel: 020 8231 2648
Fax: 020 8231 2631
Web: http://www.tvu.ac.uk

Contact: Elizabeth Ward, Audio-visual Librarian. Learning Resource Centre.

E-mail: elizabeth.ward@tvu.ac.uk

The main collection supporting media-related pathways is located in the St Mary's Road Learning Resources Centre. It supports media arts and creative arts pathways, not just film and television. Subjects include broadcasting, cinema and film, communications, film industry, media studies, radio, television and video production. There is a large film collection on video, mainly off-air recordings, which covers all genres, independent and classic films and some foreign feature films. There is a growing collection of short films recorded off-air and some television programmes. There is a collection of about 60 radio programmes, particularly plays, comedies, and some illustrating the history of radio.

Video and film holdings: Approx. 2,000.

Music holdings: 20 film soundtracks on CD.

Sound holdings: Approx. 150.

Stills holdings: 674 transparencies (35mm), mainly film stills (within a collection of 45,000 slides).

Books holdings: 20,000 books.

Datasets holdings: *Film Index International, British Humanities Index* and more general databases.

Journals holdings: small number of relevant titles, approx. 6.

Library OPACs with major holdings on moving image and radio: Yes – not yet Z39.50 compliant.

Catalogue(s) available via the Internet: Yes.

Digitised collection: No. No plans to do so.

Access: No external access to slide collection, electronic databases (or PCs), or ERA licensed off-air recordings. External access for students is allowed via SCONUL scheme and UK Libraries Plus. Otherwise by written arrangement, but restricted.

Access to researchers from outside: M25 universities' academics.

Viewing and listening facilities: Video players and audio players in Learning Resources Centre at St Mary's Road site (teaching facilities available for TVU staff).

Charges: By arrangement with LRC Manager.

THOMAS COOK FILM ARCHIVES

PO Box 36
Thorpe Wood
PETERBOROUGH
PE3 6SB
Tel: 01733 502025/502024
Fax: 0I733 502022

Contact: Mr Paul Smith, Company Archivist. Ms Jill Lomer, Archives Administrator.

A series of 45 short films on a variety of travel destinations *c.*1948–70, made or used by Thomas Cook to promote holidays for the new mass market created by the 1938 Holidays With Pay Act. (Films available for research purposes only.)

Video and film holdings: Video: 31 cassettes. Documentary.
Video components: VHS Video, hi-band U-matic, Beta/Beta-SP.

Storage: Video storage cupboard and shelving.

Printed catalogue: Available, indexed.

Cataloguing: Catalogue published by Optomen Television. Time codes for each film.

Access: Access available. Mon-Fri 10.00–16.00, by arrangement only.

Viewing and listening facilities: Viewing on premises.

Copyright: Some films are Thomas Cook copyright; others are not.

THREE S FILMS LTD – ACTION SPORTS IMAGE LIBRARY

12 Regent Square
PENZANCE
TR18 4BG
Tel: 01736 367912
Fax: 01736 350957

Contact: Mr John Adams, Managing Director. Ian Jenkin, Assistant to Managing Director.

Archive and contemporary collection of surfing films on video. Action Sports Image Library originated in 16mm, 35mm and Beta. The Library holds also *Made in Cornwall*, a collection of films and programmes concerning Cornwall.

Video and film holdings: Video components: VHS Video, hi-8, hi-band U-matic, lo-band U-matic, Beta/Beta-SP, 1-inch Video.
Film components: 16mm, negative film.

Storage: Storage on site.

Printed catalogue: Available, indexed.

Computerised database: Available.

Documentation: Time-coded shotlists.

Access: Access available. Mon-Fri 10.00–17.00.

Viewing and listening facilities: Viewing on premises. Viewing off premises. Duplicating. Sales. BITC, VHS and U-matic facilities.

Charges: Charges for research for broadcast productions. Charges for research for academic purposes. Charges for facilities and handling. A price list is available upon request.

Copyright: Copyright held. Copyright advice available.

TIBET FOUNDATION

1St James Market
LONDON
SW1Y 4SB
Tel: 020 7930 6001
Fax: 020 7930 6002
Web: http://www.tibet-foundation.org

Contact: Mr Phuntsog Wangyal, Director.

E-mail: getca@tibet-foundation.org

The Tibet Foundation holds video material relating to Tibetan Buddhist teachings and Tibetan cultural programmes.

Video and film holdings: Video: Tibetan Buddhist teachings and culture.
Video components: VHS Video, hi-8.

Storage: Storage at Tibet Foundation.

Cataloguing: Printed sheet.

Access: Access available. By arrangement.

Charges: A price list is available upon request.

Copyright: Copyright held. Copyright advice available. Copyright adviser: Tibet Foundation.

TOWER FM

The Mill
Brownlow Way
BOLTON
Greater Manchester
BL1 2RA
Tel: 01204 387000
Fax: 01204 534065
Web: http://www.towerfm.co.uk

Contact: Mr Barry Machin, Programme Director.

E-mail: info@towerfm.co.uk

The radio station holds 42 days' output to meet legal requirement.

TOWER HAMLETS LOCAL HISTORY LIBRARY AND ARCHIVES

Bancroft Library
277 Bancroft Road
LONDON
E1 4DQ
Tel: 020 8980 4366 ext 129
Fax: 020 8983 4510

Contact: Mr Chris Lloyd, Local History Librarian.

Library formed by amalgamating the local history collections of three former metropolitan boroughs of Bethnal Green, Poplar and Stepney in 1965. Some films of local interest in the Poplar and Stepney collections have been added to in recent years with films mostly copied from those in the National Film and Television Archive.

Video and film holdings: Video: 90 reels/cassettes, 100 hours. Amateur, documentary, feature films, news and current affairs.
Video components: VHS Video.
Film: 5 hours. The collection consists of documentary and newsreel films about Tower Hamlets. 100% black and white film. Documentary, news and current affairs.
Film components: Super 8mm, 16mm, positive film.

Storage: No special facilities.

Card catalogue: Available, indexed.

Conservation policy: All items are permanently preserved.

Access: Access available. Tue, Thu, 09.00–20.00. Fri 09.00–18.00. Sat 09.00–17.00. Access for disabled. There is a ramp to the front door of the building and a lift.

Viewing and listening facilities: Viewing on premises. Appointments required.

Copyright: Copyright not held.

TRADES UNION CONGRESS LIBRARY COLLECTIONS

University of North London Learning Centre
236 Holloway Road
LONDON
N7 6PP
Tel: 020 7753 3184
Fax: 020 7753 3191
Web: http://www.unl.ac.uk/library/tuc

Contact: Ms Christine Coates.

E-mail: c.coates@unl.ac.uk

The TUC Library Collection was transferred to the University of North London in 1996. The collection was first established in 1922 for the use of the TUC and affiliated unions, but its specialisation led to its parallel development as a major research library in the social sciences. The library holds material collected by the TUC up to the end of 1995. although later material will continue to be deposited on an annual basis. The core areas of the collection are reference and historical works on the trade union movement, union publications from the UK and overseas, documents relating to working conditions and industrial relations in various industries, and material collected from the various campaigns and policy areas in which the TUC has been involved since its foundation in 1868. Major strengths of the Library are the large holdings of pamphlets and other ephemera from unions, pressure groups and campaign movements which have survived here as in few other comparable libraries. The majority of this material dates from the 1920s onwards, although some earlier pamphlets date back to the 19th century.

Video and film holdings: TUC video collection.

Books holdings: Relevant material includes publications of media and entertainment unions and related organisations.

Manuscripts holdings: Workers Film Association records.

Journals holdings: Trades unions material.

Newspapers holdings: Trades unions material.

Ephemera holdings: Large holdings of ephemera.

Card catalogue: The video collection, recently

deposited by the TUC, is not yet catalogued or fully operational.

Access: Mon-Fri, 09.15–16.45. Access for all users is by appointment only. Normally, academic users must be at postgraduate level but undergraduates may use the collection with the written authorisation of their supervisor.

Access to researchers from outside: Yes. TUC staff and other trade union staff and officials will be given access, as will external users who are pursuing research interests which cannot be met elsewhere. The collections are available for reference only.

TRAINING SERVICES

Brooklands House
29 Hythegate
Werrington
PETERBOROUGH
PE4 7ZP
Tel: 01733 327337
Fax: 01733 575537
Web: http://www.trainingservices.demon.co.uk

Contact: Ms Christine Tipton, Proprietor.

E-mail: tipton@trainingservices.demon.co.uk

Library of approximately 100 titles on management, health and safety training video packages.

Video and film holdings: Video: 100 reels/cassettes, 4,500 hours. Management training, health and safety training.
Video components: VHS Video, hi-band U-matic, lo-band U-matic, Beta/Beta-SP.

Storage: Masters stored in safe at duplicators. Rest stored in warehouse.

Printed catalogue: Available, indexed.

Documentation: Individual sheets available on various subjects. Small catalogue available on equal opportunities.

Access: Access available. 09.00–17.00.

Viewing and listening facilities: Viewing on premises.

Copyright: Copyright held.

TREADWELL LTD

Euston House
21 Soulbury Road
Linslade
LEIGHTON BUZZARD
LU7 7RL
Tel: 01525 852242
Fax: 01525 851002

Contact: Ms Lin McConnell, Sales Director.

A continually expanding library of materials (1890s to 1990s), including a number of private collections. Wide range of subjects. Represented materials include collections from the United Kingdom, Russia, Germany and North America. Offices in Paris and Moscow.

Video and film holdings: Video: 2,000 hours. Documentary, news and current affairs, science and education, travelogues.
Video components: VHS Video, hi-band U-matic, lo-band U-matic, Beta/Beta-SP, 1-inch Video, 2-inch Video, M2.
Film: 75,000 feet, 640 cans. Amateur, documentary.
Film components: 8mm, Super 8mm, 16mm, 35mm.

Computerised database: Available.

Cataloguing: Claris Filemaker Pro Software – PC and Mac formats.

Conservation policy: According to commercial requirements.

Access: Access available. 09.00–18.00, by arrangement. Staff are available to assist. Access for disabled.

Viewing and listening facilities: Viewing on premises. Viewing off premises. Duplicating. Sales. Subject to copyright restrictions.

Charges: Charges for research for broadcast productions. Charges for research for academic purposes. Charges for facilities and handling. A price list is available upon request.

Copyright: Copyright held. Representatives of copyright holders. Copyright advice available. Copyright adviser: Lin McConnell.

TRILITH RURAL VIDEO UNIT

Corner Cottage
Brickyard Lane
Bourton
GILLINGHAM
Dorset
SP8 5PJ
Tel: 01747 840750/840727

Contact: Mr John Holman, Joint Director. Mr Trevor Bailey.

E-mail: johnholman@hopstep.demon.co.uk

Trilith is a media charity, based in Bourton, Dorset. As part of its general activities, which include video, television and radio production and community media training, Trilith has gathered an extensive collection of moving images, mainly of Dorset but also from Wiltshire, dating from 1905 to the present day, including both amateur and professional work. In partnership with the county record offices in Wiltshire and Dorset, Trilith actively seeks archive film material and arranges for storage and preservation with the above partners where appropriate. Trilith's main aim is to put these images back into circulation and, to this end, it works on high quality video copies to assemble locally targeted programmes for public showings in the communities of Wiltshire and Dorset which also feature an increasing amount of newly-shot material providing a context for the archive material. There is also a steadily growing amount of audio material which is being produced by the various community radio production projects run by Trilith. This mainly consists of short, documentary type material but also includes some original short drama.

Masters holdings: Masters of Trilith's own productions held. No film originals held.

Sound holdings: Short radio documentaries and drama, from various Trilith community radio projects.

Digitised collection: Audio material digitised, but not moving images.

Access: By prior arrangement.

Viewing and listening facilities: At Trilith's Rural Media Centre, Gillingham, Dorset.

Charges: Search fees and costs of provision of viewing copies charged.

Copyright: Most of the copyrights reside with the original film owners.

The TSW FILM AND TELEVISION ARCHIVE FOR THE SOUTH WEST

Melville Building
Royal William Yard
Stonehouse
PLYMOUTH
Devon
PL1 3RP
Tel: 01752 202650
Fax: 01752 205025

Contact: Ms Elayne Hoskin, Director. Mike Brewis.

E-mail: elayne@tswfta.co.uk

The core collections are the TSW Film and Video Library, which includes all Channel 3 material for the area from 1961 to 1992 and the BBC South West Film Collection, dating from 1961 onward. In addition to the core collection, the Archive has acquired and continues to acquire a large number of non-broadcast collections. The Archive also holds other materials.

Video and film holdings: Video: The holdings comprise advertising (5%), documentary (30%), news and

current affairs (50%) and science and education (15%). Advertising, documentary, news and current affairs, science and education.

Video components: VHS Video, S-VHS Video, 8mm Video, hi-8, hi-band U-matic, lo-band U-matic, Beta/Beta-SP, 1-inch Video, 2-inch Video.

Film: The holdings comprise documentary (40%), news and current affairs (50%) and science and education (10%). 65% colour film, 35% black and white film. Documentary, news and current affairs, science and education.

Film components: 16mm, 35mm, positive film, negative film, fine grain print.

Storage: Fixed racking systems.

Card catalogue: Available, indexed.

Computerised database: Available.

Cataloguing: There is a continuing programme of transfer of all card/manual index to computer. Material from 1976–1984 is currently being reviewed and indexed. 1961–1976 is card indexed. 1984–1992 is computer indexed.

Documentation: Programme information files held including issue sheets, dope sheets, transcripts, shooting scripts, press clippings, contracts etc. Files are still being catalogued.

Conservation policy: As per National Film and Television Archive guidelines.

Access: Access available. By arrangement only. Staff are available to assist. Access for disabled.

Viewing and listening facilities: Viewing on premises. Viewing off premises. Duplicating. Sales. Duplicating facilities from/to most formats.

Charges: Charges for research for broadcast productions. Charges for facilities and handling. Charges for other services. A price list is available upon request. Two tier pricing, price list available.

Copyright: The TSW collection is owned by the Archive. Clearances, etc. provided: some third-party interests to be taken into account. Copyright advice available. Copyright adviser: Elayne Hoskin.

TUA FILM COLLECTION

17 Kingsway
LEICESTER
LE3 2JL
Tel: 0116 289 0531
Fax: 0116 289 0531

Contact: Mr Rob Foxon, Owner.

The TUA Film Collection was established in the 1970s to support Rob Foxon's archive *Railway* film shows. It has subsequently developed to encompass other forms of transport (road, aircraft, shipping, etc.) and British history and forms a useful resource for researchers seeking specialised documentary footage. The collection dates from 1895 to the present day and forms the source material for Rob's nationwide *Railways Remembered* and *Bygone Britain* archive film shows. The local history collection is now formed into the *Leicestershire Film Archive* (see separate entry). The specialised 16mm *Railway* collection is probably one of the finest in the UK and covers all aspects of British and world railway operations. It includes pioneer footage from the birth of the cinema, melodrama, publicity, documentary and instructional films, together with footage of amateur shot railway film records. The British history collection includes many scarce travelogue and instructional titles.

Video and film holdings: Film: 1,000 cans. 60% black and white, 40% colour film, film. Amateur and professional, documentary, news and current affairs, science and technology.

Film components: 8mm, 9.5mm, 16mm, 35mm, positive and negative material.

Storage: Special room in purpose-built accommodation.

Card catalogue: Available.

Printed catalogue: No printed catalogue at present.

Computerised database: Partly computerised database.

Conservation policy: Viewing prints made from preservation masters. Repatriation of non-core material to other archives with owners' consent. No usable material is junked.

Access: Public film shows via touring *Railways Remembered* and *Bygone Britain* archive film shows. Film shows

are also presented to institutions, groups and societies by invitation and to schools and colleges. The Archive has also produced a small number of videos of local interest. Footage can be made available for film, video and television use, subject to copyright clearance.

Viewing and listening facilities: Normally VHS viewing copy by arrangement.

Charges: Archive search fee. Charges for VHS copies, broadcasting and production. Enquire for current rates. The Archive is self-financing and all income from charges and film shows is used in the restoration and preservation of material held.

Copyright: Some copyright held. Copyright advice available. Copyright adviser: Rob Foxon.

TWI ARCHIVE

Axis Centre
Burlington Lane
LONDON
W4 2TH
Tel: 020 8233 5500
Fax: 020 8233 5301
Web: http://www.twiarchive.com (launching March 2001)

Contact: Mr Togo Keynes, Commercial Director.

E-mail: twiarchive@imgworld.com

Extensive experience in archive management, acquisitions and commercial exploitation of the rights to many of the world's most prestigious sporting events. The collection includes major sporting federations and an array of non-sporting footage and stockshots. These include Rugby World Cup, ITF, AELTC (Wimbledon), The Nobel Foundation, The PGA European Tour, the Ruppersberg Collection of American History and many more.

TYNE AND WEAR ARCHIVES SERVICE

see *Northern Region Film & Television Archive.*

TYNE TEES TELEVISION/CHANNEL 3 NORTH EAST

see *Granada Media Clip Sales – Tyne Tees Television/Channel 3 North East.*

ULSTER FOLK AND TRANSPORT MUSEUM

National Museums and Galleries of Northern Ireland
Cultra
HOLYWOOD
County Down
Northern Ireland
BT18 0EU

Replica of Stevenson's 'Rocket' made for Henry Ford, outside the Robert Stevenson works in Darlington, 1929 (photo courtesy of the TUA Film Collection)

Tel: 02890 428428
Fax: 02890 428728

Contact: Mr Clifford Harkness. Ken Anderson.

Founded in 1958, the Museum holds a sizable audio-visual archive which includes film and videotape material. Material from BBC Northern Ireland is also held in the collection. Northern Ireland's new Digital Film Archive (*see note below*) includes newsreel footage of the Belfast-built *Titanic*, World Wars I and II, aviatrix Amelia Earhart's accidental landing at Derry in the 1930s, and the reconstruction years of the 1950s. Television footage includes the Beatles interviewed on UTV in the early 1960s, documentaries, television news, drama and feature films. The Digital Film Archive is available free of charge on PCs to six educational centres around Northern Ireland – St Patrick's Trian in Armagh, Omagh College, the University of Ulster at Coleraine, the Nerve Centre in Londonderry, W5 at the Odyssey in Belfast and at the Ulster Folk and Transport Museum.

Video and film holdings: Video components: VHS Video, hi-band U-matic, lo-band U-matic, 1-inch Video, 2-inch Video.
Film: The subject matter of the collections covers all aspects of everyday life in the Province.
Film components: Positive Film, negative film, final mix.

Storage: Magnetic materials are held in an environmentally controlled store, e.g. 16°C plus or minus 1 1/2%; 50% relative humidity plus or minus 5%. Film is held in a non-controlled area.

Cataloguing: Various retrieval techniques. All material is classified under a museum system.

Digitised collection: Northern Ireland's first Digital Film Archive was launched at the Ulster Folk and Transport Museum in November 2000. This gives the public access to over 50 hours of moving images reflecting the history and culture of Northern Ireland from 1897 to 2000.

Conservation policy: Policy under development.

Access: Access varies, depending on source of collection agreements etc. Generally, material is available for educational and research use.

ULSTER TELEVISION FILM LIBRARY

Ulster Television Limited
Havelock House
Ormeau Road
BELFAST
BT7 1EB

Tel: 028 9032 8122
Fax: 028 9024 6695

Contact: Mr Bill Garrett, Archives Supervisor.

E-mail: bgarrett@utvplc.com

Ulster Television holds the Independent Television Commission's franchise to broadcast on Channel 3 in Northern Ireland. A selection of material has been kept since the inception of the station on 31 October 1959.

Video and film holdings: Video: Since 1984 news is shot on 1/2-inch Betacam. Programmes on 2-inch VTR have all been transferred to 1-inch VTR. Material on 1-inch VTR is being transferred to Beta-SP.
Video components: Beta/Beta-SP, 1-inch Video, DigiBeta.
Film: Local newsfilm and magazine items form the bulk of the collection which includes important footage on the troubles. This can be broken down roughly as 35% news, 15% current affairs, 35% magazine and 15% arts and other general programming. Prior to 1984 all news and programmes were shot on 16mm film.
Film components: 16mm.

Storage: 1/2-inch and 1-inch VTR all stored on site in the Film Library. 16mm film is stored in the O.B. Building at Dargan Road. Both environments are temperature and humidity controlled.

Cataloguing: In 1991 a computer was introduced with a STRIX search system. All previous card index information is being entered on the computer along with all contemporary material.

Conservation policy: All transmitted news stories are kept. News/current affairs editors, in consultation with the Archives Supervisor, decide what camera /road tapes to junk. Tapes containing unwanted material are recycled.

Access: Film Library staff will try to answer queries from any source. Due to security problems access to the Library is limited and must always be on an appointment basis. Most material can be transferred to VHS for external viewing for an appropriate fee. Programme sales are arranged through Mike McCann, Ulster Television Enterprises, at the same address.

UNDERCURRENTS

Undercurrents Productions
16b Cherwell Street
OXFORD
OX4 1BG
Tel: 01865 203661/Mobile: 0797 329 8359
Web: http://www.undercurrents.org

Contact: Mr Paul O'Connor, Director.

E-mail: underc@gn.apc.org

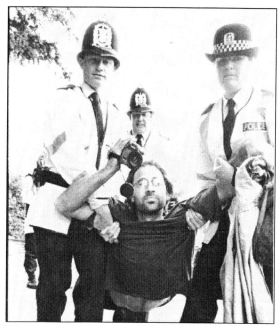

(photo courtesy of Undercurrents)

Undercurrents is an alternative news video magazine distributed via VHS and the Internet. Since 1993 Undercurrents has distributed and archived environment and social justice news of direct action protest which have been recorded by both activists and video journalists on camcorders. Many of the 'micro documentaries' have won international awards. The perspective comes from the direct viewpoint of the community in struggle. Undercurrents the organisation also offers video training and archives all tapes on Betacam SP.

Video and film holdings: Video: 2,000 hours unedited footage of protests. 50 hours of various documentary features on protests.
Video components: VHS, S-VHS, hi-8, Dv, DvCAM, Beta-SP, video 8.

Printed catalogue: Available for alternative news video.

Access: Limited access. Access for disabled.

Viewing and listening facilities: Viewing off premises. Sales, duplicating Beta SP to VHS with Timecode in view.

Charges: Charges for research for broadcast, academic purposes, facilities and handling. Price list available on request.

Copyright: Copyright held. Copyright advice available. Copyright adviser: Paul O'Connor.

The UNITED SOCIETY FOR THE PROPAGATION OF THE GOSPEL (USPG)

Partnership House
157 Waterloo Road
LONDON
SE1 8XA
Tel: 020 7928 8681
Fax: 020 7928 2371

Contact: Ms Catherine Wakeling, Archivist.

Films date from the 1920s to the 1970s. Films were produced by the Society for the Propagation of the Gospel in Foreign Parts (SPG) and the Universities Mission to Central Africa (UMCA), which merged in 1965 to form USPG. Films were produced to educate supporters about the work of the societies and to assist in raising funds. The subject matter reflects the diversity of work under taken around the world.

Cataloguing: The National Film and Television Archive has produced a brief handlist compiled from the accession notes.

Access: Access available. USPG's film collection is deposited with the National Film and Television Archive. Researchers should contact the NFTVA to view the material.

Copyright: Copyright held for part of the collection. Copyright advice available.

UNIVERSITY COLLEGE CHICHESTER

Learning Resources Centre
College Lane
CHICHESTER
West Sussex
PO19 4PE
Tel: 01243 816085
Fax: 01243 816080
Web: http://www.ucc.ac.uk

Learning Resources Centre.

The book collection supports the teaching of modules and includes standard undergraduate text books, introductions and readers on film theory, film history and film studies. Other areas include: the development of Hollywood and its politics, sexuality as portrayed in films. national cinemas, popular television in Britain, television comedy, soap operas, children and television, Bakhtin theories, etc. The collection of films and videos is also closely related to what is taught and thus, is a mixed one.

Journals holdings: 15.

Library OPACs with major holdings on moving image and radio: Yes. Talis.

Catalogue(s) available via the Internet: TalisWeb via Internet site.

Digitised collection: No. No plans to do so.

Access to researchers from outside: Yes, for reference purposes.

Viewing and listening facilities: 6 machines in the Library. 1 is bookable.

Charges: Free to borrow for students. Fines if late back. Range of fees for external borrowing.

Copyright: ERA, CLA licences.

UNIVERSITY OF BIRMINGHAM BARBER MUSIC LIBRARY

Edgbaston
BIRMINGHAM
B15 2TT
Tel: 0121 414 5851
Fax: 0121 414 5853
Web: http://www.is.bham.ac.uk

Contact: Ms Anna Greig, Music Librarian, Music Library Information Services, Barber Music Library.

E-mail: a.greig@bham.ac.uk

Video and film holdings: Approx. 300.

Music holdings: Approx. 12,000, including LPs, CDs, cassettes and 78s.

Card catalogue: Pre-1971 items not yet added to computerised catalogue.

Computerised database: Talis.

Digitised collection: No.

Access to researchers from outside: Yes.

Viewing and listening facilities: Yes, individual and group viewing.

Charges: None to University members. Non-members pay annual charge for membership.

UNIVERSITY OF BIRMINGHAM LIBRARY

University of Birmingham
Main Library
Edgbaston
BIRMINGHAM
B15 2TT
Tel: 0121 414 5817
Fax: 0121 471 4691
Web: http://www.is.bham.ac.uk

Contact: Ms Lydia Priestley, Language & Media Resource Centre.

E-mail: l.c.priestley@bham.ac.uk

The Language and Media Resource Centre was established to support the multimedia needs of students and staff.

Video and film holdings: Video: 3,200 cassettes. Documentary, feature films, news and current affairs, science and education.

Video components: VHS and NTSC video.

Storage: Videos in resource centre.

Computerised database: Available.

Access: Access available by arrangement for non-University members.

Viewing and listening facilities: In-house viewing facilities are available.

Charges: Charges for access apply in excess of 3 visits per year.

Copyright: ERA licence held. Copyright advice on request.

The UNIVERSITY OF BIRMINGHAM WESTHILL

Westhill
14–16 Weoley Park Road
BIRMINGHAM
B29 6LL
Tel: 0121 415 2339
Fax: 0121 415 2273

Contact: Mr G A Harris, Director, Orchard Learning Resources Centre, Information Services.

E-mail: olrc@westhill.ac.uk

Primary education and religious education are particular strengths at the University of Birmingham Westhill.

Video and film holdings: 1,750 VHS cassettes.

Digitised collection: No.

Access: Prior warning requested.

Access to researchers from outside: Yes.

Viewing and listening facilities: VCR available.

UNIVERSITY OF BRIGHTON, DEPARTMENT OF INFORMATION SERVICES

Watts Building
Lewes Road
BRIGHTON
BN2 4GJ
Tel: 01273 642769
Fax: 01273 606093
Web: http://www.library.bton.ac.uk

Contact: Media Librarian, Media Services.

E-mail: slc2@brighton.ac.uk (*For general enquiries*)

The Department of Information Services has 4 libraries which are open to the public. Each library has a substantial video collection as part of its subject resources. Although the majority of programmes are off-air recordings, there are also a large number of commercially available specialist programmes in each library. Three of the libraries are located in or near Brighton town centre: St Peter's House Library, Aldrich Library and Falmer Library. The fourth, Queenswood Library, is in Eastbourne. Each library has a telephone line for enquiries and it is recommended that visitors phone the relevant site in the first instance or search the library catalogue online. All stock is catalogued and searchable via the Web OPAC at http://library.bton.ac.uk. *St Peter's House Library* (Richmond Terrace, Brighton BN2 2NA, Tel: 01273 643220, Fax: 01273 607532) supports a broad range of courses in the arts and design, including editorial photography, fashion textiles, fine art, graphic design, humanities, illustration, interior design, performing arts and three-dimensional studies in craft and production. Studies in culture and society and in visual culture encompass film and television. There is a slide library and a trade literature collection. Access to the slide library is limited to registered students and staff due to copyright restrictions. St Peter's House Library has been described by the Higher Educational Funding Council for England as being of national importance. *Aldrich Library* (Cockcroft Building, Brighton BN2 4GJ, Tel: 01273 642760/642764, Fax: 01273 642988) supports the following areas of study: computing, maths and IT, information and media studies, library and information studies, pharmacy and biochemistry, microbiology, business studies. finance and accountancy, engineering, construction, environment, architecture and interior design. The Information and Media Studies degree is relatively recent and staff are actively developing the collection. Aldrich Library is the largest of the site libraries and has the largest video collection. The audio-tape collection mostly comprises language learning material. *Falmer Library* (Falmer, Brighton BN1 9PH, Tel: 01273 643569, Fax: 01273 643560) houses resources to support many courses in education, languages, health studies, nursing and social sciences. There is a large collection of schools broadcasts and language learning audio-visual material. *Queenswood Library* (Darley Road, Eastbourne BN20 7UN, Tel: 01273 643682, Fax: 01273 643825) supports service management, leisure and tourism, sports science, physiotherapy, podiatry and nursing. The video collection is an intrinsic part of overall resources.

Video and film holdings: About 25,000 across the four site libraries.

Masters holdings: Not in the libraries, though Media Services (in the same department) has its own collection.

Music holdings: St Peter's House Library has a small collection of recordings of mainly contemporary classical composers.

Sound holdings: 1,200.

Books holdings: Approx. 2,000.

Theses holdings: Approx. 50 – mainly MA relating to media-assisted language learning.

Datasets holdings: Access to AVANCE.

Journals holdings: Approx. 20 titles.

Posters holdings: Not specifically, though holds books about posters.

Computerised database: Library OPAC.

Library OPACs with major holdings on moving image and radio: All library materials catalogued and searchable online.

Catalogue(s) available via the Internet: http://www.bton.ac.uk

Digitised collection: Not yet, although looking to use digital recordings/capture technology.

Access: Ring to confirm opening hours.

Access to researchers from outside: The libraries are open to the public.

Viewing and listening facilities: All libraries have audio and VHS playback facilities and CD-ROM; all except Falmer have Video8 playback.

Charges: None.

Copyright: None directly. However, Media Services, also in the Department of Information Services, holds the rights to material it produces. Copies of the Services' productions are in the University libraries or can be purchased from Media Services.

UNIVERSITY OF BRISTOL, DEPARTMENT OF DRAMA – THEATRE, FILM, TELEVISION

Cantocks Close
Woodlands Road
BRISTOL
Avon
BS8 1UP
Tel: 0117 928 7833

Contact: Dr Jacqueline Mainguard, Lecturer, Film and Television Studies.

E-mail: jacqueline.mainguard@bris.ac.uk

Video and film holdings: 4,000 VHS tapes.

Masters holdings: 500 masters of student film material.

Music holdings: CDs for use by film production students.

Printed catalogue: Yes.

Digitised collection: No.

Access to researchers from outside: No.

Viewing and listening facilities: Video (VHS).

UNIVERSITY OF BRISTOL, DEPARTMENT OF RUSSIAN

17 Woodland Road
BRISTOL
BS8 1TE
Tel: 0117 928 7596

Contact: Dr Birgit Beumers. Department of Russian.

E-mail: birgit.beumers@bris.ac.uk

Masters holdings: c.100.

Printed catalogue: Russian feature films.

Catalogue(s) available via the Internet: No.

Websites relating to radio and moving images: http://www.bris.ac.uk/Depts/Russian

Digitised collection: No.

Access: 09.00–17.00.

Access to researchers from outside: No.

Viewing and listening facilities: Language Laboratory.

UNIVERSITY OF CAMBRIDGE SCHOOL OF EDUCATION

Shaftesbury Road
CAMBRIDGE
CB2 2BX
Tel: 01223 369631
Fax: 01223 324421

Contact: Ms Emma-Jane Batchelor, Deputy Librarian.

E-mail: ejb40@cam.ac.uk

Sound holdings: Radio programmes on education and related subject area.

Computerised database: Cambridge University Library Online Catalogue System.

Catalogue(s) available via the Internet: http://www.lib.cam.ac.uk/catalogues/OPAC

Digitised collection: No, not at present.

Access to researchers from outside: Yes, for reference only.

Copyright: ERA licence.

UNIVERSITY OF CENTRAL LANCASHIRE LIBRARY & LEARNING RESOURCES SERVICE

St Peter's Square
PRESTON
Lancashire
PR1 2HE
Tel: 01772 892280
Fax: 01772 892960

Contact: Ms Marion E Seed, Library & Learning Resources Service, User Support.

E-mail: m.seed@uclan.ac.uk

Large collection of feature films on video from early years compilations to latest blockbusters. Small but growing collection of video art. Fashion collections videos.

Music holdings: c.160 CDs, tapes, LPs, etc.

Books holdings: c.2,500.

Datasets holdings: 1,500+.

Journals holdings: c.26 titles.

Computerised database: Yes.

Library OPACs with major holdings on moving image and radio: Talis OPAC.

Websites relating to radio and moving images: http://www.uclan.ac.uk/library/visres.htm

Digitised collection: No. No definite plans but interested.

Access: Library opening hours.

Access to researchers from outside: Reference only or possibly inter-library loan.

Viewing and listening facilities: Mostly open access. for 4-week (normal), 1-week (short) or restricted (24 hours') loan.

Charges: Only for external users (membership fee).

Copyright: None.

UNIVERSITY OF DERBY LIBRARY & LEARNING RESOURCES

Britannia Mill
Mackworth Road
DERBY
DE22 3BL
Tel: 01332 594050
Web: http://www.derby.ac.uk

Library enquiries, Library & Learning Resources.

Materials cover books, journals, videos, and slides. Film indexes held on CD-ROM: *International FilmArchive*, *Film Index International*.

Video and film holdings: Purchased videos and off-air recordings.

Masters holdings: Stock figures not available.

Stills holdings: Slides.

Books holdings: Yes.

Theses holdings: Yes.

Datasets holdings: Yes.

Journals holdings: Yes.

Digitised collection: No.

Access: As advertised on the University's website.

Access to researchers from outside: Yes, for reference.

Viewing and listening facilities: Video playback in learning centres. Cinema facilities in Metro Cinema at Green Lane site where main film stock is held.

Charges: £30 per annum for external borrowers.

UNIVERSITY OF EXETER
BILL DOUGLAS CENTRE

School of English
Queen's Building
The Queen's Drive
EXETER
EX4 4QH
Tel: 01392 264321
Fax: 01392 264361
Web: http://www.ex.ac.uk/bill.douglas

Contact: Dr Hester Higton, Curator.

The Bill Douglas Centre collection consists of all types of objects and writing related to the history of the cinema and pre-cinema (such as magic lanterns, zoetropes, panorama, shadow show, etc.). The Centre itself does not collect films, but does acquire anything relating to them. The collection of pre-cinema artefacts and texts is one of the best in the country. Within those materials which relate to the history of cinema there are important collections of sheet music from films, biographies of film stars and directors, film annuals, fiction connected to the film industry, film stills, postcards, posters and cigarette cards. Other items include toys linked to films, a good library of technical film books (especially from the early years of the century), film scripts, academic histories and critical studies, and a wide range of periodicals. There is a small number of books relating to television and radio, but this does not form a major part of the collections.

Music holdings: Approx. 3,500 records and pieces of sheet music.

Stills holdings: Approx. 4,000.

Books holdings: Approx. 17,000.

Manuscripts holdings: Approx. 200.

Journals holdings: Approx. 5,400.

Newspapers holdings: Approx. 200.

Posters holdings: Approx. 700.

Ephemera holdings: Approx. 15,000.

Equipment holdings: Less than 100.

Computerised database: Yes. Complete inventory (some catalogued) on Microsoft Access available at the Centre.

Catalogue(s) available via the Internet: Preliminary catalogue available at http://www.ex.ac.uk/bill.douglas/database.htm

Websites relating to radio and moving images: Yes. http://www.ex.ac.uk/bill.douglas

Digitised collection: No. Plans for eventual digitisation.

Access to researchers from outside: Yes.

Viewing and listening facilities: Galleries open Mon-Fri, 10.00–16.00. Research Centre Mon-Fri, 10.00–13.00 and 14.00–17.00.

UNIVERSITY OF GLASGOW
MEDIA SERVICES

64 Southpark Avenue
GLASGOW
Scotland
G12 8LB
Tel: 0141 330 5676
Fax: 0141 330 5674
Web: http://www.gla.ac.uk/media

Contact: Ms Ann Drummond, Director. Elaine Kinee, Production Secretary Media Services.

E-mail: a.drummond@udcf.gla.ac.uk

The subject matter of the master material does not relate to the subject of moving images as such, in fact no specific titles in this area spring to mind. Subjects relate predominantly to the teaching in all eight faculties, ranging from lab techniques to documentaries and promotional videos. The Services' audio collection is negligible.

Masters holdings: Media Services holds its own collection of master video recordings dating back to the 1960s, programmes which have been made by the in-house production team.

Sound holdings: Few.

Stills holdings: Main university collection of 250,000 stills held by Photographic Unit.

Theses holdings: In Central Library.

Equipment holdings: A few 1-inch VTRs.

Card catalogue: For archive stock.

Printed catalogue: No.

Computerised database: In process of setting up an Access-based database for the collections.

Library OPACs with major holdings on moving image and radio: No.

Catalogue(s) available via the Internet: No.

Websites relating to radio and moving images: No.

Digitised collection: Have begun process for stills. Considering video collections.

Access: Prior permission.

Access to researchers from outside: By arrangement.

Viewing and listening facilities: By arrangement.

Copyright: Glasgow University.

UNIVERSITY OF GREENWICH LIBRARY

Woolwich Campus
Beresford Street
LONDON
SE18 6BU
Tel: 020 8331 8197
Fax: 020 8331 8464
Web: http://www.gre.ac.uk/directory/library/index.html

Contact: Mr David Evans, Reader Services Librarian. Library.

E-mail: d.h.evans@gre.ac.uk

The University of Greenwich library service is spread out over six campus libraries. All comments and statistics relate to Woolwich Campus Library only. The teaching of our Media and Communication and Media and Society courses takes place at Woolwich and the materials detailed will cater for these courses. Although our collections are modest at present, we would hope to develop them over the next few years, especially in the field of film studies.

Books holdings: 600.

Datasets holdings: 3,126.

Library OPACs with major holdings on moving image and radio: Yes.

Catalogue(s) available via the Internet: Yes.

Digitised collection: No.

Access: Mon-Thu, 09.00–21.00. Fri-Sat, 09.00–17.00 during termtime.

Access to researchers from outside: Individuals are asked to contact the Campus Librarian who will make arrangements for admission on a discretionary or charge basis.

Viewing and listening facilities: Video playback machines.

Charges: None for registered students or individual subscribers.

Copyright: Off-air recordings.

UNIVERSITY OF KENT AT CANTERBURY, THE TEMPLEMAN LIBRARY

CANTERBURY
Kent
CT2 7NX
Tel: 01227 764000
Fax: 01227 475495
Web: http://www.ukc.ac.uk/library

Contact: Mr D Whittaker, Subject Librarian. Subject Division.

E-mail: d.whittaker@ukc.ac.uk

The book collection is very broad-based and reflects teaching and research interests. it includes: History and Film, Film and Philosophy, Film analysis, Documentary Interpretation and Criticism, British Cinema, American Cinema, European Cinema, Gender, Narrative Cinema, Experimental and Fantastic Cinema.

Video and film holdings: 4,500 videos. Modest collection of DVDs.

Masters holdings: No.

Sound holdings: c.100 audiocassettes relating to radio.

Stills holdings: c.1,000 slides on films.

Books holdings: c.4,500 books.

Theses holdings: 50.

Datasets holdings: *Film Index International. International FilmArchive. International Index to the Performing Arts.*

Journals holdings: 49 journals (subscriptions); c.1,770 volumes.

Posters holdings: c.20.

Computerised database: Yes.

Library OPACs with major holdings on moving image and radio: Yes. All holdings can be traced through the Library Catalogue which is available on the website.

Catalogue(s) available via the Internet: Yes, plus Internet Movie Database and other links to film journals.

Websites relating to radio and moving images: Yes.

Digitised collection: No.

Access: Mon-Thu, 09.00–22.00. Fri, 09.00–20.00, Sat, 12.00–19.00, Sun, 14.00–19.00. Reduced hours in vacations (all on Internet site).

Access to researchers from outside: Yes. During 1999/2000 a smart-card entry system was installed. Students and staff from other universities will have access.

Viewing and listening facilities: 17 video viewing stations.

Charges: No charges for students and staff. For any developments consult website.

UNIVERSITY OF NEWCASTLE UPON TYNE ☐
SCHOOL OF MODERN LANGUAGES

NEWCASTLE UPON TYNE
NE1 7RU
Tel: 0191 222 7492
Fax: 0191 222 5442
Web: http://www.ncl.ac.uk/crif

Contact: Mr Phil Powrie. School of Modern Languages.

E-mail: p.p.powrie@ncl.ac.uk

VHS collection of mainly off-air recordings of main national cinemas. Extra in University Library holdings of books (not periodicals) in all areas of film.

Video and film holdings: 2,000+ VHS videos (USA, UK, Spanish, German, Russian).

Computerised database: Yes.

Library OPACs with major holdings on moving image and radio: University Library.

Digitised collection: No.

Access: Prior permission.

Access to researchers from outside: Yes.

Viewing and listening facilities: VHS and monitors.

Charges: By negotiation.

UNIVERSITY OF NORTH LONDON, ☐
THE LEARNING CENTRE

236–250 Holloway Road
LONDON
N7 6PP
Tel: 020 7607 2789 ext 2720
Web: http://www.unl.ac.uk/library/aishums/film.shtml

Contact: Mr Crispin Partridge, Humanities & Education Faculty Librarian.

E-mail: c.partridge@unl.ac.uk

The University offers many undergraduate modules in the moving image, e.g. Hollywood melodrama of the 1950s, Realist cinema, Introduction to national cinemas, Questions of authorship, Post-revolutionary cinema in Soviet Russia, 1917–1928, The French New Wave, Greek tragedy on film, British cinema 1958–1973, Television drama, Comedy and gender, Black British cinema, Contemporary American cinema from 1977 to the present, The film industry, Women's cinema, Caribbean cinema. The collection's subject strengths are in these areas. Modules new in 1999 are National cinemas, Mobilising the photographic image, and Italian Neo-Realism; consequently, there is very little stock in these areas at present.

Video and film holdings: 3,000 or so videos and film-related documentaries on VHS videotape.

Theses holdings: One or two only.

Datasets holdings: *Film Index International, MLA, IIPA Full text.*

Journals holdings: See website for details. Most major academic journals held.

Library OPACs with major holdings on moving image and radio: WEBCAT. http://opac.unl.ac.uk

Catalogue(s) available via the Internet: WEBCAT. A description of the video stock, list of periodical titles, abstracts and indexes is available on the Web.

Digitised collection: N/A.

Access to researchers from outside: Yes, but written permission needed and no access to the Web or databases.

Viewing and listening facilities: Large number of open access video playback machines; DVD playback available 2000–2001 session.

UNIVERSITY OF READING, FACULTY ☐
OF LETTERS AND SOCIAL SCIENCES

Whiteknights
READING
RG6 6AA
Tel: 0118 931 8878
Fax: 0118 931 8873
Web: http://www.rdg.ac.uk/libweb

Contact: Mr J Hillier, Head of Department. Mr C B Cipkin. Department of Film & Drama.

E-mail: j.m.hillier@reading.ac.uk

Video and film holdings: Numerous small departmental collections of off-air recordings. Not available to external visitors.

Music holdings: Very small number of CDs/tapes of film music and television themes.

Stills holdings: Slide and microfiche collection of theatre stills at Bulmershe Library. (See also below under Ephemera.)

Books holdings: Extensive collection of books relating to film studies.

Manuscripts holdings: Papers relating to Sir David Lean.

Theses holdings: PhD and MPhil theses are in the Library; MA theses are with the Departments.

Journals holdings: Wide range of dead and current subscriptions to film journals.

Ephemera holdings: Film and radio advertisement materials and movie stills in the Rickards Collection, Centre for Ephemera Studies, Department of Typography.

Card catalogue: Yes – gradually being retrospectively converted, especially at Bulmershe Library.

Library OPACs with major holdings on moving image and radio: Yes – especially books and periodicals. Z39.50 compliant.

Catalogue(s) available via the Internet: Yes – http://www.unicorn.rdg.ac.uk

Digitised collection: No. No plans to do so.

Access: Limited access for children under 10 at Main Library, Whiteknights. Restrictions on loan of software and AV material and access to special collections.

Access to researchers from outside: Libraries are generally available for reference.

Viewing and listening facilities: Video-playback machines at Bulmershe Library, Main Library at Whiteknights and Music Library.

Charges: Charges apply for external membership of Library, granted at Librarian's discretion.

UNIVERSITY OF SALFORD, AIS (Library)

Adelphi Campus
Peru Street
MANCHESTER
M3 6EQ
Tel: 0161 295 6183/7246
Fax: 0161 295 6083

Contact: Ms Sue Slade, Faculty Coordinator. Mr Andy Callen, Information Officer AIS.

E-mail: s.m.slade@salford.ac.uk

A collection of books and videos to support the media and performance courses at the Adelphi Campus. Subjects covered include performance, drama, film, television, radio, culture, mass media, broadcast industry, and computing (Internet/multimedia). Areas of special interest are: film scripts; off-air recordings, including many examples of films, documentaries, drama productions and other television programmes. Videos cover a good selection of world cinema. CDs of BBC sound effects and background music.

Video and film holdings: Yes.

Music holdings: Yes.

Sound holdings: Yes.

Books holdings: Yes.

Theses holdings: A few only; most are undergraduate.

Datasets holdings: CD-ROMs (stand alone): *Audio Visual Materials for Higher Education (AVANCE); Film Index International; International Index to the Performing Arts (IIPA)*.

Journals holdings: 60.

Digitised collection: Not at present.

Access: External users should apply in writing to the Campus Manager.

Viewing and listening facilities: Video viewing facilities available.

Charges: Not made, except for overdue loans. There is a charge of £30 per year for external borrowers.

UNIVERSITY OF SALFORD, DEPARTMENT OF MEDIA & PERFORMING ARTS

Adelphi Campus
Peru Street
SALFORD
Tel: 0161 295 6044

Contact: Dr Gareth Palmer, Head of Division. Ian Calloway, Media & Performing Arts.

E-mail: g.palmer@salford.ac.uk

Contemporary Documentary Archive: the collection consists of mainly documentaries dealing with crime and the police (e.g. *Crimewatch UK, Mersey Blues*, etc.). The collection also includes fly-on-the-wall documentaries and programmes which use 'hidden cameras', (e.g. *Neighbours from Hell, Beadle's About*). However, the collection is expanding to include documentaries in general and will perhaps branch out to include current affairs programmes and drama.

Masters holdings: Approx. 1,000 hours.

Card catalogue: No.

Printed catalogue: Yes.

Computerised database: Access.

Library OPACs with major holdings on moving image and radio: No.

Catalogue(s) available via the Internet: No.

Websites relating to radio and moving images: No.

Digitised collection: No.

Access to researchers from outside: Research from postgraduates only with prior arrangement.

Viewing and listening facilities: Yes, on site in archive.

Copyright: ERA licence.

UNIVERSITY OF STRATHCLYDE ARCHIVES

University of Strathclyde
McCance Building
Richmond Street
GLASGOW
G1 1XQ
Tel: 0141 548 2318
Fax: 0141 552 0775
Web: http://www.strath.ac.uk/Departments/Archives

Contact: Dr Jim McGrath, Archivist.

E-mail: suarchives@mis.strath.ac.uk

Small collection relating to University activities, development of campus, etc. Chiefly 1960s and after but includes film of Edward VII unveiling foundation stone of Royal College building in May 1903.

Video and film holdings: Video: Science and education. Film: The 1903 film has been copied through the Scottish Film Archive. Science and education.

Storage: Archive storage (to BS 5454 standard, not specific to film needs).

Cataloguing: Printed catalogue for internal use only.

Conservation policy: As required; seek advice from the Scottish Film Archive.

Access: Access available. 09.00–17.00, but preferably by arrangement.

Viewing and listening facilities: Viewing off premises. No viewing facilities available in the Archive.

Charges: Charges for facilities and handling. Charges for other services.

Copyright: Copyright held.

UNIVERSITY OF STRATHCLYDE LIBRARY

Jordanhill Campus
76 Southbrae Drive
GLASGOW
Tel: 0141 950 3309
Fax: 0141 950 3150
Web: http://www.lib.strath.ac.uk

Contact: Ms Linda Emery, Media Librarian. Library.

E-mail: l.r.emery@strath.ac.uk

The media collection covers a broad spectrum of subjects, age-levels and physical formats. It is designed to support all courses taught in the Faculty of Education. Its principal role is to provide resources for students when on placement, mainly teaching (all levels), community education and speech and language therapy. The collection therefore covers most subjects taught in schools from pre-school to secondary, further and adult education and higher education. There are also media resources supporting the teaching of social work, speech and language therapy, music, sport and all education courses. The physical formats include sound recordings (audio cassettes, compact discs and jazz records), video recordings (commercial and off-air), slides, wallcharts, multimedia packs and a range of software.

Video and film holdings: 3746 videos including off-air.

Sound holdings: 4069 tape cassettes and 589 CDs – includes music.

Catalogue(s) available via the Internet: Yes – http://library-server.lib.strath.ac.uk/webpac-1.2

Digitised collection: No.

Access: Library opening hours.

Access to researchers from outside: Yes.

Viewing and listening facilities: 7 video players.

UNIVERSITY OF SUNDERLAND INFORMATION SERVICES

Chester Road
SUNDERLAND
SR1 3SD
Tel: 0191 515 2900
Fax: 0191 515 2904
Web: http://www.library.sunderland.ac.uk

Contact: Miss Joan Hetherington. Chester Road Library Information Services.

E-mail: joan.hetherington@sunderland.ac.uk

This is a university library collection which includes all subject areas. The University has four site libraries; Chester Road Library, St Peter's Library, Hutton Library and Ashburne Library.

Video and film holdings: 4,000+.

Music holdings: 250.

Sound holdings: 1,400+.

Stills holdings: 4,800+ slides of art material in Art Library.

Books holdings: 4,553 in relevant subject areas.

Datasets holdings: CD-ROMs, e.g. *Film Index International, Complete Index to World Film.*

Journals holdings: Approx. 30 journal titles in relevant subject areas.

Computerised database: CD-ROM databases.

Library OPACs with major holdings on moving image and radio: Access via Internet to Higher Education OPACs.

Catalogue(s) available via the Internet: http://webcatalogue.sunderland.ac.uk/webclient.html

Websites relating to radio and moving images: Access via Internet.

Digitised collection: No.

Access to researchers from outside: Available for reference to non-University of Sunderland users.

Viewing and listening facilities: Video and audio facilities available in all 4 site libraries.

Charges: None.

UNIVERSITY OF SURREY, ROEHAMPTON – INFORMATION SERVICES

Roehampton Lane Learning Resources Centre
Roehampton Lane
LONDON
SW15 5SZ
Tel: 020 8392 3765
Fax: 020 8392 3259
Web: http://www.roehampton.ac.uk/support/infoserve/info_library/ftv.asp

Contact: Ms Felicity Lander, Faculty Information Officer. Mrs Judith Hegenbarth, Assistant Information Adviser, Information Services.

E-mail: F.Lander@roehampton.ac.uk

Roehampton offers a broad range of courses at undergraduate, postgraduate and research level in the arts and humanities, social and life sciences and education. There are two Learning Resource Centres which between them house 370,000 books and other material to support the academic needs of its users. The Roehampton Lane Learning Resources Centre in particular houses a strong collection of performing arts material in the areas of drama and theatre, dance, film and television. In line with the modules taught at undergraduate level the College has good collections of material on film and video productions, audience studies, film history, narrative, criticism and theory, European cinema, Shakespeare on film, and social and political aspect of cinema.

Video and film holdings: 7,105 videos,

Books holdings: 2,287.

Journals holdings: 20 current journal subscriptions.

Computerised database: CD-ROMs.

Catalogue(s) available via the Internet: http://helios.roehampton.ac.uk:8001/www-bin/www_talis

Digitised collection: No. No plans to do so.

Access: Not currently.

Access to researchers from outside: Currently, yes.

Viewing and listening facilities: Two group viewing rooms. 18 video viewing stations (with headphones).

Charges: External borrowers pay £50 per year for two items concurrently.

UNIVERSITY OF SUSSEX LIBRARY

Falmer
BRIGHTON
BN1 9QL
Tel: 01273 877097
Fax: 01273 678 441
Web: http://www.sussex.ac.uk/library

Contact: Ms Dheirdre Mitchell, AV Librarian. The Library.

E-mail: library.av@sussex.ac.uk

Video and film holdings: 3,500+.

Music holdings: Very few.

Sound holdings: 12,000+ (mostly University of Sussex lectures).

Printed catalogue: Printed in-house catalogue available in the Library for film and television productions and audio items. (Holdings of film and television productions only on the website.)

Library OPACs with major holdings on moving image and radio: Talis – AV items can be searched separately – also available on the Web.

Digitised collection: No.

Access: Prior arrangements must be made for weekends and evenings. Opening hours weekdays. Mon-Fri 10.00–17.00. Borrowing only permitted with a University of Sussex library card.

Access to researchers from outside: Yes – in-house use only and subject to restrictions above.

Viewing and listening facilities: 12 video players, 1 record player. 1 CD player, 5 cassette players, and 1 large-screen video player.

UNIVERSITY OF THE WEST OF ENGLAND, BOLLAND LIBRARY

Frenchay Campus
Coldharbour Lane
BRISTOL
BS16 1QY
Tel: 0117 965 6261
Fax: 0117 976 2509

Contact: Ms Maggie Shrubshall, Assistant Librarian, Bolland Library.

E-mail: maggie.shrubshall@uwe.ac.uk

There are 8 libraries on different UWE campuses. Off-air recordings and bought-in videos reflect the subjects taught at each campus, e.g. health and social care, humanities, engineering. At Frenchay the Faculty of Languages and European Studies runs a European Cinema Module so this library's book and video stock includes material for this subject. The Bower Ashton campus includes material for film and media studies.

Catalogue(s) available via the Internet: Yes. http://www.uwe.ac.uk/library

Access: Library open to the public for reference use. Limited borrowing facilities available on subscription – phone for details. Usual copyright restrictions apply to all materials.

Viewing and listening facilities: VHS for student use. Group viewing rooms in some libraries.

UNIVERSITY OF ULSTER ART & DESIGN LIBRARY

York Street
BELFAST
Northern Ireland
BT15 1ED
Tel: 028 9026 7269
Fax: 028 9026 7278
Web: http://www.ulst.ac.uk

Contact: Ms Olivia Fitzpatrick, M Khorsidian, Faculty of Art & Design.

E-mail: o.fitzpatrick@ulst.ac.uk

As this is a general art and design library, mainly undergraduate, there is no specialist collection. This is only one of four libraries in the University. See also Department of Humanities, Coleraine Campus.

Video and film holdings: About 1,000 videos of classic films, cartoons, techniques for jewellery, fashions, ceramics, etc.

Books holdings: 150 on history, criticism and techniques of cinema.

Datasets holdings: *Film Index International.*

Journals holdings: *c.*3.

Newspapers holdings: Small number on Irish film in index to *Irish Times.*

Library OPACs with major holdings on moving image and radio: Not major holdings.

Catalogue(s) available via the Internet: University of Ulster catalogue.

Digitised collection: N/A.

Access: Staff and students.

Access to researchers from outside: On request.

Viewing and listening facilities: 4 video playback machines in Library.

Charges: None.

UNIVERSITY OF ULSTER AT COLERAINE LIBRARY

University of Ulster
Cromore Road
COLERAINE
Northern Ireland
BT52 1SA
Tel: 02870 324546
Fax: 02870 324357

Contact: Ms Kay Ballantine, Sub-Librarian Humanities.

The moving image collection in the Library is designed to support teaching and research in media studies at the University. It contains published material only: books, journals and videos relating to film, video, television and radio, and does not contain any unique material.

Video and film holdings: Approx. 500.

Books holdings: Approx. 2,200.

Theses holdings: Approx. 23.

Datasets holdings: *Film Index International* and *FIAF* – access for UU staff and students only.

Journals holdings: 16 current and 25 additional backruns.

Library OPACs with major holdings on moving image and radio: Yes.

Catalogue(s) available via the Internet: http://library.ulst.ac.uk

Digitised collection: No.

Viewing and listening facilities: Video viewing facilities, single user.

UNIVERSITY OF ULSTER AT COLERAINE, THE FILM AND SOUND RESOURCE UNIT

Cromore Road
COLERAINE
Northern Ireland
BT52 1SA

Tel: 028 7032 4625
Fax: 028 7032 4952

Contact: Ms Gillian Coward, Senior Technician.

E-mail: ga.coward@ulst.ac.uk

The collection was established in 1970 to locate and collect local archive films and film relating to course teaching, primarily in the Faculty of Humanities. Attention has increasingly focused on the acquisition of audio-visual material relating to the history of the last 30 years in Northern Ireland. Amateur, documentary, feature film, news and current affairs material is included. There is also over 85 hours of programme material from Ulster Television reflecting its range of output from 1959. In addition there are sound broadcasting tapes on history and current affairs. The University is one of the 6 public sites in Northern Ireland to house a PC based digital film archive containing over 50 hours of Northern Ireland's archive film (see *Northern Ireland Digital Film Archive* description under entry for *Ulster Folk and Transport Museum*).

Video and film holdings: Video: 2,800 VHS cassettes. 5,000 hours.
Film: 90 black and white 16mm positive film prints. 10 colour 16mm positive film prints.

Masters holdings: None.

Sound holdings: 400 sound tape hours – 1/4-inch tape.

Datasets holdings: *British Newsreels: Pathe news scripts.*

Journals holdings: *Sight & Sound/Monthly Film Bulletin* 1934 to present (on microfilm); 'Little Cinema' magazines (early cinema magazine collection on microfilm). Various other journals.

Newspapers holdings: *Irish News* 1919–1939 (some references).

Card catalogue: Yes.

Printed catalogue: Yes. Indexed.

Computerised database: Yes. FileMaker Pro software.

Websites relating to radio and moving images: http://cain.ulst.ac.uk/othelem/media/tvprogs.htm – disk searchable database of programmes about the Northern Ireland 'Troubles'.

Digitised collection: No plans.

Access: Opening hours; Weekdays, 09.15–16.45. Disabled access.

Access to researchers from outside: Access is mainly for staff and students for teaching and research purposes. However, all enquiries are welcome and educational and leisure use encouraged.

Viewing and listening facilities: On premises.

Charges: None.

Copyright: Not held.

UNIVERSITY OF WALES ABERYSTWYTH – THOMAS PARRY LIBRARY

Llanbadarn Fawr
ABERYSTWYTH
Wales
SY23 3AS
Tel: 01970 622417
Fax: 01970 622190

Contact: Mr A J Clark, Site Librarian.

E-mail: parrylib@aber.ac.uk

16mm films have been collected since the College's inception in 1964. Video (VHS) has been added more recently. Some film is acquired for archival purposes. The earliest film dates from 1922.

Video and film holdings: Video: 950 cassettes. Documentary, news and current affairs, science and education, librarianship and information science, agriculture and countryside matters.
Video components: VHS Video.
Film: 250 cans. Documentary, news and current affairs, science and education, librarianship and information science.
Film components: 16mm.

Storage: Films stored in racks on standard library shelving. Library shelving for video.

Computerised database: Catalogue available through Voyager online catalogue: http://voyager.aber.ac.uk

Cataloguing: Conversion of card catalogue in process.

Access: Access available. By arrangement.

Viewing and listening facilities: Viewing on premises.

UNIVERSITY OF WALES, BANGOR – MAIN LIBRARY INFORMATION SOURCES

Main Library
College Road
BANGOR
Gwynedd
LL57 2DG
Tel: 01248 382971
Fax: 01248 382979

Contact: Mrs G Hughes, Social Studies Librarian. Main Library, Information Sources.

E-mail: g.hughes@bangor.ac.uk

The main part of the collection at UWB consists of videocassette copies of motion pictures (both bought and off-air recordings) for the film studies course which has been running for the past two years. The book (including film scripts) and serials collection related to this course is being developed. In addition to the film studies collection, there are 150 videocassettes, mostly off-air recordings, relating to psychology. There are small video collections relating to Wales and the Welsh language and some education videos for children.

Video and film holdings: 1,500 videos.

Books holdings: 250 books and filmscripts.

Journals holdings: *c.*20 journals.

Library OPACs with major holdings on moving image and radio: Yes. Z39.50 compliant.

Catalogue(s) available via the Internet: http://library.bangor.ac.uk

Digitised collection: No.

Access: Restricted to UWB patrons.

Access to researchers from outside: Yes, for books and journals only. Reference only.

Viewing and listening facilities: Limited to Main Library, Education Library and Health Studies Library.

UNIVERSITY OF WALES COLLEGE, NEWPORT

Library and Learning Resources
Caerleon Campus
PO Box 179
NEWPORT
NP18 3YG
Tel: 01633 432103
Fax: 01633 432108
Web: http://library.newport.ac.uk

Contact: Mrs Lesley May, Deputy Head, Library and Learning Resources.

E-mail: llr@newport.ac.uk

Video and film holdings: Approx. 2,000 tapes in an off-air collection of videos to support the University College's teaching programmes.

Music holdings: Eclectic CD music collection.

Books holdings: Yes. To support the University College's teaching programme.

Journals holdings: Yes. To support the University College's teaching programme.

Catalogue(s) available via the Internet: Yes. http://unicorn.lib.newport.ac.uk/

Websites relating to radio and moving images: http://library.newport.ac.uk/film.html

Digitised collection: No.

Access to researchers from outside: Reference only access to books and journals is available. Viewing, borrowing or copying of videos from the off-air collection of videos is only available to staff and students at UCWN for educational purposes.

Viewing and listening facilities: Viewing the off-air collection of videos is only available to staff and students at UWCN.

UNIVERSITY OF WESTMINSTER LEARNING RESOURCES CENTRE

Harrow Campus
Watford Road
Northwick Park
HARROW
HA1 3TP
Tel: 020 7911 5956
Fax: 020 7911 5952
Web: http://www.wmin.ac.uk/harlib

Contact: Ms Sally Bannard, Librarian. Alleyne Riley (video enquiries), Learning Resources Centre.

E-mail: bannard@wmin.ac.uk

The Learning Resources Centre houses a videotape collection comprising off-air recordings, commercially produced tapes, pop music videos and feature films. A particular strength is animation and printed guides are available to this part of the collection. Books and periodicals support undergraduate and postgraduate courses.

Video and film holdings: Approx. 10,000 tapes.

Music holdings: Approx. 2000 CDs, covering mainly hit/contemporary material from the late 1950s to the present day.

Sound holdings: BBC Sound Effects CDs.

Books holdings: 8,000.

Theses holdings: Approx. 500 MA theses.

Datasets holdings: *International Index to Film Periodicals. International FilmArchive. MLA International Bibliography. Art Bibliographies Modern. Art Abstracts.*

Journals holdings: 33 current subscriptions.

Library OPACs with major holdings on moving image and radio: http://library.westminster.ac.uk/ALEPH

Digitised collection: No.

Access to researchers from outside: Yes to members of UK Higher Education institutions with current ID. Anyone else should write to the Library Manager.

Special permission is needed to consult theses. Please write to the Library Manager.

Viewing and listening facilities: 7 video presenters.

UTN: THE STOCKSHOT LIBRARY

c/o United, 4th Floor
48 Leicester Square
LONDON
WC2H 7LY
Tel: 020 7389 8750
Fax: 020 7389 8752

The Agency supplies broadcast quality stockshots. 90% of material is less than four years old. UTN specialises in world-wide (including America and Europe) locations – cities and countryside, lifestyle (village and country life), adverse weather, aerial views, archive black and white footage, sport action – sailing, extreme sports.

Video and film holdings: Video: 2,000 cassette stockshots.
Video components: Beta-SP, DigiBeta.
No film is held.
Conservation policy: To delete material over four years unless of unique interest.
Storage: Material held in archive storage with rapid access.
Computerised database: Available.
Access: Access available by arrangement.
Viewing and listening facilities: Via requested VHS videos.
Charges: Published ratecard.
Copyright: Copyright holder.

VALENCE HOUSE MUSEUM & ARCHIVES

Becontree Avenue
DAGENHAM
Essex
RM8 3HT
Tel: 020 8227 5293/4/5/6

Contact: Ms Sue Curtis, Heritage Services Manager.

The majority of the collection belongs to the two film societies operational in the borough from the 1940s to the 1970s. The Dagenham Co-operative Film Society produced drama and documentary films in the borough of Dagenham during the late 1940s and 1950s after the merger of Barking and Dagenham boroughs in 1965. The Fanshawe Film Society operated as a film club but shot some documentary footage in the 1960s and 1970s.

Video and film holdings: Video: See film holdings.

Film: The Archive holds 12 films of local interest and civic ceremonies. In addition, a large film archive was acquired from the Fanshawe Film Society in 1991. The film collection's growth is sporadic. Films of local interest.
Film components: Positive Film.

Storage: Fire proof cabinets in strong room. Temperature/humidity controlled. Temperature is kept below 60 degrees Fahrenheit.

Documentation: *Guide to Local History Resources,* accessions register, files.

Access: Access available. By appointment only.

Copyright: By individual arrangement with Heritage Services Section.

VALLEYS RADIO

Festival Park
Victoria
EBBW VALE
Wales
NP23 8XW
Tel: 01495 301116
Fax: 01495 300710

Contact: Mr Tony Peters, Programme Manager.

E-mail: admin@valleysradio.co.uk

Radio station. Holds 42 days' output to meet legal requirement.

The VICKERS ARCHIVES FILM COLLECTIONS

Cambridge University Library
West Road
Cambridge
CB3 9DR
Tel: 01223 333000
Fax: 01223 333160

Contact: Mr John Wells, Assistant Under-Librarian.

E-mail: jdw@ula.cam.ac.uk

The collection is that of the former Photographic Department of Vickers plc, which was based at the company's headquarters in London.

Video and film holdings: Video: 400 reels/cassettes. Advertising, documentary, feature films.
Video components: VHS Video, hi-band U-matic, lo-band U-matic, Beta/Beta-SP, 1-inch Video.
Film: 200 cans. 10% colour film, 90% black and white film. Advertising, documentary, feature films.
Film components: 16mm, positive film, negative film, fine grain print, final mix.

Storage: Film stored in main, environment-controlled archive stack.

Computerised database: Available.

Cataloguing: Searches on the database can be conducted by staff upon request.

Access: Limited access. By appointment only. Access for disabled. Access to video material only.

Viewing and listening facilities: Viewing on premises. By prior appointment to holders of Library reader's tickets only.

Copyright: Copyright not held. Copyright in most cases rests with Rolls-Royce plc. Copyright advice available. Copyright adviser: Mr John Wells.

VIEWTECH FILM & VIDEO

7–8 Falcons Gate
North Avon Business Centre
Dean Road
YATE
BS37 5NH
Tel: 01454 858055
Fax: 01454 858056

Contact: Ms Susan Duckett, Manager.

Viewtech Film & Video, established in 1981, is the UK's leading independent distributor of educational films and videos. Hundreds of titles are available covering all main educational topics as well as health-related subjects. From this wide range footage may be supplied for broadcast and non-theatric purposes. Leaflets and catalogues are available on request.

Video and film holdings: Video: 300,000 feet, 500 reels/cassettes, 150 hours. Science and education.
Video components: VHS Video, hi-band U-matic, lo-band U-matic.
Film: 300,000 feet, 500 cans, 150 hours. 99% colour film, 1% black and white film. Science and education.
Film components: 16mm, positive film, negative film, fine grain print, effects mix, final mix.

Printed catalogue: Available.

Access: Limited access.

Viewing and listening facilities: Viewing on premises. Viewing off premises.

Charges: Charges for research for broadcast productions.

Copyright: Copyright held.

VOICE OF THE LISTENER AND VIEWER (VLV)

101 King's Drive
GRAVESEND
Kent
DA12 5BQ

Tel: 01474 352835
Fax: 01474 351112

Contact: Ms Linda Forbes, Administrator.

E-mail: vlv@btinternet.com

VLV has an extensive archive of its own with records of all its conferences since 1984, plus a reference library of books and magazines, etc., some from overseas consumer groups which are not likely to be replicated elsewhere in Britain. There is also an archive of the former Broadcasting Consortium (of charities which lobbied around the 1990 Broadcasting Bill and subsequently for a few years). The strength of the VLV collection lies in its perspective of the listener and viewer, representing the citizen and consumer interest.

Sound holdings: Yes.

Stills holdings: Some.

Books holdings: Yes. Reference Library.

Manuscripts holdings: Archives of VLV and former Broadcasting Research Unit (1980–1991) and British Action for Children's Television (BACTV).

Journals holdings: Yes – a variety of UK and overseas journals.

Newspapers holdings: A few.

Ephemera holdings: Some.

Printed catalogue: Yes.

Websites relating to radio and moving images: http://www.vlv.org.uk

Digitised collection: No.

Access: By appointment.

Access to researchers from outside: Yes.

Viewing and listening facilities: On request.

Charges: On request.

Copyright: On request.

WALES FILM AND TELEVISION ARCHIVE / ARCHIF FFILM A THELEDU CYMRU

Unit 1
Aberystwyth Science Park
Cefn Llan
ABERYSTWYTH
Wales
SY23 3AH
Tel: 01970 626007
Fax: 01970 626008
Web: http://www.sgrin.co.uk

Contact: Administrator.

E-mail: wftva@sgrin.co.uk

Mr Lloyd George addresses the House of Commons. Still from the silent film THE LIFE STORY OF DAVID LLOYD GEORGE, Ideal Film Company, 1918 (courtesy of the Wales Film and Television Archive / Archif Ffilm A Theledu Cymru)

The collection comprises the voluntary film and video deposits and donations of filmmakers and production companies, individuals, groups, organisations and corporate bodies. All commonly used film and video formats (current and obsolete) are represented, with 16mm the most common for film (81% of total footage in the collection). The types of production can be categorised as feature fiction (20% of the total collection footage), animation (5%), art experimental (5%), documentary/ non-fiction (45%), amateur/home movie (25%). Television material is acquired via the collections of individual production companies and producers, rather than systematically from broadcasters or off-air, although Welsh-language fourth channel S4C deposits selected drama material. Non-fiction, being the largest category of material held, includes newsreels and topicals, television and film documentaries, educational films and home movies and other amateur productions. One of the collection's greatest strengths is the range and variety of certain thematic representations: an example is ex-Prime Minister Lloyd George, who appears in newsreels, educational films, home movies, amateur records of political meetings, a three-hour government-suppressed 1918 biopic, and even animation. Strongly-represented subjects include agriculture, community and social life, cultural activity (e.g. eisteddfodau), family life, and tourism and leisure. **Note:** *The Archive will join with the National Library of Wales to form a larger archive in April 2001.*

Video and film holdings: Video: 1,200 reels/cassettes, 900 hours. Amateur, documentary, science and education.

Video components: VHS Video, S-VHS Video, 8mm Video, hi-8, hi-band U-matic, lo-band U-matic, Beta/Beta-SP, 1-inch Video, 1/2-inch reel to reel, Phillips video format.

Film: 3,000,000 feet; 8,000 cans. The Archive holds over 3,000 titles to date. Much of the material is non-fiction and spans most of the 20th century. A considerable amount of amateur footage, including that of the National Eisteddfod, is also held.

The collection consists of advertising films (5%), amateur footage (40%), documentaries (30%), feature films (5%), news and current affairs (5%), science and education (2%) and travelogues (13%). 65% colour film, 35% black and white film.

Film components: 8mm, Super 8mm, 9.5mm, 16mm, Super 16, 35mm, positive film, negative film, fine grain print, effects mix, final mix.

Storage: Separate film and magnetic vaults, temperature and humidity controlled; total storage area of 200 square feet.

Books holdings: Approx. 100 items, including early film history books, technical journals and manuals, some acquired from a private collection.

Manuscripts holdings: 8 collections of various items (scripts, correspondence) relating to the filming/ commissioning activity of their depositors (individuals, companies and organisations).

Ephemera holdings: Few items only.

Equipment holdings: 15 projectors (various formats), 15 cameras (various formats).

Printed catalogue: Available, indexed, for a proportion of the collection (published 1997).

Computerised database: For internal use only.

Conservation policy: Junking only occurs when the material is of limited interest, of very poor quality, or of no relevance to the nature of the collection (i.e. not of Welsh interest). In the latter case the archive would propose the material to a relevant archive before junking.

Access: Access available. 09.00–17.30, by arrangement only. Staff are available to assist. Access for disabled. Access ramp and toilets available.

Viewing and listening facilities: Viewing on premises. VHS copies of certain titles may be supplied for viewing off premises in some circumstances.

Charges: Charges for research for broadcast and commercial productions. Special rates for academic, educational and non-commercial users. Charges for facilities and handling. A price list is available upon request.

Copyright: Most copyright is in third-party ownership.

WALSALL LOCAL HISTORY CENTRE

Local History Centre
Essex Street
WALSALL
WS2 7AS
Tel: 01922 721305
Web: http://www.walsall.gov.uk

Contact: Ms Ruth F Vyse, Archivist/Local Studies Officer.

E-mail: localhistorycentre@walsall.gov.uk

The Centre is the archive repository and local studies library of Walsall Metropolitan Borough Council and as such accepts donations and deposits of film/video material which relates to the local area. Film is transferred to video for easier access by researchers. This is only a small collection which does not represent a large part of the overall holdings.

Video and film holdings: Video: VHS professional, 16 cassettes; U-matic professional 1 tape; VHS amateur. 19 cassettes. U-matic amateur, 1 tape.
Film: 35mm professional, 1 reel; 16mm professional, 10 cans, 5 films, 2 soundtracks; 9.5 mm amateur, 12 reels, black and white; Super 8mm, amateur, 7 reels, colour.

Storage: Archive repository which conforms to BS 5454 and is air-conditioned and fitted with halon gas fire extinguishing system.

Printed catalogue: Available, indexed.

Documentation: *Handlist of Accessions 1972–1998* and annual reports.

Conservation policy: Qualified conservator on the staff. There is no separate, specific policy on film/video.

Access: Access available. Tue and Thu 09.30–17.30; Wed 09.30–19.00; Fri 09.30–17.00; Sat 09.30–13.00. Access for disabled.

Viewing and listening facilities: Viewing on premises. Duplicating. Tapes can be copied for sale.

Charges: Prices by arrangement.

Copyright: Copyright advice available.

The WAR ARCHIVE

Images of War Ltd
31A Regent's Park Road
LONDON
NW1 7TL
Tel: 020 7267 9198
Fax: 020 7267 8852
Web: http://www.warfootage.com

Contact: Mr Derek Blades.

E-mail: derek@dircon.co.uk

Winston Churchill (photo courtesy of the War Archive)

The War Archive is a collection of original film footage from both the First and Second World Wars and the preceding periods. The Archive consists of almost 200 hours of footage from Great Britain, Germany, Russia, the USA and Japan, and covers all aspects of these important periods in recent history.

Video and film holdings: Video and film holdings.
Video components: DigiBeta, Bets SP.
Film components: 16mm.

Storage: In secure vaults.

Computerised database: Not fully catalogued or computerised: searches made at clients' request.

Access: By appointment only.

Viewing and listening facilities: On or off premises.

Charges: Charges for research for broadcast or video production.

Copyright: Some copyrights held; remainder out of copyright.

WARRINGTON COLLEGIATE INSTITUTE LIBRARY

Padgate Campus
Crab Lane
WARRINGTON
WA2 0DB
Tel: 01925 494494
Fax: 01925 816077
Web: http://www.library.warr.ac.uk

Contact: Ms Lorna Crewe, Assistant Librarian, Visual Resources Media & Performing Arts, Library.

E-mail: l.crewe@warr.ac.uk

Video and film holdings: 1,200 videos.

Books holdings: Approx. 400.

Theses holdings: 20 MA theses.

Datasets holdings: *Film Index International* CD-ROM.

Journals holdings: 42 journal subscriptions.

Websites relating to radio and moving images: http://library.warr.ac.uk

Digitised collection: No.

Access to researchers from outside: Yes, for reference only.

Viewing and listening facilities: 6 television/video monitors.

Charges: None.

Copyright: FE copyright licence and Open University licence.

The WAVE 96.4 FM

965 Mowbray Drive
BLACKPOOL
Lancashire
FY3 7JR
Tel: 01253 304965
Fax: 01253 301965
Web: http://www.thewavefm.co.uk

Contact: Mr Gary Burgess, Programme Controller.

E-mail: info@thewavefm.co.uk

The radio station holds 42 days' output to meet legal requirement. Does not maintain an archive but holds a private music library.

WELLCOME LIBRARY FOR THE HISTORY AND UNDERSTANDING OF MEDICINE – ICONOGRAPHIC COLLECTIONS

183 Euston Road
LONDON
NW1 2BE
Tel: 020 7611 8582
Fax: 020 7611 8703
Web: http://www.wellcome.ac.uk/en/library/homelib/HOMlibCOL.html

The first surviving in-house film was made in 1912, the first recorded purchase in 1928. The Library was founded by Sir Henry Wellcome and reflects his interest in documentary techniques. Most items have been acquired since World War II. The Library holds original archive material of which copies on videotape are available for viewing in most cases. Some films are also available for viewing on laserdisc (videodisc). Three separate departments of the Wellcome Library hold moving image materials; the Iconographic Collections, including over 200 documentary films on medicine, hygiene, surgery, pharmaceuticals, hospitals, laboratories, anthropology, and the history of these and other related subjects; Archives and Manuscripts (formerly Contemporary Medical Archives and Western Manuscripts), including about 40 films made by or acquired by individuals whose archives have been deposited with the Library, including films on gynaecological surgery, eugenics, veterinary medicine and microcirculation; and the Medical Film and Video Library (see below for separate entry).

Video and film holdings: Video: The archive also holds some material on video – VHS and videodisc.

Video components: VHS (PAL, SECAM, NTSC); Betamax; BVU (SP), Videodisc (Laserdisc).

Film components: 8mm, 16mm, 35mm, positive film, negative film.

Storage: Shelving in a store with controlled temperature and humidity.

Printed catalogue: Available.

Cataloguing: Holdings are also included in the union catalogue *Moving Images of Medical Science and History*, 1992 (see separate entry under Wellcome Trust). Computerised catalogue available through the Wellcome Library online catalogue at http://library.wellcome.ac.uk

Documentation: Some synopses available, also accompanying material (transcripts, brochures, provenance information).

Conservation policy: None. A large collection of nitrate films was destroyed in 1970 (list available).

Access: Access available. Mon, Wed, Fri 09.45–17.15; Tue, Thu, 09.45–19.15; Sat, 09.45–13.00. Staff are available to assist. Access for disabled. By prior arrangement. Large reference library on medical history and related subjects available.

Viewing and listening facilities: Viewing on premises. Duplicating. Sales. No viewing charge. Viewings available by appointment.

Charges: Charges for other services. A price list is available upon request. There is a charge for copying.

Copyright: Copyright held for some of the material. Copyright advice available. Copyright adviser: William Schupbach.

WELLCOME TRUST MEDICAL FILM AND VIDEO LIBRARY

The Wellcome Trust
210 Euston Road
LONDON
NW1 2BE

Tel: 020 7611 8596/7
Fax: 020 7611 8765
Web: http://www.wellcome.ac.uk/en/1/homlibmfv.html
Contact: Dr Michael Clark. Marie Williams.
E-mail: mfvl@wellcome.ac.uk

Built up by donations and selective acquisitions from the 1950s onwards; approximately four-fifths of the present holdings, including film and video of mainly archival interest, has been acquired since the late 1970s. The core of the present collection consists of some 40 medical, biomedical and veterinary films dating from the 1940s, '50s and '60s, made over to the Trust by the Wellcome Foundation in 1988 and subsequently reissued on video; 13 videos on contemporary and historical aspects of tropical diseases and medicine and the work of the Wellcome Trust, made by the Wellcome Trust Film Unit between 1985 and 1990; and the three most recent (1957, 1971 and 1978) editions of the film *William Harvey and the Circulation of the Blood,* transferred to the Trust by the Royal College of Physicians in 1989–90. Since 1988, nearly all Wellcome Trust copyright films have been transferred to video and made available for purchase in VHS format, and the 8mm, 16mm and 35mm film masters deposited with the Wellcome Library Iconographic Collections (*see entry for Wellcome Library for the History and Understanding of Medicine – Iconographic Collections*). During the same period, most of the non-copyright films belonging to the Iconographic Collections and the Contemporary Medical Archives Centre have also been transferred to video, and viewing copies added to the Trust collection. Finally, in 1990–91, the Trust assumed joint responsibility for two special medical videotape collections, the Institute of Neurology Cine Film Library and the medical videotape collection of the former University of London Audio-Visual Centre (some 120 titles dating mainly from the 1970s in the *Scientific Basis of Medicine* and *Up to Date* series). The Trust's main collection continues to grow at a rate of about 100 new titles a year.

Video and film holdings: Video: About 1,200 titles in main collection and another 220 in two special collections (see above). Main subject areas represented include physiology and pharmacology, the neurosciences, cell biology, parasitology and tropical medicine, but clinical medicine and surgery and the history of medicine are also well represented. The main collection consists largely of Beta-SP, BVU and hi-band U-matic video masters and/or sub-masters, together with VHS viewing copies (including viewing copies of nearly all the archival medical films in the Wellcome Library Iconographic Collections). The Institute of Neurology special collection is held in the form of 1-inch master videotapes and VHS viewing copies, the University of London Audio-Visual

Centre collection in a variety of video formats, including 3M 1-inch reels, 1-inch Memorex Chroma tapes, and lo-band U-matic. Amateur, documentary, news and current affairs, science and education, promotional films, drama documentary.

Video components: VHS (PAL, SECAM, NTSC), hi-band U-matic, lo-band U-matic, Beta/Beta-SP, 1-inch Video, BVU, Videodisc (Laserdisc); CD-ROM; DVD.

Film: All film masters of titles in the Wellcome Trust Collection originally held as film (*c.*250 cans) have been deposited with the Iconographic Collections of the Wellcome Library for the History and Understanding of Medicine. 75% colour film, 25% black and white film. Amateur, documentary, news and current affairs, science and education, drama documentary.

Film components: 8mm, 16mm, 35mm, positive film, negative film, final mix.

Storage: All 8mm, 16mm and 35mm film stock, together with some video masters and submasters, have now been deposited in the Wellcome Library Iconographic Collections store. Viewing copies (nearly all VHS) available for viewing on request in the Wellcome Trust Information Service. Video masters stored in the Medical Film and Video Library.

Ambient temperature and humidity under some control in both locations, but not at ideal or constant levels.

Printed catalogue: Available, indexed.

Cataloguing: About three-quarters of the main collection and roughly half of the two special collections have been properly catalogued. Basic information and, in some cases, detailed summaries of contents are available on request for most of the remaining uncatalogued titles. New, updated and enlarged version of Catalogue is available as an online database via WISDOM (Wellcome Trust Information Service Databases on Medicine) – http://www.wisdom.wellcome.ac.uk/wisdom/mfvlhome.html

Documentation: Handlists of special collections; subject guides; printed information sheets on the Wellcome Trust Film and Video Collection. Printed catalogue of audio-visual programmes in the Wellcome Library relating to the history of medicine forthcoming (February 2001).

Conservation policy: No film stock junked since 1970s, except for a small amount of nitrate film recopied onto safety stock. No videotape stock junked yet, except duplicates.

Access: Access available 09.15–18.00, preferably by appointment. Staff are available to assist. Access for disabled viewers possible, but advance notice required. Most loanable items in the general collection available on request to anyone with a serious academic or professional interest in the materials. Film and television researchers, academics, secondary school science teachers and students welcome. A few items in the general collection, plus 95 titles in the Institute of Neurology special collection, restricted to bona fide medical and scientific audiences.

Viewing and listening facilities: Viewing on premises. Viewing off premises. Sales. Viewing facilities are available in the Wellcome Trust Information Service, preferably by appointment, for VHS and U-matic (PAL, NTSC) videotapes, and for Beta-SP (PAL, NTSC), Videodisc and CD-ROM in the Medical Film and Video Library offices.

Charges: Charges for facilities and handling. A price list is available upon request. No charge made for viewing, but sales of footage from Wellcome Trust copyright material charged for in the usual way.

Copyright: About 15% only of the collection is in copyright to the Wellcome Trust. Copyright advice available. Copyright adviser: Dr Michael Clark.

WESSEX FILM AND SOUND ARCHIVE

Hampshire Record Office
Sussex Street
WINCHESTER
SO23 8TH
Tel: 01962 847742
Fax: 01962 878681

Contact: Mr David Lee, Film and Sound Archivist.

E-mail: sadedm@hants.gov.uk

The Wessex Film and Sound Archive was established in February 1988 by the Hampshire Archives Trust in association with the Hampshire County Council, which now administers the archive. Film, video and sound recordings of interest to Hampshire and the surrounding counties are collected for preservation. The material dates from 1890 to the present. Particular subject strengths are the military: army, navy, royal marines, parachute regiment, army air corps. royal observer corps; merchant shipping, including shipbuilding and technical material; amateur films; British Powerboat Company (Scott-Paine films); the seaside; local radio, including BBC Radio Solent, Radio Victory, Ocean Sound and Radio 210; oral history; towns like Southampton, Portsmouth, Bournemouth and Winchester; Bournemouth orchestras; off-air recordings of classical music performances on the radio in the 1960s made by Constantin Silvestri; and original footage concerning the raising of the ship *Mary Rose*. WSFA also holds viewing copies of documentaries made by local broadcasting companies BBC South, Meridian, TVS

and Southern Television. The Archive is a member of the Film Archive Forum.

Video and film holdings: Video: 1,000 reels/cassettes. Video recordings are also collected, and some filming is done around the region by the archive itself.

Video components: VHS Video, S-VHS Video, 8mm Video, hi-8, hi-band U-matic, lo-band U-matic, Beta/Beta-SP, 1-inch Video, Phillips 1500 and 1700, Sony 1/2-inch and 1/4-inch, Betamax, V2000, DV, Digital Betacam.

Film: 7,000 cans. Nearly all non-fiction material. Amateur films are well represented, along with documentaries and technical subjects. Film collections which reflect the region include maritime and shipping and technology, civic occasions, military and aviation subjects. The Portsea Island Mutual Co-operative Society collection is now held by the archive, as are the film holdings of Southampton City Museums and Record Office, and Portsmouth City Records Office. The rate of expansion varies, but appears to be about 500 films per annum. 50% colour film, 50% black and white film, 1% nitrate film.

Film components: 8mm, Super 8mm, 9.5mm, 16mm, 35mm, positive film, negative film, fine grain print, effects mix, final mix.

Storage: Purpose-built in new premises at Hampshire Record Office. Two areas of strong room – one for originals and one for research copies. Nitrate in separate store out of town.

Printed catalogue: Short guide to collections available on request.

Computerised database: Available.

Cataloguing: Full catalogue only available on computer database, which was tailor-made for Wessex Film and Sound Archive. Recently converted to CALM 2000 system (Windows); uses ISAD(G) cataloguing rules.

Earl Haig at the foundation-stone laying ceremony for Gosport War Memorial Hospital, July 1921 (still from cine-film courtesy of the Wessex Film and Sound Archive)

Documentation: Background material about holdings is kept on file. Receipts are held for deposited items, along with details about ownership and copyright.

Conservation policy: Archive policy is to make VHS video viewing copies, plus viewing prints on 16mm. Nitrate films are given priority. To repair and store items to the best standards possible, in a purpose-built repository. Nitrate films stored temporarily in separate place, pending duplication to safety stock.

Access: Access available. Mon-Fri 09.00–17.00. Staff are available to assist. Access for disabled. Researchers are welcome. Wessex Film and Sound Archive is not a commercial film archive; material is collected for study and research use. Any television or production requests must be cleared with copyright owners before items are released for use in film or video programmes.

Viewing and listening facilities: Viewing on premises. Viewing off premises. Duplicating. Video copies of cleared items for reference purposes (viewing on and off premises) only. Master material may not be viewed, but viewing copies are available on VHS video cassettes or 16mm prints.

Charges: Charges for research for broadcast productions. Charges for facilities and handling. A price list is available upon request. Facility fees are charged for any commercial use of the Archive.

Copyright: Very little copyright is owned by Wessex Film and Sound Archive, which largely provides custody for other's material. Copyright advice available.

WEST GLAMORGAN ARCHIVE SERVICE

County Hall
Oystermouth Road
SWANSEA
SA1 3SN
Tel: 01792 636589
Fax: 01792 637130
Web: http://www.swansea.gov.uk/archives

Contact: Miss S G Beckley, County Archivist.

E-mail: archives@swansea.gov.uk

West Glamorgan Archive Service is the joint service of the City and County of Swansea and the County Borough of Neath Port Talbot. From the mid-19th century onwards, it was Swansea Council's policy to make still photographic records of major works, showing the sites before, during and after the works. From the 1930s, the Council began to make movie films of important civic events. At first the films were shot by contracted commercial firms, but in the late 1940s, a small filmmaking unit was set up in the central library. The films produced by these means, together with films donated to the Council, were held in the library until 1974. They were then transferred to the former Swansea City Archives Office and in 1996 into the custody of the West Glamorgan Archive Service.

Video and film holdings: Video: 110 cassettes. Mayoral films 1985 – present; miscellaneous subjects, including copies of cine film and documentaries regarding Swansea. Video components: VHS Video.
Film: 115 films are held. There are two main classes: Mayoral films, 1952–1983; miscellaneous subjects, from 1936 onwards, including visits of royalty, opening of public buildings, etc.; amongst this category most notable is amateur footage of the Mumbles train and the Swansea-Pontarddulais railway line. Also held are gifts of documentaries, newsreel, etc., regarding Swansea, from television companies (69 films and 58 videocassettes). 90% colour film, 10% black and white film. Amateur, documentary.
Film components: 16mm, positive film, negative film.

Storage: Films are stored flat in cans in an unheated strong-room. Relative humidity is controlled by dehumidifiers at 55%. Air in room is kept circulating by ducting. Films with magnetic sound tracks kept on plastic or aluminium spools in non-magnetic cans. Limited facilities for repair of films.

Card catalogue: Available, indexed.

Cataloguing: A small number of films await sorting and listing. These are not available for consultation until they have been properly arranged.

Documentation: Handlists.

Conservation policy: Once accessioned, films and videotapes are kept indefinitely.

Access: Access available only by prior arrangement. Access for disabled.

Viewing and listening facilities: Viewing on premises. Duplicating.

Charges: Charges for research for broadcast productions. Charges for research for academic purposes. Charges for facilities and handling. A price list is available upon request.

Copyright: Copyright held for most films.

WEST SUSSEX RECORD OFFICE

County Hall
CHICHESTER
West Sussex
PO19 1RN
Tel: 01243 753600
Fax: 01243 533959
Web: http://www.westsussex.gov.uk/RO/home.htm

Contact: Mr Richard Childs, County Archivist.

E-mail: records.office@westsussex.gov.uk

Since 1992 the Record Office has been a founding partner of the South East Film and Video Archive (SEFVA) (q.v.) and is its Repository and Conservation Centre.

Video and film holdings: A growing collection, now of several hundred films of local interest – amateur and professional. Includes the collection of the Royal Sussex Regiment, 1914–1960.

Video components: Betamax, VHS, S-VHS.

Film components: Positive film, 8mm, 9.5mm, 16mm, 35mm. No nitrate.

Storage: Air conditioned strongroom.

Computerised database: On SEFVA database (in progress).

Access: Access.

Viewing and listening facilities: Viewing facilities; film and video, by appointment only.

Charges: Information on charges available on request.

WESTMINSTER CITY ARCHIVES

10 St Ann's Street
LONDON
SW1P 2DE
Tel: 020 7641 5180
Fax: 020 7641 5179
Web: http://www.westminster.gov.uk

Contact: Ms Susannah Rayner, City Archivist.

There is no special collection of films and videos. Covering dates are 1935–1990, but Liberty plc is likely to deposit videos regularly.

Video and film holdings: Video: 52 reels/cassettes, 9 hours. The rate of acquisition is approximately five videos per annum. Mostly Liberty plc material; also some video of views of St Marylebone (c.1950) and a publicity video for the Langham Hotel. Advertising, amateur, news and current affairs, arts and fashion programmes.

Video components: VHS Video, lo-band U-matic, Beta/Beta-SP.

Film: 1.25 hours. Eleven films are held, including civic ceremonies, royal visits, Liberty plc material and some BBC and ITN newsfilm footage. A selection of material has been copied onto VHS video. 34% colour film, 66% black and white film. Advertising, amateur, documentary, news and current affairs.

Film components: 16mm, positive film.

Storage: In purpose-built negative store with temperature and humidity control in strong rooms of new archive building, St Ann's Street, London SW1.

Cataloguing: Typed catalogues of three films (in English); draft lists of other films including title, date and run time (except for two films); draft list of video titles and dates.

Documentation: Detailed synopsis for three films (two Liberty films and one of St Marylebone).

Conservation policy: Stored indefinitely.

Access: Access available. By arrangement. Staff are available to assist. Access for disabled. By arrangement. As much notice as possible required, especially for 16mm films. Open: Tue, Thu, Fri, 09.30–19.00. Wed, 09.30–21.00. Sat, 09.30–17.00.

Viewing and listening facilities: Viewing on premises. Viewing off premises. Viewing on premises – VHS videos and 16mm films.

Viewing off premises – loans of broadcast format and Beta videos with permission of Liberty and copyright holders (BBC, ITN, ITV).

Charges: Charges for facilities and handling. Broadcast productions and other researchers are expected to do their own research. There is a viewing charge.

Copyright: Copyright rests with BBC, ITN, ITV, St Marylebone Society, Paddington Society and Hilton International. Copyright advice available.

WESTMINSTER MUSIC LIBRARY

Westminster Libraries and Archives
Victoria Library
160 Buckingham Palace Road
LONDON
SW1W 9UD
Tel: 020 7641 4286
Fax: 020 7641 4281

Contact: Mrs Ruth Rogers, Westminster Music Librarian.

The full subject strength of the Music Library's collection is as follows: 16,117 Books; 450 periodicals (100 current, 350 back titles); 50,989 printed music (including 1,166 sets orchestral parts and 970 vocal score sets); 536 manuscripts of which about 500 are by Emanuel Moor. The Edwin Evans (1871–1945) collection holds press cuttings, mainly from 1930s and 1940s, and about 500 letters from musicians of the same period. Pre-1800 printed music (approx. 400 scores, 40 books as listed in RISM and BUCEM). Oriana Madrigal Society collection of sets of past songs and madrigals. Extensive collection of collected editions/Denkmaler available for loan. No audio-visual materials for loan. (There is a small sound collection of CDs available for loan administered by the Victoria Library on the same site.)

Music holdings: Approx. 150 film scores.

Books holdings: Small collection (approx. 20 volumes in each) relating to film music scoring and radio.

Journals holdings: 4 titles held: *Gramophone, Hi Fi News, Sound on Sound, Audio-Visual Librarian.*

Card catalogue: For printed music only.

Printed catalogue: For orchestral sets only.

Computerised database: For orchestral sets only.

Digitised collection: No. Yes, within the next 3–4 years.

Access: Free access for any member of the public during library opening hours. Registered users unrestricted. Orchestral sets service limited to permanent orchestras.

WINCHESTER SCHOOL OF ART

Park Avenue
WINCHESTER
Hampshire
S023 8DL
Tel: 0238 059 6941/7015
Web: http://www.wsa.soton.ac.uk

Contact: Ms Linda Newington, Librarian, Winchester School of Art Library.

Winchester School of Art Library is a specialist art and design library comprising books, exhibition catalogues, special collections, journals, slides and videos. It has been developed primarily as a teaching collection and, as a result, reflects the academic disciplines taught within the School.

Video and film holdings: Over 5,000 television programmes and films on video

Stills holdings: The Slide Library contains over 100,000 slides and covers images of works of art, contemporary fashion designers and architecture.

Books holdings: On film approx. 328; on television, approx. 65; on video, approx. 63; on radio, 10.

Theses holdings: Approx. 5.

Journals holdings: The Library takes over 170 titles.

Computerised database: Yes.

Library OPACs with major holdings on moving image and radio: Yes. WEBCAT, the University of Southampton (Z39.50 compliant).

Websites relating to radio and moving images: ADAM: The Gateway to Art, Design, Architecture and Media Information on the Internet at www.adam.ac.uk

Digitised collection: Not in the immediate future.

Access to researchers from outside: Yes, for reference only.

Viewing and listening facilities: VCR players available. (No official borrowing rights; reference only.)

Charges: None.

WIRRAL, METROPOLITAN BOROUGH

Information Services
Central Library
Borough Road
BIRKENHEAD
Merseyside
L41 2XB
Tel: 0151 666 3902
Fax: 0151 653 7320

Contact: Ms Janice Taylor, Archivist.

E-mail: archive@wirral-libraries.net

Small collection of films of local interest are held as part of the archive's service.

Video and film holdings: Video: 30 reels/cassettes. Amateur, documentary.
Video components: VHS Video.
Film: 48 cans. 1933; civic movies. 10% colour film, 90% black and white film. Advertising, amateur, documentary, news and current affairs.
Film components: 16mm, 35mm, positive film.

Storage: Items mostly stored boxed with related archives.

Cataloguing: Films and tapes usually appear as items on an archive list. There is no film/audio-visual collection as such.

Conservation policy: Items stored in controlled conditions. Nitrate films or films in poor condition are copied, and the originals usually sent to the North West Film Archive.

Access: Limited access. By arrangement only. Access for disabled.

Viewing and listening facilities: Viewing off premises. There are no viewing facilities at the library, but the films can be viewed by arrangement at the Wirral Museum, Town Hall, Hamilton Square, Birkenhead. Available on loan to local film societies only.

Copyright: Copyright held for certain civic films.

The WOLF

10th Floor
Mander House
WOLVERHAMPTON
WV1 3NB
Tel: 01902 571070
Fax: 01902 571079
Web: http://www.thewolf.co.uk

Contact: Mr Tim Page, Programme Controller.

E-mail: studio@thewolf.co.uk

The radio station holds 42 days' output to meet legal requirement.

WOLVERHAMPTON ARCHIVES & LOCAL STUDIES

42–50 Snow Hill
WOLVERHAMPTON
West Midlands
WV2 4AG
Tel: 01902 552480
Fax: 01902 552481
Web: http://www.wolverhampton.gov.uk/library/archives

Contact: Mr Peter Evans, Borough Archivist.

E-mail: wolvarch.and.ls@dial.pipex.com

Films and videos have been acquired as an incidental part of the Borough Archives collection policy.

Video and film holdings: Video: 100 reels/cassettes. Advertising, amateur, documentary, news and current affairs, industrial processes.
Video components: VHS Video, lo-band U-matic.
Film: 500 cans. Over 100 films made in or about the Wolverhampton local area. 40% colour film, 60% black and white film. Advertising, amateur, documentary, science and education.
Film components: 8mm, Super 8mm, 16mm, 35mm, positive film, negative film.

Storage: Stored in archive strong rooms to BS 5454.

Card catalogue: Available.

Printed catalogue: Available.

Computerised database: Being compiled.

Documentation: General background information is available for many of the items held.

Access: Limited access. For video only: Mon, Tue, Fri, 10.00–17.00 Wed, 10.00–19.00. 1st and 3rd Sat of each month, 10.00–17.00. Access for disabled. Disabled visitors should contact the archivist prior to visiting. Access to film and U-matic material by arrangement only. Unrestricted access to the video collection.

Viewing and listening facilities: Viewing on premises.

Charges: Charges for research for broadcast productions. Charges for facilities and handling. Copies of videos can be made for sale.

Copyright: Some copyrights reside in the Wolverhampton Borough Council. Copyright advice available.

WOLVERHAMPTON COLLEGE, KEY SKILLS AND LEARNING RESOURCES UNIT

Westfield Road
Bilston
WOLVERHAMPTON
WV14 6ER
Tel: 01902 317700

Contact: Mrs Ros Roberts, Library Manager. Sue Walsgrove.

E-mail: rroberts@bilston.co.uk

Wolverhampton College was known as Bilston Community College until 30 September 1999.

Video and film holdings: 1,200.

Books holdings: 100.

Library OPACs with major holdings on moving image and radio: Genesis.

Digitised collection: N/A.

Access to researchers from outside: Public access for reference. Local community may join.

Viewing and listening facilities: 2 video playback machines.

Charges: None at present.

Copyright: Television recordings.

WOMEN'S JAZZ ARCHIVE

8 Chaddesley Terrace
Mount Pleasant
SWANSEA
Wales
SA1 6HB
Tel: 01792 466083
Web: http://www.jazzsite.co.uk/wja/

Contact: Ms Jen Wilson.

E-mail: jenjazzarchive@aol.com

The Archive is currently (October 2000) in storage awaiting rehousing by the City and County of Swansea. The Archive's website is part of the Channel 4 Black History Map of Britain (http://www.blackhistorymap.com).

WORLD BACKGROUNDS FILM PRODUCTION LIBRARY

Imperial Studios
Imperial Place
Maxell Road
BOREHAMWOOD
WD6 1WE
Tel: 020 8207 4747
Fax: 020 8207 4276
Web: http://www.world-backgrounds.com

Contact: Mr Ralph Rogers, Director.

Started operating in 1964 to service the requirements of the television and film industry.

Video and film holdings: Video components: VHS Video, lo-band U-matic, Beta/Beta-SP, 1-inch Video, DigiBeta. Film: 5,000 cans. A wide range of locations and subjects as the company name 'World Backgrounds' implies. Feature films – all unused scenes. 95% colour film, 5% black and white film. Feature films.
Film components: 35mm, negative film.

Storage: All film and facilities stored on premises.

Computerised database: Available.

Access: Limited access. Preferably sending clients VHS copies.

Viewing and listening facilities: Viewing off premises. Telecine transfer from negative to VHS and U-matic. Showreel tape supplied on request.

Charges: Charges for research for broadcast productions. Charges for research for academic purposes. Charges for facilities and handling. A price list is available upon request.

Copyright: Copyright held. Copyright advice available. Copyright adviser: Ralph Rogers.

WORLD IMAGES

1 Host Street
BRISTOL
BS1 5BX
Tel: 0117 930 4099
Fax: 0117 930 4088
Web: http://www.worldtelevision.net

Contact: Ms Bryonie Baxter. Ms Molly Haig or Dominique O'Regan.

E-mail: world.images@worldtelevision.net

World Television is a specialist archive management and stock footage service, representing the collections of NGOs such as Amnesty International, International Fund for Animal Welfare (IFAW), Greenpeace UK and the World Wide Fund for Nature (WWF). Smaller collections include Ocean in Motion and Shark Bay Films (award-winning oceanography.) The Archive represents one of the most comprehensive collections of environment, animal welfare and human rights footage in the world.

Video and film holdings: Video: Approx. 10,000 hours of broadcast standard videotape. Material dates from the 1970s to the present.
Video components: Beta SP or Digital Betacam.
Film components: 16mm.

Storage: Mobile shelving, housed on site in a secured area.

Computerised database: Collections are shotlisted and indexed using a computerised database. Searching is by subject, titles, format, date, location, type of production and/or generation. Free-text searching enables specific shots to be located.

Access: Limited access, available by arrangement with Archive staff.

Viewing and listening facilities: On-site viewing can be arranged. Preview VHS tapes and catalogue entries available on request. Some holdings can be viewed in digital format over the Internet. A VHS showreel is also available on request; catalogue entries can be supplied by e-mail or fax. Footage can be transferred in-house to virtually any video format or broadcasting standard. Themed compilations can be produced to order.

Charges: Research fees and duplication charges apply. Royalty fees are negotiated on an individual basis.

Copyright: World Images acts on behalf of its archive clients and is the sole copyright clearance body.

YORK MINSTER ARCHIVES

Dean's Park
YORK
YO1 7JQ
Tel: 01904 611118
Fax: 01904 611119

Contact: Mr L Hampson, Archivist.

Haphazard from 1942, but more systematic since the 1980s.

Video and film holdings: Video components: VHS Video. Film: Films relating to York Minster including enthronements, special services and television programmes.
Film components: 16mm, positive film.

Storage: Stored in archive strong room.

Cataloguing: Typed list.

Viewing and listening facilities: Viewing off premises by prior arrangement only.

Copyright: Various. Please consult the Archivist for more information.

YORKSHIRE FILM ARCHIVE

University College of Ripon and York St John
College Road
RIPON
HG4 2QX
Tel: 01765 696264
Fax: 01765 600516
Web: http://www.ucrysj.ac.uk/dialect/yorkshire_film_archive.htm

Contact: Ms Sue Howard, Director.

E-mail: s.howard@ucrysj.ac.uk

The Yorkshire Film Archive exists to locate, preserve and show film made in, or about the Yorkshire region. Material dates from 1897 and includes newsreels, documentaries, advertising and amateur films.

Video and film holdings: Video: 50 reels/cassettes. Advertising, amateur, documentary.

Video components: VHS Video, S-VHS Video, lo-band U-matic, Beta/Beta-SP, 1-inch Video.

Film: 3,000 cans. 30% colour film, 70% black and white film, 10% nitrate film. Advertising, amateur, documentary, science and education.

Film components: 8mm, Super 8mm, 9.5mm, 16mm, 35mm, positive film, negative film, fine grain print.

Storage: Temperature and humidity controlled film storage vaults.

Card catalogue: Available, indexed.

Computerised database: Available.

Documentation: Further printed information on the collection and activities of the Archive is available on request.

Conservation policy: Film and video kept for long term preservation. Very little material is junked.

Access: Access available. Staff are available to assist. Access for disabled.

Viewing and listening facilities: Viewing on premises. Viewing off premises.

Charges: Charges for research for broadcast productions. Charges for facilities and handling. A price list is available upon request.

Copyright: Part of the copyright held.

YORKSHIRE TELEVISION

see *Granada Media Clip Sales – Yorkshire Television*

ZURICH FINANCIAL SERVICES (UKISA) LTD

UK Life Tower
Montpellier Drive
CHELTENHAM
GL53 7LQ
Tel: 01242 511227
Fax: 01242 630874

Contact: Ms Isabel Syed, Group Archivist.

The Zurich Financial Services (UKISA) Ltd archive comprises three films. **Note:** *Eagle Star is now part of the Zurich Financial Services Group.*

Video and film holdings: Video: *Eagle Star Museum Video* (1991; 11 min). This was made for Eagle Star News

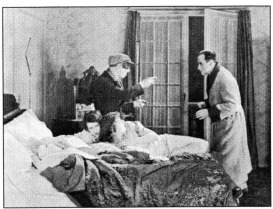

Still from THE MAGIC SCROLL (courtesy of Zurich Financial Services [UKISA] Ltd)

to show the history of Eagle Star, using items from the Museum then at Oriel Lodge, Cheltenham. Commentary spoken by Charles Harrison.

Videos of the *The Magic Scroll* and *Gloria Regina* have been made.

Film: 1) *The Magic Scroll* (1930; 6 min). This was the second advertising film commissioned by the company (known at that date as the Eagle, Star and British Dominions Insurance Company). The script was written by Ernest Spater (1886–1975) who joined British Dominions in 1915, and retired in 1951. From the historic point of view the most valuable feature of this film is the appearance and voice of Sir Edward Mountain, the founder of Eagle Star, and of Sydney Bennett, his general manager. Original film of *The Magic Scroll* held at NFTVA.

2) *Gloria Regina* (1953; 22 min). This film of the Coronation was made by Ron English, formerly a senior Eagle Star inspector in the West End, from 79 Pall Mall, originally built in 1867 as the Eagle's head office. The shots of London, of the procession passing 79 Pall Mall and of the interior of 79 Pall Mall were filmed by Ron English. The official footage of the ceremony was taken by him from a film on public sale at the time. The interior scenes are of Eagle Star senior management and staff who gathered at the office to watch the occasion on specially-installed television sets.

Access: Zurich Financial Services (UKISA) Ltd allows in general access to these films; reproduction is possible in appropriate circumstances provided that the company's name would be included. Any charge would be according to circumstances, although as a general rule the company would not expect to charge, provided that the company's name was clearly visible.

Copyright: Copyright held.

Film, Television, Radio and Related Documentation Collections – Republic of Ireland

ANNER INTERNATIONAL – DIGITAL, POST PRODUCTION LTD

50 Upper Mount Street
DUBLIN 2
Ireland
Tel: +353 1 661 2244
Fax: +353 1 661 2252
Web: http://www.annerinternational.com

Contact: Mr Andy Ruane, Managing Director.

E-mail: bookings@annerinternational.com

The company started in 1975. The collection has been built up since, and includes some material dating from before that year. It is being added to on an ongoing basis. The collection is very strong on news footage of the Northern Ireland Troubles and holds footage of many prominent Irish politicians including Gerry Adams and Charles Haughey. News footage of Sinn Fein Ard-Fheises and IRA kidnappings is also held.

Video and film holdings: Video: c.5000 reels/cassettes. Advertising, documentary, news and current affairs.
Video components: Hi-Band U-matic, Beta/Beta-SP, 1-inch Video.
Film components: 16mm, 35mm.

Storage: Material is well stored, some outhoused.

Computerised database: Available.

Cataloguing: Printouts are not available, but searches can be carried out by staff.

Conservation policy: News and other master tapes are normally kept indefinitely, footage tape for about five years.

Access: Limited access.

Viewing and listening facilities: Viewing on premises. Viewing off premises.

Charges: Charges for research for broadcast productions. Charges for research for academic purposes. Charges for facilities and handling. Prices by quotation.

Copyright: Copyright held for most of the material. Copyright advice available.

EMDEE INTERNATIONAL PRODUCTIONS

90 Lower Baggott Street
DUBLIN 2
Ireland
Tel: +353 1 662 7276
Fax: +353 1 662 7224
Web: http://www.scorpiotvcommercials.com

Contact: Mr Seamus O'Neill.

Emdee Productions has been in operation since 1986 specialising in 16mm documentary films in addition to television cinema commercials. The company has a large aerials collection.

Video and film holdings: Video: 500 reels/cassettes, 250 hours. Advertising, documentary, news and current affairs, corporate films.
Video components: VHS Video, hi-8, hi-band U-matic, lo-band U-matic, Beta/Beta-SP, 1-inch Video.
Film: 900,000 feet, 450 cans, 425 hours. 98% colour film, 2% black and white film, 1% nitrate film. Advertising, documentary, news and current affairs.
Film components: 16mm, Super 16, 35mm, positive film, negative film, effects mix, final mix.

Storage: Film stored in temperature and humidity controlled facility.

Printed catalogue: Available, indexed.

Computerised database: Available.

Cataloguing: Only the film collection has been computerised; the database is currently semi-complete.

Documentation: Printed index of shots, now out of date.

Conservation policy: For film only.

Access: Limited access. Not open to the public.

Viewing and listening facilities: Sales.

Charges: Charges for research for broadcast productions. Charges for research for academic purposes. Charges for facilities and handling. Charges for other services. A price list is available upon request.

Copyright: Copyright held.

FOYNES FLYING BOAT MUSEUM

FOYNES
Ireland
Tel: +353 69 65416
Fax: +353 69 65416
Web: http://www.webforge.net/foynes

Contact: Ms Margaret O'Shaughnessy, Curator.

The Museum is a non-profit making community-funded institution. The collection comprises material from 1937–47 relating to the beginnings of Atlantic passenger travel. It is the only museum of its kind in the world. The collection is still being added to.

Video and film holdings: Video components: Hi-Band U-matic.

Cataloguing: No catalogue available.

Documentation: Other material and also books relating to Atlantic passenger travel.

Access: Research facilities very limited. By arrangement only.

Copyright: Copyright held for part of the collection.

IRISH FILM ARCHIVE

Film Institute of Ireland
6 Eustace Street
DUBLIN 2
Ireland
Tel: +353 1 679 5744
Fax: +353 1 677 8755
Web: http://www.fii.ie

Contact: Ms Sunniva O'Flynn, Archive Curator. Kasandra O'Connell, Head of Archive. Eugene Finn, Archivist – Collections. Emma Keogh, Librarian.

E-mail: archive@ifc.ie

The Irish Film Archive has been located in custom-built premises in the Irish Film Centre since 1992. Collections of Irish and Irish-related materials are preserved and freely accessed by researchers, programme-makers and members of the public. It has been a provisional member of FIAF since 1989.

Video and film holdings: Video: 1,500 reels/cassettes. Advertising, amateur, documentary, feature films, news and current affairs, short films.
Video components: VHS Video, hi-band U-matic, lo-band U-matic, Beta/Beta-SP, 1-inch Video, 2-inch Video.
Film: 15,000 cans. The archive section of the Irish Film Institute was established in 1986. Since then the collection has grown to over 10,000 (catalogued) cans of film, comprising some 5,000 titles. The collection dates from 1908 to the present day. The collection comprises advertising material (750 titles), amateur films (125 titles), documentaries (400 titles), feature films (71 titles), news and current affairs (244 titles), science and educational films (300 titles), shorts (40 titles) and travelogues (30 titles). 65% colour film, 35% black and white film, 5% nitrate film.
Film components: 8mm, Super 8mm, 9.5mm, 16mm, 35mm, positive film, negative film, fine grain print, effects mix, final mix.

Storage: Three recently commissioned master vaults holding colour film/black and white and magnetic film/and film-related documents where temperatire and humidity are maintained at optimal level for long-term preservation. These vaults and the larger viewing copy store are fitted with comprehensive fire detection and prevention systems.

Stills holdings: The Archive holds a rapidly increasing collection of stills from Irish cinema.

Manuscripts holdings: The Archive holds valuable collections of private archives relating to film production and distribution in Ireland.

Posters holdings: The Archive holds a rapidly increasing collection of posters from Irish cinema.

Computerised database: Computerised database. Access is provided to database for public via archive staff. Searches can be conducted under any information entry point.

Catalogue(s) available via the Internet: Information on elements of the film collection are available on the Film Institute of Ireland website – http://www.fii.ie

Documentation: The Tiernan MacBride Library, maintained by the Librarian, is an extensive publicly-accessible resource of books and periodicals relating to Irish and world cinems. The Library is open to the public on weekday afternoons. Information on the library holdings is available on the Film Institute of Ireland website.

Conservation policy: Access is only permitted to viewing copies. Where films exist only as unique master material access must be denied.

Access: Access available. By appointment made by phone or mail. Staff are available to assist. Researchers can apply to the Curator for information about the Archive's holdings.

Viewing and listening facilities: Viewing on premises.

Charges: Charges for research for broadcast productions. Charges for research for academic purposes. Charges for facilities and handling. Charges for other services. A price list is available upon request. The Archive charges research and access fees.

Copyright: Copyright not held. The Archive acts as intermediary between users and rights holders. Copyright advice available.

IRISH FOLKLIFE FILM ARCHIVE

Irish Folklife Division
National Museum of Ireland
7–9 Merrion Row
DUBLIN 2
Ireland
Tel: +353 1 677 7444
Fax: +353 1 661 5155

Contact: Mr Paul Doyle, Keeper/Manager, Irish Folklife Division.

Film on crafts in rural Ireland; shot in the 1950s,1960s and1970s. **Note:** *The division is moving to County Mayo in 2001.*

Video and film holdings: Video: Film holdings transferred to video. Documentary.
Video components: VHS Video.
Film: 25 hours. 100% colour film. Documentary.
Film components: 16mm.

Storage: Metal cupboards; no temperature and humidity control.

Cataloguing: A computerised database is being prepared. The National Museum of Ireland is currently preparing a more detailed catalogue.

Conservation policy: All 16mm converted to video.

Access: Limited access. Access for established film personnel only.

Viewing and listening facilities: Viewing on premises. Plans to have film for sale are under way.

Charges: Charges for research for broadcast productions. Charges for facilities and handling. A price list is available upon request.

Copyright: Copyright held.

LIMERICK FILM ARCHIVE

c/o Belltable Arts Centre
69 O'Connell Street
LIMERICK CITY
Ireland
Tel: +353 61 341435/319866. Mobile: 087 298 3180.
Fax: +353 61 418552

Contact: Mr Declan McLoughlin, Coordinator.

Formed in March 1992, to locate and acquire film, video and cinema material of Irish interest, with particular emphasis on 50 items relating to the mid-West region (Limerick and Clare counties). Since its inception, the Archive has been successful in acquiring over 30 film titles, both 35mm and 16mm, over 500 hours of video material, a large file on local and national cinemas (their history, photographs, programmes and related memorabilia, etc.). The Archive also has the largest collection of data and stills on Irish film players in Ireland. All archive holdings were purchased or donated.

Video and film holdings: Video: 500 hours. Amateur, documentary, feature films, news and current affairs.
Video components: VHS Video, Beta/Beta-SP, NTSC tapes, DVD, Laserdisc.
Film: 95 hours. 30% colour film, 70% black and white film. Advertising, amateur, documentary, feature films, travelogues.
Film components: Super 8mm, 9.5mm, 16mm, 35mm.

Storage: Kept in private storage in a room with temperature-control.

Card catalogue: Available, indexed.

Printed catalogue: Available, indexed.

Cataloguing: The above mentioned catalogues are basic in design and layout; photocopies can be made available to researchers. A computerised database will be available from summer 2001.

Documentation: Large collection of posters, stills, press packs, production notes on the films and videos held, for reference, etc. Large reference library on Irish cinema also, with an ongoing collection on the history of cinemas in Ireland.

Conservation policy: To continue our research and to save as much film and related material from destruction which is still the fate of so much of our film heritage.

Access: Access available. By prior arrangement only. Access for disabled.

Viewing and listening facilities: Viewing on premises. Viewing off premises. Sales. Film to video and video to video transfer facilities. Sales video finding service. (VHS, PAL and NTSC) available.

Charges: Charges for research for broadcast productions. Charges for research for academic purposes. Charges for facilities and handling. Price list available after consultation.

Copyright: Copyright not held on all holdings.

NATIONAL ARCHIVES OF IRELAND

Bishop Street
DUBLIN 8
Ireland
Tel: +353 1 478 3711
Fax: +353 1 478 3650
Web: http://www.nationalarchives.ie

Contact: Mr Ken Hannigan, Senior Archivist.

E-mail: mail@nationalarchives.ie

Very small collection of video recordings of official conference proceedings, but it is likely to grow. At present, only recordings of the National Education Convention, October 1993, are available for inspection.

Video and film holdings: Video: 50 hours. Conference proceedings.
Video components: VHS Video.

Storage: Not suitable for storage of archive film or video, but provision of area with appropriate temperature and humidity controls is under consideration.

Documentation: National Education Convention transcripts of proceedings and other papers.

Conservation policy: Permanent preservation

Access: Access available. Mon-Fri 10.00–17.00.

Viewing and listening facilities: Viewing on premises.

Copyright: Copyright not held. Copyright adviser: Ken Hannigan.

OLLSCOIL EDUCATIONAL EXPERIENCES

Audiovisual Centre
University College Dublin
Belfield
DUBLIN 4
Ireland
Tel: +353 1 706 7020
Fax: +353 1 283 0060

Contact: Ms Freda Kavanagh, Administrative Officer.

The collection comprises adult educational series, including: *Archaeology* – five part series; *Science* – five part series; *Economics* – five part series; *Women's Studies* – five part series; *Animals, Science and Society* – five part series; *The Story of Irish Expression* – ten part series; *The World of Psychology* – five part series; *The Act of Reading* – five part series; *Questioning the System* – ten part series; *Computers: Common Sense* – five part series; *Philosophy* – five part series; *Remote Control: Rural Development* – five part series; *N to End* – five part series.

Video and film holdings: Video: science and education.
Video components: VHS Video.

Printed catalogue: Available.

Documentation: Notes accompanying the various series.

Access: Limited access.

Viewing and listening facilities: Sales.

Copyright: Copyright not held. Copyright advice available. Copyright adviser: RTE.

The RADHARC FILMS ARCHIVE

43 Mount Merrion Avenue
BLACKROCK
Ireland
Tel: +353 1 288 1939
Fax: +353 1 283 6253

Contact: Mr Peter Kelly, Managing Director of Esras Films Ltd and Management Company of Radharc Archive.

E-mail: esras@iol.ie or peterkelly@esras.com

36 years of religious documentary production for Irish television. Produced by Ireland's oldest independent production company, and Ireland's longest running television series – *Radharc*. The Archive comprises over 400 titles from all over the world.

Video and film holdings: Video: 60 hours. Religious documentaries.
Video components: VHS Video, lo-band U-matic, Beta/Beta-SP.
Film: 150 hours. 75% colour film, 25% black and white film. Documentary.
Film components: 16mm, positive film, negative film, effects mix, final mix, v/o tracks.

Storage: In storage at office address and at the Irish Film Archive, Dublin, q.v.

Printed catalogue: Available.

Documentation: Production files are separately kept for each production. Press cuttings.

Conservation policy: All finished Radharc films are held for posterity.

Access: Limited access. On application.

Viewing and listening facilities: Viewing on premises. Duplicating. Sales.

Charges: Charges for facilities and handling. There is a charge for viewing.

Copyright: Copyright shared with RTE. Copyright advice available. Copyright adviser: RTE Commercial Enterprises.

RTE STILLS LIBRARY

Radio Telefís Eireann
Donnybrook
DUBLIN 4
Ireland
Tel: +353 1 208 3127
Fax: +353 1 208 3031
Web: http://www.rte.ie

Contact: Ms Margaret-Mary O'Mahony, Assistant Librarian. Stills Library.

E-mail: omahonmm@rte.ie or stillslibrary@rte.ie

Stills holdings: 100,000 images on CD, many relating to broadcasting.

Books holdings: 3,000 titles, many relating to television and film.

Computerised database: Yes. Image database.

Digitised collection: Yes, CD-ROM.

Access: Prior permission. Open, Mon-Fri, 09.30–17.30.

Access to researchers from outside: Yes.

Viewing and listening facilities: Yes.

Charges: £30 access charge plus copyright charges. Contact Library for more information.

Copyright: RTE copyright. Other copyrights – contact library.

RTE TELEVISION ARCHIVES

Radio Telefís Eireann
Donnybrook
DUBLIN 4
Ireland
Tel: +353 1 208 3369
Fax: +353 1 208 4354
Web: http://www.ret.ie/about/archive.html

Contact: Ms Norma O'Connor. Mr Stephen D'Arcy.

RTE (Radio Telefís Eireann) is the Irish National Public Service Broadcasting Organisation. Television in Ireland was inaugurated in 1961. The collection consists of a selection of news, current affairs and programme material dating back to 1961, and a large selection of stockshot material. Additionally there is a selection of material of Irish interest acquired from international news agencies and local sources dating from about 1913.

Video and film holdings: Video holdings: 2-inch and 1-inch formats all now transferred to to Digital Beta as well as a selection of film material. Remaining film and SP tapes and legacy formats are in the process of transfer to Digital Beta as part of the ongoing Archive digitisation project.
Film holdings: News inserts, programme selection on 16mm film: black and white positives and negatives 1962–1974 and colour print and reversal 1974–1985. Archive film of Irish interest from c.1913 on 35mm and 16mm.

Storage: On site storage of recent SP material; off-site storage of legacy tape and film formats and digital transfers.

Stills holdings: *See separate entry for RTE Stills Library.*

Manuscripts holdings: Selection of programme information files on hard copy held separately.

Card catalogue: News card catalogue.

Computerised database: Computerised database. Library staff catalogues news and a selection of programmes. A project is in place to update the cataloguing on legacy holdings.

Conservation policy: Transmitted news, current affairs and documentary programmes are held permanently. Other material is held depending on content.

Access: Opening hours: Mon-Fri, 09.15–17.30. Wheelchair access.

Viewing and listening facilities: Viewing on premises. Sale.

Charges: Research charges for all requests. Charges for facilities and handling. Royalty charges. A price list is available upon request.

Copyright: Copyright held on RTE productions, rights permitting. Illustrations and music copyright information is held separately.

UNIVERSITY COLLEGE DUBLIN, DEPARTMENT OF IRISH FOLKLORE

University College
Belfield
DUBLIN 4
Ireland
Tel: +353 1 706 8216
Fax: +353 1 706 1144
Web: http://www.ucd.ie/~arts/folklore.htm

Contact: Professor Séamas Ó'Catháin.

E-mail: seamus.ocathain@ucd.ie

Built up from 1935, since the foundation of the Irish Folklore Commission. In 1971, the commission was transferred, staff and holdings, to University College Dublin, where it became the Department of Irish Folklore. The material has been collected from various sources – field work, loan, gift, etc. All of the collection deals with some aspect of folklore and folk life. Most of it relates to Ireland.

Video and film holdings: Video: 300 hours. Amateur, documentary, folklore material (own productions).
Video components: VHS Video, hi-band U-matic, lo-band U-matic, Beta/Beta-SP.
Film: 3 hours. 1% colour film, 99% black and white film. Documentary.
Film components: Positive Film.

Storage: Purpose built storage in archive.

Computerised database: Available.

Documentation: Written accessions book in Irish and English.

Access: Access available. Mon-Fri 14.30–17.30. (By arrangement only for video and sound.)

Viewing and listening facilities: Viewing on premises.

Copyright: Copyright for most of the collection is held by the Department of Irish Folklore. Copyright advice available.

Film and Televison
Researchers

John ABBOTT

3 Roland Gardens, London SW7 3PE. Tel: 020 7370 4810. Fax: 020 7373 8865 E-mail: abbott@ibis.hi-net.co.uk

Services offered: Principal of IBIS Media Concepts, a media consultancy which offers advisory services for the development of inter-archive research access through electronic image databasing services. Also offers general research, legal services and rights management.

Special skills and interests: International sourcing. Military and aerospace. Pacific Rim developments.

Jack AMOS

106A Torriano Avenue, London NW5 2SD. Tel: 020 7424 9929.

Services offered: Film and video researcher for all types of production.

Special skills and interests: 20th-century politics and history.

TV programme/film credits: *Film Century; Mission – Berlin; From Princess to Queen; Ride On (II and III); The Windsors; The Churchills; A-Z of TV; 1001 Nights of TV; TV Heaven; Century, The Real Prince Philip, The Real Queen Mother.*

Jim ANDERSON

51 Smithy Brow, Croft, Warrington WA3 7DA. Tel: 01925 765409. E-mail: andersonjim2000@aol.com

Services offered: Producer/Director/Assistant producer/Film researcher for television and film, especially archive-based programming. Format development and consultancy. Copyright clearance UK and worldwide.

Special skills and interests: Sport, the history of television, award shows, comedy, business, science, environment, farming.

TV programme/film credits: *BAFTA Awards 2000* (ITV), *Eye On the World series – The Role of the Camera in Entertainment, Medicine and War* (Discovery), *Fever Pitch* (Feature film/C4), *They Think It's All Over* (BBC1); *Fantasy Football League* (BBC2*)*, *Glory Glory '68* (ITV), *TV's Finest Failures* (BBC1), *Great Speeches – Mandela* (BBC Choice*)*, *The Best of British – Barbara Windsor/Cliff Richard* (BBC 1), *EC"92, Improving Performance, GNVQs and IT in Business* (BBC Select).

Helen BENNITT

213 Tufnell Park Road, London N7 0PX. Tel: 020 7609 8568. Mobile: 07775 994508.
E-mail: helenbennitt@hotmail.com

Services offered: Freelance film, video and stills research world-wide for television, feature films, commercials and publications covering current affairs, social documentary, features and entertainment. Copyright clearances and negotiations undertaken.

TV programme/film credits: *South Bank Shows; Smashie and Nicey – End of an Era; Gettys – Rags to Riches, BAFTA 1996 – 100 Years of Cinema, Bob's Fab Ads, Who's Line Is It Anyway, The Aliens Are Coming, Heroes of Comedy, This Is Your Life.*

Rosalind BENTLEY

46 Clockhouse Road, Beckenham, Kent BR3 4JP. Tel: 020 8658 3164. Fax: 020 8658 3164.
E-mail: rosalindbentley@cwcom.net

Services offered: Experienced in international co-productions with good contacts in libraries and collections, both in UK and abroad. Copyright negotiations and clearances obtained within a set budget. Member of FOCAL and BUFVC.

Special skills and interests: Twenty years experience in all fields of film and stills research for BBC television and independent companies. Particular interests include World War I, World War II, all areas of history, geography, art, film and current affairs.

TV programme/film credits: BBC: *World About Us; Great Journeys; Arafat; Burma Road; Dunkirk; D-Day; China – Red Dynasty; What Did You Do in the War Auntie?* Antelope: *Midas Touch; Royal Collection; Royal Gardens; Mao; Baden-Powell.* Paravision: *Spaceship Earth; Seven Wonders of the World.* Uden: *History of Technology.* RAF: *Bomber Command.* 3BM Television: *Hiroshima; Suez.* IMAX: *Antarctica.* TV New Zealand: *Freyberg; Spanish Civil War, New Zealand at War.* ABC Australia: *Indonesia; RAAF Anniversary; History of the BBC; Berlin Airlift; Desert Rats; John Betjeman; Holocaust on Trial.* Jigsaw, USA: *Pacific Century.* Longhow, USA: *Tiananmen Square.* WDR, Germany: *Hungerstrike* Jeremy Isaacs: *Millennium.* Twenty Twenty: *Singapore Mutiny.* Full list available on application.

Steve BERGSON

15 Marden Road, Staplehurst, Kent TN12 0NF. Tel: 01580-893242. Fax: 01580-890143

E-mail: 00416.312@compuserve.com or E-mail: 56004@ port.almac.co.uk

Services offered: Research, acquisition and clearance of all materials – film, video, stills, audio for all kinds of production – TV, corporate, features, print and multimedia. Own facilities.

Special skills and interests: All-round production experience, some languages, computer literacy, wide range of interests.

TV programme/film credits: *Twentieth Century* (ABC Television); *Cold War* (Jeremy Isaacs Productions); *The New Jerusalem* (Barraclough Carey); *Sleeping Beauty Rediscovered* (Gold Winner, Houston; TVS); *Unit 731* (Gold Winner, New York; TVS); *The Duel* (JBM TV); *Finest Hour* (Brook Lapping); *Coppers* (Historic Films).

Jane BIGGER

36 Ross Street, Cambridge CB1 3BX. Tel: 01223 415526. Fax: 01223-415526

Services offered: Associate Producer, researcher, consultancy.

Special skills and interests: Popular culture, social history, comedy, cinema.

TV programme/film credits: Associate producer: *Scotland v. England* (Absolutely Productions/Channel 4); *Jack Dee's Glamorama* (Open Mike/Channel 4); *Paul Merton's Life of Comedy* (Tiger Aspect/BBC); *Rory Bremner...Who Else* (Kudos/Channel 4); *40 Years of Children's ITV* (LWT). Consultant: *1996 BAFTA Awards – 100 Years of Cinema* (LWT). Researcher/film researcher: *The Moon Walk – 25th Anniversary* (BBC); *History of Technology* (Uden/BBC); *Birth Night* (BBC); *Weather Night* (BBC); *Arena – Punk and the Sex Pistols* (Wall to Wall TV/BBC); *Fear in the Dark – the Horror Movie* (Classic Films/Channel 4); *Saturday Night at the Movies* (Initial/ITV); *The Word* (24 Hour Productions/Channel 4); *Whose Line Is It Anyway?*; *This Is David Lander*; *Norbet Smith – A Life* (Hat Trick/ Channel 4). Jane Bigger has also worked in the ITN and BBC Film Archives.

Jo CHILES

111 Holmefield Crescent, London W10 5FR. Tel: 020 8960 2193

Services offered: I am a senior archive film and stills researcher with eleven years of experience in TV, corporate video and multimedia. My responsibilities have included bringing in extra researchers according to project needs and managing and training junior researchers.

TV programme/film credits: (2000/2001) *Tarrant on TV* (LWT); (2000) *Lost Worlds – The Story of Archaeology* (C4); *Loves Like a Dog* (4Later); (1999) *Pornography – A Secret History of Civilization* (C4); *The Trip* (Series 2, C4). (1998) *The Adam and Joe Show* (C4); *Find a Fortune* (ITV); *The Trip*, (Series 1, C4); *Turn On TV – 4* (Home Box Office Channel; *The Complete Cosmos* (C4). (USA, 1997) *Tomorrow Never Dies* (18th James Bond feature film). Full list of series and programmes available on application.

Karen COLBRON

126 Gibson Gardens, Stoke Newington, London N16 7HH. Tel: 020 7249 7510. E-mail: k.colbron@virginnet. co.uk

Services offered: Film and stills research.

Special skills and interests: Specialising in architectural footage and stills. A well developed interest in commercials, both domestic and foreign.

TV programme/film credits: *Bowie at Fifty*; *Country Night* (BBC); *Bookmark Special – H.G. Wells*; *Bookmark – A.S. Byatt*; *Skinhead Farewell*; *Saturday Night Clive*; *Sunday Night Clive*; *One Foot in the Past*; *The Other House of Windsor*, *Bookmark – Charles Bukowski*; *Peter York's Eighties*; *Clive James on the Eighties*.

Maggi COOK

E-mail: plex@dircon.co.uk

Services offered: Film researcher with special interest in new media. Twenty years experience working as film researcher across the full range of television programming.

Special skills and interests: Special interest in nonfiction film for documentary and social history productions. Since gaining MA in Interactive Media from the RCA in 1996 has combined film research with designing CD-ROM/Internet projects. Please contact for full credit list.

Alex COWAN

12 The Stile, Heath and Reach, Leighton Buzzard, Bedfordshire LU7 0BL. Tel: 01525-237602. Mobile: 07768 213719. Fax: 01525-237602. E-mail: alex.jane@mcmail. com. Website: http://www.archive.research.mcmail. com

Services offered: Film and general research; copyright clearance; film archiving.

Special skills and interests: Regional film archives, amateur film.

TV programme/film credits: *People's Century*; *Fine Cut*; *Secret Lives*; *Dispatches*; *A Bill Called William*; *The American Dream*; *Without Walls*; *Secret History, Disabled Century, War in Europe, Equinox, Everyman, Modern Times*.

Tony DALTON

185 Wandsworth Bridge Road, Fulham, London SW6 2TT. Tel: 020 7736 1009. Fax: 020 7734 1052. Mobile: 07831 434346. Email: dalton@chronicles.demon.co.uk

Services offered: Archive consultancy/research. Writer, director and producer.

Special skills and interests: Wide knowledge of feature films (especially with reference to public domain), copyright clearances, feature film stills and historical footage.

TV programme/film credits: *Fame in the 20th Century*; *The Promised Land*; *Secret Lives: Edward VIII The Traitor King*; *Errol Flynn*; *Princes Margaret*; *Margot Fonteyn*; *Arena – Tony Bennett's New York*; *Hamlet* (feature*); Century in Motion: History of Transportation*; *The Cleopatra Files*; *Return to Normandy*; *The Lolita Story*; *Animal Farm* (feature); *The Final Day: Illuminations* (8-part series on cinema); *The Stork & the Syringe*; *How to Get Ahead in Film*; *And the World Was Bond*; *Dispatches: GM Foods*; *When Brendan Met Trudy* (feature); *Sinatra: The Millennium Movies Show*; *Star Wars: The Making of a Myth*; *Working With Dinosaurs* (Ray Harryhausen); *British Academy Awards* (film awards).

Valerie EVANS

54 Mackenzie Road, Beckenham, Kent BR3 4RZ. Tel: 020 8776 7251. E-mail: val_evans@cwctv.net

Services offered: Freelance film, television and stills research. Copyright clearance and negotiation of UK and World rights.

Special skills and interests: Fourteen years experience of archive research for comedy, documentary, political and entertainment programmes, including fee negotiation and world copyright clearances, working within a budget to tight deadlines.

TV programme/film credits: *The Way They Were* (ITV); *Bremner, Bird & Fortune* (C4); *Rory Bremner Who Else?* (C4); *TV Nightmares* (ITV); *World's Weirdest Television* (Sky1); *End of the Year Show with Angus Deayton* (BBC); *Moving Pictures* (BBC); *Saturday Night Clive* (BBC); *Clive James on 1993* (BBC); *Ceausescu: Behind the Myth* (BBC); *South Bank Show* (ITV); *The Thatcher Factor* (C4); *A Week in Politics* (C4).

Liz FAY

Fay Research, 17 West Grove, Greenwich, London SE10 8QT. Tel: 020 8691 0242. Fax: 020 8691 2336. E-mail: liz.fay@bt.click

Services offered: Complete film and video research service. Archive, feature film and stockshots sourced worldwide. Copyright negotiations and artists' clearances. 25 years' experience in television production and film research.

Special skills and interests: Research undertaken for factual television, television commercials, corporate videos, pop promos and videos.

TV programme/film credits: BBC – Corporate promotions. News 24, BBC World. Local Radio – *The Lipstick Years, Great Speeches of the World, The Foxhunting Debate*. Granada TV – *I've Got the Music in Me, Countdown to the Millennium*. LWT – *The Hidden Talents of the Rich and Famous*. Channel 4 – *The Real Peter Mandelson; So You Wanna Be on TV?*. Carlton TV – *The Guccis; The Roots of Rock*. Television commercials for *Financial Times,* Irish National Lottery, Smethwicks Brewery, Age Concern.

FILM RESEARCH & PRODUCTION SERVICES

Amanda Dunne, James Webb, Rooms 211-213, Mitre House, 177 Regent Street, London W1B 4JN. Tel: 020 7734 1525. Fax: 020 7734 8017. E-mail: frps@aol.com

Services offered: Film research – all types. All third-party copyright clearances. Access to international sources in the UK, Europe, the United States and Australia.

Special skills and interests: Cinema and TV commercials. Also Pop promos, documentaries, corporates and TV series.

TV programme/film credits: Major newspaper commercials. *Five Women Painters*; *After the Warming*; *Oceans of Wealth*; *Acid From the Sky*; *Mission Impossible*; *Double Acts*; *Dance With a Stranger*; *Good Looks*. Numerous pop promos including *Culture Club, AC/DC, Cliff Richard* and *Ultravox*.

Margaret FRANK

33 Mary Peters Drive, Greenford, Middlesex UB6 0SS. Tel: 020 8864 2578. E-mail: mafrank@madasafish.com

Services offered: Film research and copyright clearance.

TV programme/film credits: *Have I Got News for You* (BBC; Winner of BAFTA and British Comedy Award); *History File: The World Since 1945* (BBC); *Landmarks* (BBC); *Clean Slate* (BBC); *The Education Programme* (BBC); *Watch: Weather* (BBC Schools); *The Royle Family* (BBC); *The Viewing Room* (BBC); *Numbertime* (BBC).

Gerard HEALY

68 Kempe Road, London NW6. Tel: 020 8969 7654. E-mail: gerry.healy@online.rednet.co.uk

Services offered: Freelance film researcher/archive consultant.

TV programme/film credits: Senior film archivist to British Movietonenews 1987-1994; film archivist to British Pathe News 1981-1987. *Margaret Thatcher, The Path to Power and Beyond* (David Paradine Productions, BBC); *The Minefield* – programme dealing with psychoanalysis (Diverse Productions, Channel 4); *Jancis Robinson's Wine Course* (Eden Productions, BBC); *50th Anniversary D-Day* (Outside Broadcast Programme, BBC); *Presley Meets the President* (Illuminations Television; Channel 4); *Life of Louis Mountbatten* (Atlantic Productions, Channel 4); *Anglia at War* (Fourth Estate Productions, Anglia Television); *Battle for Goose Green* (Barraclough Carey, Channel 4); *Living Forever* (BBC); *The Promised Land* (BBC); *Children of the Revolution* (BBC); *Violent Earth* (CD-ROM); *Electricity and Magnetism* (CD-ROM); *Habitats* (CD-ROM).

Liz HEASMAN

8 Lansdowne House, Lansdowne Road, London W11 3LP. Tel: 020 7229 9770. Fax: 020 7229 9770. E-mail: lizheasman@compuserve.com

Services offered: Film, stills, copyright and factual research for television, exhibitions and publishing.

Special skills and interests: Research on all; additional specialisation in cinema, television and performing arts.

TV programme/film credits: Projects include: *A Walk Through the 20th Century* (Centennial Exhibition, Lisbon); *London on Film* (Museum of London*); Sir – Letters to The Times 1914–1918* (BBC); *The Worlds of Charlie Chaplin* (MOMI); The Museum of the Moving Image; London Film Commission.

Susan HUXLEY

15 Rockells Place, London SE22 0RT. Tel: 020 8299 4156.

Services offered: Film research in TV, feature film and factual archive. Copyright clearances for moving images, music and actors. Programme research, celebrities,

people and ideas. London and UK location research. Multimedia – corporate stills/picture research.

Special skills and interests: Working on factual documentaries, light entertainment and current affairs. Knowledge of feature film history. Archive and library resources in the UK and world-wide. Film and TV exhibition research.

TV programme/film credits: (2000) – *People's Planet – Cities, Nature, Searching for Paradise* (Antelope/NHK/ CNN); *20th Century Roll of Honour* (Saatchi/BA Commercial). (1999) – *The History of the Pop Video* ((C4/VH One); *Millennium Dome – Journey Zone* (Imagination); *The Best of British* (BBC). (1998) – *TV Nightmares* (LWT); *Twiggy's People* (Granada); *Mata Hari* (C4); (1997) – *U2 Pop Mart World Tour* (Dreamchaser). (1996/97) – *The Great Sell Off* (BBC1). (1995/96) - *How Do They Do That?* (BBC1). Earlier credits include: *Cold War* (Jeremy Isaacs/BBC); *The Palladium Story* (BBC); *Voltaire* (Channel Arte, Paris); *The Beat* – Film reviews (Carlton); *This Morning* (Granada); light entertainment and documentaries for LWT; documentaries for Channel 4 including *The Tommy Cooper Story*. Film Acquisitions Assistant at Channel 4. Exhibition Research at The Museum of the Moving Image, London, on many changing exhibitions e.g. *Ray Harryhausen, Jim Henson, Muybridge, The History of the Pop Video.*

Martin LEONARD

14 Chartwell Court, Manor Road, Barnet, Hertfordshire EN5 2JY. Tel: 020 8449 6049

Services offered: Media consultant and freelance film researcher. Archivist with over 30 years experience.

TV programme/film credits: Recent credits include *The Big Story* (ITV, 1993-97);

Dispatches (C4 1995-99); *Canterbury Tales* (C4 1996); *Ian Hislop's School Rules* (C4 1997); *The Real Story of...* (C4 1999-2000); *Queen Mother 100* (BBC 2000*); The War Behind the Wire* (BBC 2000).

Alison McALLAN

70 Half Acre Road, London W7 3JJ. Tel: 020 8567 4448. Fax: 020 8567 4448.

Services offered: Film research, negotiation and copyright clearance world-wide. Some experience with stills research.

Special skills and interests: Historical documentaries, current affairs; extensive research in Russia.

TV programme/film credits: (Carlton/C4): *Hell in the Pacific; Danger UXB;* (Twenty Twenty Television/C4):

Boer War. Jeremy Isaacs Productions: *Cold War* (for Turner Original Productions); BBC: *Timewatch, 25 Bloody Years, States of Terror, Reputations; Panorama.* Thames TV: *This Week, Waldheim – A Commission of Enquiry, Blake Escape* and many other documentaries.

Aileen MCALLISTER

50 Forest Road, Walthamstow, London E17 6JR. Tel: 07957 460314

Services offered: Film research and copyright clearance.

TV programme/film credits: *Battle Stations* (8-part series for A&E); *Hitler's Brides* (C4); *History in Action* (6-part series for C4); *I Witness* (5-part series for The History Channel); *Duel in the Desert* (A&E); *Cold War* (Film Archivist) (Turner Original Productions).

Janet McBRIDE

5 Buchanan Gardens, London NW10 5AD. Tel: Mobile: 0973-255473. E-mail: jmcbride@freeuk.com

Services offered: Producer of archive-based television programmes. Project development and consultancy.

Special skills and interests: Use of archive film in light entertainment and comedy programmes. Production skills ranging from project development to post-production. Languages: Turkish.

TV programme/film credits: ITV: *Fantasy World Cup Live; TV's Naughtiest Blunders.* BBC: *Shooting Stars; Fantasy Football League; The Frank Skinner Show; Staggering Stories of Ferdinand de Bargos; Rory Bremner; A Christmas Night With the Stars; Lenny Henry; Shooting Stars; Newsnight; Reportage.* Channel 4: *Almost Complete History of the Twentieth Century; Jo Brand through the Cakehole.*

Lin McCONNELL

Treadwell Ltd, Euston House, 21 Soulbury Road, Linslade, Leighton Buzzard, Bedfordshire LU7 7RL. Tel: 01525 852242. Fax: 01512 851002

Services offered: World-wide film, stills and information research for TV, film, advertising, corporate and publishing. Copyright clearance and negotiation; library management consultancy.

Special skills and interests: Social history, domestic and foreign news and current affairs, World War II, Russia.

TV programme/film credits: *One Day in September;*

Historyfile Russia; The Underworld (British crime); *Timewatch; History of Shopping.*

Stuart McKAY

30 Addison Road, Hove, East Sussex BN3 1TP. Tel: 01273 326356

Services offered: Archive research and copyright clearances.

Special skills and interests: Twenty years experience in the film and video archive industry, including fifteen years for ITN. Wide knowledge of events, personalities and politics, especially the from the 1950s onwards. Particular interest: youth culture and music.

TV programme/film credits: *Howard Goodall's Big Bangs* (major events in the history of music; *The Rise and Fall of the Mafia; Western Sahara: A Forgotton War; The American Nightmare* (horror movie directors talk about their early influences); *Biography* (including Prince Charles, Prince Philip. Mick Jagger, Idi Amin, Mikhail Gorbachev and Pol Pot); *Hellraisers* (excessive lifestyles of famous Brits from Oliver Reed to Liam Gallagher); *Diana: Her Life; Diana: The People's Princess; Disaster* (13-part series); *Faces of Islam; The Saudi Century* and various other education and corporate productions about Saudi Arabia.

Kathy MANNERS

48 Mervan Road, London SW2 1DU. Tel: 020 7326 4865. Mobile: 0976 924380. E-mail: kathymanners@hotmail.com

Services offered: Film researcher. Copyright Clearance.

TV programme/film credits: *Crawfie; The Nanny Who Couldn't Keep Mum; The 20th Century Garden* (C4); *Timewatch: The Germans We Keep* and *Sleeping With the Enemy; War of the Century* (4-part series); *Reputations; Kenneth Williams* (BBC); *A Parcel of Rogues* (C4); *Reputations: Bertrand Russell* (BBC); *Secret Lives: Lord Beaverbrook* (C4); *Inside Story* special: £830,000,000 – *Nick Leeson and the Fall of the House of Barings; The Late Show* (BBC).

Jane MERCER

10 Dallington Square, London, EC1V 0BZ. Tel: 020 7251 1009. E-mail: janemercer@compuserve.com

Services offered: Research to find and select film and television material internationally and covering all disciplines from light entertainment and feature films through to documentary and news and current affairs: preparing budgets.

Special skills and interests: Costings: clearing copyright and third-party rights: organising the transfer of material onto required formats. Languages: French, Italian. Special interests: 20th-century history, political, cultural, social and economic history.

TV programme/film credits: *Fame in the 20th Century* (BBC); *Korean War* (BBC); *Clive James Programmes* (BBC); *History of Television* (Granada TV); *Sword of Islam* (Granada TV); *Automania* (Central TV); *Viewpoint Kennedy* (Central); *The World of Arthur C. Clarke* (YTV).

Judy PATTERSON

26 Avenue Road, Highgate, London N6 5DW. Tel/Fax: 020 8340 1130. E-mail: judy@mailbox.co.uk

Services offered: Archive film research/consultancy. Programme Research and Associate Producer.

Special skills and interests: Extensive experience in documentary research and production. Special interest in medicine and health. Archive Consultant to Nobel Museum Stockholm for *2001 Centennial Exhibition*.

TV programme/film credits: Credits include *The Facts of Life* (C4); *Mau Mau (Secret History,* C4); *Windrush* (BBC series); *Science of the Impossible* (Discovery); *Pioneers* (BBC series); *Divine Magic* (Discovery/C4).

Bill RUDGARD – CCTV ARCHIVE

14 Ardilaun Road, London N5 2QR. Tel: 020 7226 4580. Fax: 020 7226 3317 E-mail: info@cctvarchive.com Website: http:www.cctvarchive.com

Services offered: Specialist in 'reality' TV and video.

Special skills and interests: Producer, director, researcher and musician.

TV programme/film credits: *American Robot Wars*; *Police Stop!* series; *Look at That* series; *Really Caught in the Act* series.

Peter SCOTT

63 Grove Lane, Camberwell, London SE5 8SP. Tel: 020 7701 3296. Mobile: 0468 594701. E-mail: pjscott21@hotmail.com

Services offered: World-wide film research.

Special skills and interests: Historical, arts and political documentaries. Contacts and knowledge of archives and sources world-wide.

TV programme/film credits: *Royal Biographies* (ITV); *Hitler and Stalin: Twin Tyrants* (C4); *The Real Diana*

Mosley (C4); *1939: Did We Have to Fight?* (C4); *About Face* (C4/WGBH); *Science At War* (BBC); *Reputations: John Wayne* (BBC). *Gulf War: A Television History* (BBC/WGBH); *Thatcher: The Downing Street Years* (BBC TV); *Reputations: Harold Macmillan* (BBC); *Decisive Weapons* (BBC/Discovery); *Wasted Windfall: 25 Years of North Sea Oil* (Channel 4); *Charles and Diana: The First Decade* (BBC Video).

Henry SCOTT-IRVINE

7 Shamrock Street, Clapham, London SW4 6HF. Tel: 020 7498 8202

Services offered: Rock and music TV archive consultant. Rock music TV documentary producer.

Special skills and interests: History of rock and pop on TV. Archive TV programming. Copyright. Digital remastering/audio and visual.

TV programme/film credits: *Abba – Winner Takes It All* (Iambic/ITV); *Dr John – Anutha Zone* (Dreamchaser/C4); *Music of the Millennium – The Top 100 Albums* (Archive Producer – The Means of Production/C4); *Elton at 50* (Producer – W A Bong/John Reid for TX on 36 networks/global); *Song Stories – A Whiter Shade of Pale* (Producer/Director – Initial); *All Back to Mine* (Associate producer of 16 x 30 minute programmes for Channel X/C4); *The Real John Lennon* (Planet Wild for C4); *Classic Albums – Series 3* (Isis for ITV); *Two Rooms – Celebrating the Songs of Elton John* (LWT/Polygram); *George Martin Presents Music* (6 x 1-hour programmes for Walt Disney and Buena Vista TV); *Elton John's Greatest Hits* (Polygram Video); *Marc Bolan – The Legendary Years* (Channel 4); *The White Room* (music series, Initial TV for Channel 4).

Diane SEDGWICK

11 Manor Court Road, London W7 3EJ. Tel/Fax: 020 8567 8286. Mobile: 0976-294324. E-mail: diana.sedgwick@ntlworld.com

Services offered: Film, stills and copyright clearance.

Special skills and interests: Comprehensive knowledge of television programme-making from budgeting and shooting to editing, copyright clearance and post-production paperwork.

TV programme/film credits: Film research credits include *Brendel at 70* (Rosetta Pictures/BBC); *Why Trains Crash* (Darlow Smithson/C40; *After They Were Famous* (Yorkshire TV/ITV); *Fortean TV Xmas Files* (Rapido/C4); *Southern Eye* (BBC); *Leslie Crowther – A Tribute* (BBC); *Auntie's TV Favourites* (BBC); *Murder in*

Belgravia (BBC); *Inside Story* (BBC); *Cine Memo* (Third Eye/BBC); *Forty Minutes* (BBC).

Gill SHEPHERD

87 Elm Park Mansions, Park Walk, London, SW10 0AP. Tel: 020 7352 1770. E-mail: rgbshepherd@msn.com

Services offered: Film and stills researcher with copyright clearances and negotiation skills.

Special skills and interests: Politics and history.

TV programme/film credits: *Great Romances of the 20th Century* (BBC World-wide*)*; *Sex Bomb* (series on the sexual revolution for C4); *Secrets of World War II* (History Channel); *Spy Web* (series on espionage for the History Channel); *The Affair* (World War II drama documentary, BBC/HBO); *Proximity* (World War II documentary, American PBS TV); *What Has Become of Us?* (4 x 60 mins series about post-war Britain, Channel 4); *All the Presidency Men* (Winner of Europe's Prix Stendhal, *Dispatches* Special); *Democracy in Danger* (*Dispatches* Special); *Frontiers* (documentary about the Northern Ireland border, BBC); *A Vote for Hitler* (drama documentary, Channel 4); *Low* (documentary about political cartoonist David Low, Channel 4).

Declan SMITH

134 Coronation Avenue, Victorian Road, London N16 8DX. Tel/Fax: 020 7241 4510. E-mail: declansmith@hotmail.com

Services offered: Archive film and picture research and copyright clearance.

Special skills and interests: Good working knowledge of German, Italian and French.

TV programme/film credits: *Weekend World* (LWT); *The Media Show* (Wall to Wall TV/C4); *A Night With Alan Bennett*; *Granadaland, Python Night* and other television history projects for BBC2; *Walking the (Berlin) Wall, Bauhaus – Face of the 20th Century, Fellowship of the Air* (BBC2); biographical documentaries for BBC2's *Reputations* and Channel 4's *The Real...*, including films on Muhammed Ali, Alfred Kinsey, Alfred Hitchcock, Dr Benjamin Spock, Lee Strasberg, Billie Jean King, Simon Wiesenthal, Erich von Daeniken, etc. *One Foot in the Past; The Gay Rock and Roll Years* and *It's Not Unusual; Endgame in Ireland* (series on the peace process); *TV Heroes – Rolf Harris; Pinky and Perky; Fanny Craddock.*

Catherine SUROWIECW

34 Saint Paul's Road, London N1 2QW. Tel: 020 7704 2794. Fax: 020 7704 2794. E-mail: catherine_surowiec@compuserve.com

Services offered: Research for publications, filmographies, bibliographies, chronologies. Film history. Also editing and proof-reading.

Special skills and interests: Film and cultural history. Silent film, transition to sound; early talkies; musicals; vaudeville and music hall. Art direction, set and costume design. Computer literate. Language: French, some Italian.

Deborah TOWNSEND

Tel: 020 8340 2008. Mobile: 07747 606274. E-mail: debbie.townsend@walltowall.co.uk

Services offered: World-wide film, video and stills research and copyright clearance.

TV programme/film credits: *When Dinosaurs Ruled* (TLC); *Naked Planet* (C4); *Deluge* (C4); *When Money Went Mad – Story of the South Sea Bubble* (C4); *Into the Flames* series 1 & 2 (C5/TLC); *Building the Biggest* (C4/TLC); *How Do They Do That?* (BBC); *Disneytime* (BBC/Buena Vista); *Extreme Machines* (TLC); *BAFTA Advertising Awards* (BSKB); *Jameson Tonight* (Sky TV); *Kilroy* series (BBC); *Surprise Chefs* (Meridian/Action Time).

Philip VAUGHAN

215 Goldhawk Road, London W12 8E. Tel: 020 8743 4432. Fax: 0181-740 1435

Services offered: Film, tape and library research. Copyright clearance.

Special skills and interests: Military, World War I, World War II and NATO. Language: French.

Evelyn VELLEMAN

79 Canfield Gardens, London NW6 3EA. Tel: 020 7624 7807. Fax: 020 7624 7807 E-mail: classmuse@attglobal.net

Services offered: Freelance film researcher specialising in classical music.

TV programme/film credits: *The Art of Conducting – Great Conductors of the Past*, a 120-minute archive-based programme co-produced by the BBC, IMG Artists and Teldec Classic International; promotional video for Sony Classical, Masterworks Heritage Series; *Art of Conducting II*, a 120-minute archive-based programme produced by Teldec Classics International; University of California Press – CD-ROM research for international dictionary of conductors.

Christine WHITTAKER

12 Mayfield Avenue, London W4 1PW. Tel/Fax: 020 8995 0333. Mobile: 07967 646509.

E-mail: christine@whittgc.demon.co.uk

Services offered: Archive research, production and consultancy. I have years of experience working for the BBC and independent companies, and have been in charge of archive research on many major series. I have extensive knowledge of world-wide sources and speak French and German.

Special skills and interests: Social and political history; archive based documentaries.

TV programme/film credits: *All Our Working Lives*; *Now The War Is Over*; *An Ocean Apart*; *Out of the Doll's House*; *Nippon – Time Watch*; *Pandora's Box*; *People's Century*; *Dangerous Company*; *Sex and Shopping*; *The Hunt*.

Cy YOUNG

58 Oliphant Street, Queen's Park, London W10 4EF. Mobile: 07768 844273 Fax: 020 8968 9086

Services offered: Comprehensive archive (film and video) consultancy. Prints located, copyright established, royalties negotiated, budgets prepared, from pre-production to post-production.

Special skills and interests: Other activities include – magazine articles on film and television history, background research for Kevin Brownlow's official biography of David Lean. Illustrated lecture on film research at the National Film School in Beaconsfield – all supported by a personal collection of vintage film and television ephemera for reference.

TV programme/film credits: Granada Television: *Clapperboard* (movie history and new releases); Open Media for C4; *Equinox – The Big Sleep* (hypnotism); LWT: *South Bank Show – David Bailey* (arts biography); *River Thames* (oral history documentary series); Thames Television: *A Hard Act to Follow* (Buster Keaton biography – Emmy Award for Film Research); *Heroes of Comedy* (performance footage, 3 series*); Paul Merton's Palladium Story* (2-part documentary); Teliesyn for SC4 and C4: *Reel Truth?* (silent newsreel fakes); BBC: *Laughter in the House (Omnibus* 3-part history of sitcom); Tiger Aspect Productions: *Not 'Arf* (on disc jockeys) for Sky; *Kevin and Perry's Girlfriends* (teenage documentary) for BBC. Many others.

Research Services and Organisations

BRITISH UNIVERSITIES FILM & VIDEO COUNCIL (BUFVC)

77 Wells Street, LONDON W1T 3QJ Tel: 020 7393 1500
Fax: 020 7393 1555 E-mail: ask@bufvc.ac.uk
Web: http://www.bufvc.ac.uk

Research and Viewing Services

During the last two decades the BUFVC has expanded and extended its services to underpin the scholarly use of film and television. These services are available to BUFVC members and to staff working in BUFVC member institutions. Viewing services are charged at a discount rate to members and there is a special grade of membership tailored to researchers.

BUFVC Information Service

The BUFVC's Information Service maintains a number of databases of value to researchers which are available online, or may be interrogated by visitors to BUFVC's premises in central London.

The British Universities Newsreel Project (BUNP) – a database of British cinema newsreel stories released between 1910 and 1979. Online access restricted to UK higher and further education and to BUFVC member institutions and researcher members. at http://www. bufvc.ac.uk/newsreels. *(See entry below for further details.)*

AVANCE – a list of some 25,000 film and television programmes which may be suitable for use in higher and further education. AVANCE includes a comprehensive listing of distributors' information enabling searches to identify publishers of audio-visual material. Online access free to all at http://www.bufvc.ac.uk/databases.

Television Index – a selective database of British television programmes transmitted via terrestrial services. On card index and classified by subject from 1987, and online for programmes from 1 July 1995. Online access free to all at http://www.bufvc.ac.uk/databases. The Television Index will not be added to beyond the end of 2001, when it will be replaced by the BUFVC's developing *Television and Radio Index for Learning and Teaching (TRILT)*, a comprehensive listing of UK television and radio at http://www.bufvc.ac.uk/databases.

BUFVC Gateway – an online gateway of websites relevant to the use of moving images and sound in higher and further education. All sites have been evaluated by BUFVC staff, and the categories include academic disciplines such as Art, Drama, History, Media Studies and Science, as well as general resources for film and television. The gateway will be available from April 2001 at http://www.bufvc.ac.uk/gateway

Researcher's Guide Online (RGO) – the online version of this *Researcher's Guide* has been developed with funding from the Researcher Support Libraries Programme. The RGO enables users to define searches by collection title, subject, index term and medium. Each record has live e-mail and weblinks, and the data will be constantly updated by the BUFVC's Information Service at http://www.bufvc.ac.uk/rgo

The BUFVC's Information Service holds a reference library holding over 3000 books, some 100 periodicals and newsletters, current catalogues from more than 1000 British and overseas distributors of audio-visual materials, and a number of special documentation collections, all of which are of value to those researching film and television sources.

Visits and reader facilities available by appointment. Contact BUFVC Information Service. Tel: 020 7393 1506.

Viewing Services

The Council has facilities for viewing the following media:

Film

35mm (comopt/commag) Steenbeck, 16mm (comopt/commag/sepmag) Steenbeck and projection facilities, 9.5mm and 8mm projection facilities.

BUFVC also has a 16mm 'video Steenbeck' capable of creating (from commag, comopt and sepmag material) viewing/audition copies with burnt-in identification and running time.

Videocassette

VHS, S-VHS, Hi-8, Betamax, Philips 1500, U-matic lo-band, U-matic hi-band, Betacam, DV, DVCAM, DVPRO.

Videotape

1/2-inch Sony CV2100, 1/2-inch Sony EIAJ

Videodisc

LaserVision CAV/CLV

BUFVC has the capability to playout video recordings from PAL, NTSC and SECAM standards in all formats via low-cost standards converting device.

Multimedia

BUFVC has CD-ROM playout facilities for both PC and Mac platforms.

Viewing services available by appointment, differential charges for BUFVC members and non-members. Further details from the Assistant Director, BUFVC. Tel: 020 7393 1503.

BRITISH UNIVERSITIES NEWREEL PROJECT

British Universities Film & Video Council,
77 Wells Street, LONDON W1T 3QJ
Tel: 020 7393 1508 Fax: 020 7393 1555
E-mail: newsreels@bufvc.ac.uk

Contact: Luke McKernan

At the heart of the British Universities Newsreel Project (BUNP) is a database of 160,000 newsreel stories shown in British cinemas between 1910 and 1979, which is available on CD-ROM (PC/Mac) and online at www.bufvc. ac.uk/newsreels. It is the only centralised index of British newsreel production, and marks the culmination of over twenty-five years' commitment from the BUFVC to the newsreels as a source of academic study and a resource for film researchers.

The BUNP is based on the data originally gathered for the Slade Film History Register, which was created over thirty years ago. The launch of the *British National Film Catalogue* in 1963 guaranteed future historians a comprehensive listing of all films produced in Britain. Yet this made the absence of an earlier catalogue even more apparent, and in 1969 Thorold Dickinson, Professor of Film at the Slade School of Fine Art, University College London, established the Slade Film History Register, with the aid of a grant from the Social Science Research Council. His intention was to complement the *British National Film Catalogue* with a central register of film material created before 1963, and it was hoped that the Slade Film History Register would do for historic films what the National Register of Archives, established in 1945, was already doing for the nation's historic written documents.

The Register was to include all films of historical significance, but its first priority was to collect the surviving newsreel issue sheets. These list the contents of each bi-weekly issue, and form an invaluable guide to the estimated 200,000 cinema news stories released between the launch of *Pathé's Animated Gazette* in 1910 and the closing of the *British Movietone News* in 1979. An archive of issue sheets was quickly assembled, and the Register staff also compiled two selective card catalogues, one a subject index to the 30,000 newsreel stories considered of particular historical significance, and the other a title catalogue of 6,000 documentary and non-fiction films produced between 1914 and 1960.

The newsreel companies and film archives gave their assistance to the project, and the copies are now held of the issue sheets for the following British newsreels and cinemagazines:

Topical Budget	1917–1931
Gaumont Graphic	1910–1932
Pathé Gazette/Pathé News	1919–1970
Eve's Film Review	1921–1933
Empire News Bulletin	1926–1932
Gaumont Sound News	1929–1933
British Movietone News	1929–1979
Universal News	1930–1956
Pathétone Weekly	1930–1941
Pathé Pictorial	1931–1969
British Paramount News	1931–1957
Gaumont British News	1934–1959
Warwork News	1942–1945

The grant from the Social Science Research Council came to an end in 1973. For two years the Slade Film History Register continued its work with financial support from University College and, latterly, from the British Universities Film & Video Council, but this also ceased in 1975. Without funds the Register's work of cataloguing and indexing had to be suspended, its staff dispersed, and its records were transferred for safekeeping to the BUFVC. The BUFVC was able to maintain a small enquiry service for these records, which were consulted by as many film and television producers as by academics, but in 1976 it was felt necessary to establish a Working Party to consider the future of the whole project.

The Working Party reported in 1977. It recommended that the Register should be relaunched as 'a staffed register...in constant direct contact with the owners or keepers of collections', and should be enlarged to include television. This was impossible without additional funding, but the BUFVC did respond to an additional recommendation for a comprehensive directory 'of film and television collections in the United Kingdom'. In 1981 it published the first edition of the *Researcher's Guide to British Film & Television Collections*, edited by Elizabeth Oliver. This gave details of more than 120 audiovisual archives, which rose to 160 for the second edition in 1985, over 200 for the third edition in 1989, almost 250 for the fourth in 1993, and over 300 for the fifth edition in 1997. This sixth edition contains almost 550 entries, and the data has been made available over the Internet as the Researcher's Guide Online (RGO) for the first time.

The BUFVC continued to search for sufficient funding to relaunch the Slade Film History Register, and in the meantime maintained its enquiry service for academics and film researchers, based around the newsreel issue sheets. The BUFVC also encouraged research into British newsreels through a series of specialist publications, beginning in 1983 with the first volume of the

Researcher's Guide to British Newsreels, edited by James Ballantyne. This was followed by the publication of the complete *British Newsreels Issue Sheets 1913-79 on Microfiche* in 1984, whilst the second volume of the *Researcher's Guide to British Newsreels* appeared in 1988, and the third and final volume in 1993.

Then, in 1994, came a breakthrough in funding, when the BUFVC made a successful application to the Higher Education Funding Council for money to computerise the newsreel issue sheets. The original British Universities Newsreel Project ran from 1995 to 1999, and with a staff of four (three based at the BUFVC offices in London, and a fourth in the British Movietonews office in Denham) 160,000 newsreel stories were even-tually transferred to the database. The British Universities Newsreel Project Database was made available as a cross-platform CD-ROM and online (accessible to UK higher and further education, BUFVC member institutions and member researchers only) in March 2000.

The Newsreel Project involved more than the computerisation of the issue sheets. Each newsreel issue was broken into its component stories, which were then key-worded to assist searching. The keywording was based on the systems used in film libraries and photographic archives, but was tailored to the peculiarities of the news-reels and the needs of academics. Each story also carries a note of the number of items on the reel in which it appeared, and the position of that story in the reel, in order to preserve the context of the original release. The full text of the database can be scanned for particular events or individuals, or single fields can be searched. It is also possible to access the material by date, or to search chronologically through one company's output.

In 1998 Reuters Television generously donated to the BUFVC a collection of some 40,000 newsreel documents relating to *British Paramount News, Gaumont British News* and *Universal News*. These documents included assignment sheets, cameramen's dope sheets, commentary scripts, shot lists and ephemera such as newspaper clippings, sports programmes and leaflets which the cameramen used as guidance in shooting a news story. This collection formed the basis of a four-year extension to the BUNP, the British Universities Newsreel Scripts Project (BUNSP), with funding 1999-2003 from the Arts and Humanaties Research Board. The aim of the BUNSP is to add between 80,000 and 100,000 digitised newsreel documents to the existing newsreel database. Two staff in the BUFVC's London offices are adding these documents online, as well as additional data and subject keywords, under the supervision of the BUFVC's Head of Information. Supporting documentation, articles, a biographical database of newsreel staff, and audio files of interviews with newsreel cameraman are all

to be added as well. Work continues to identify new resources to augment the newsreel database, and two significant possible developments will be links to the moving images themselves, and an expansion into television news data.

FILM ARCHIVE FORUM

British Universities Film & Video Council
77 Wells Street
LONDON W1T 3QJ
Tel: 020 7393 1500
Fax: 020 7393 1555
E-mail: faf@bufvc.ac.uk
Web: http://www.bufvc.ac.uk/faf

Contact: Luke McKernan, Chair

The Film Archive Forum (FAF) was established in 1987 with the object of fostering an informal network of British moving image archives. Four archives sent representatives to the first meeting, but the Forum now contains twelve institutional members, representing all the national and regional public sector moving image archives of the UK. The Forum is chaired by the Head of Information at the British Universities Film & Video Council (BUFVC), currently Luke McKernan. Full membership remains institutional, although others can be invited to attend Forum meetings as Observing Members.

The Forum takes an interest in all the archival aspects of the moving image. It has particular interest in the preservation of nitrate film, acetate film, and video-tape; the training of archivists, acquisitions policy, standards for archives, copyright, co-operation with film laboratories, and contacts with foreign archives. The twelve archives represent the best practice in preservation, access, and exhibition for film collections in the UK, and are separated from the main run of film libraries by their commitment to the preservation of the country's moving image heritage, not simply its commercial reuse.

Over the years a handful of national archives has developed into a network covering the whole country. The oldest members of the FAF are the Imperial War Museum Film and Video Archive, which dates back at least to 1920, and the National Film and Television Archive, which was founded in 1935 as a division of the British Film Institute, itself founded in 1933. The next creation of a national public film archive came forty years later, when in 1976 what is now the Scottish Screen Archive was established as the Scottish Film Archive by the Scottish Film Council. In 1989 the Wales Film and Television Archive was set up in Aberystwyth under the auspices of the Welsh

Arts Council, becoming part of Sgrin-Media Agency for Wales in 1997.

1976 also saw the creation of the first of the regional film archives, with the formation of the East Anglian Film Archive in Norwich, using pump-priming money from the University of Essex, the University of East Anglia, and the Eastern Arts Association. This was followed in 1977 by a research project based at Manchester Metropolitan University which led to the identification of significant volumes of local film material, and the creation of the North West Film Archive. In 1984 the Yorkshire Film Archive was initiated, originally as the Yorkshire Archive Film Search, and based at what is now the University College of Ripon and York St John.

In 1988 the Wessex Film and Sound Archive was created by the Hampshire Archives Trust, in 1992 the South East Film and Video Archive was established within the University of Brighton, and in 1993 the TSW Film & Television Archive for the South West was established in Plymouth.

By this time the areas which did not have archive provision were readily apparent, and the FAF has been instrumental in the creation of new regional archives to fill these gaps. The Northern Region Film and Television Archive, located in Newcastle and Middlesborough, was created in 1998, and in 2000 the Media Archive for Central England was initiated in Birmingham and is now located within the University of Nottingham. The FAF helps to bind these archives together as a network, through informal links and the exchange of news and ideas.

From the outset the Forum was particularly eager to establish a postgraduate course in film archiving at an institution of higher education in the UK. After much hard work, this became a reality in 1990 with the start of two one-year pilot courses at the University of East Anglia, leading to an MA degree. These pilot courses were a great success, and in 1992 the one-year MA in Film Archiving was formally recognised by the University of East Anglia. The annual intake is 8-10 students, and placements are arranged at the National Film and Television Archive, the Imperial War Museum Film & Video Archive and other regional archives.

With the imminent completion of the archive network, it became clear that the FAF should raise its profile as a body representing the best practice in UK film and moving image archiving, and as an advisor on national archive policy. At its meeting in December 1998 it was proposed that the FAF should give itself 'a clear voice and a set of principles', and through a series of meetings drew up the document *Moving History* (available free from the BUFVC), which was eventually published in April 2000. This document indicates how the national network of public sector moving image archives can be strengthened and consolidated. The lobbying conducted by the FAF has helped towards the acknowledgement by the Film Council, in its document *Film in England: A Development Strategy for Film and the Moving Image in the English Regions* (November 2000), of the need for regional film archives in England to be properly recognised and resourced.

Full members:

BFI Collections (National Film and Television Archive)
East Anglian Film Archive
Imperial War Museum Film & Video Archive
North West Film Archive
Scottish Screen Archive
South East Film & Video Archive
TSW Film & Television Archive for the South West
Wales Film and Television Archive
Wessex Film and Sound Archive
Yorkshire Film Archive

Emerging archive:

Media Archive for Central England
Northern Region Film and Television Archive

Observers:

Film Institute of Ireland
Northern Ireland Film Commission
Re:source

FEDERATION OF COMMERCIAL AUDIO VISUAL LIBRARIES INTERNATIONAL LTD (FOCAL)

South Hill Avenue,
SOUTH HARROW,
HA2 0DU
Tel: 020 8423 5853 Fax: 020 8933 4826
E-mail: info@focalint.org
Web: http://www.focalint.org

Contact: Anne Johnson

The Federation of Commercial AudioVisual Libraries (FOCAL) was founded in 1985 as an international professional trade association to represent commercial film/audiovisual libraries, large and small, general and specialized. FOCAL is unique and dedicated to the promotion of library and archive audio visual material in all media. FOCAL offers content holders and archive researchers an unparalleled opportunity to keep abreast of developments and to publicise and promote their own activities.

FOCAL is non-profit making and receives no sponsorship monies or financial support beyond its membership.

In order to give the organisation as broad a working base as possible, it was decided right from the start to create a wide-ranging membership. This now encompasses professional researchers and consultants, producers using substantial amounts of bought-in audiovisual material, the facility houses which handle the material, and any other related organisations or individuals such as lawyers, consultants manufacturers of stock and equipment, and specialised freight companies.

FOCAL now has a membership of over 360 companies, organisations and individuals on all six continents. To celebrate its tenth anniversary in 1995, a highly successful international meeting hosted by INA and Pathe Television Archive, was held in Paris, at which FOCAL's commitment to facilitating international liaison between a wide range of footage suppliers and their users was seen at its best and most convivial. In its fifteenth year (2000) the third international Conference was held in Berlin. This event provided a platform for a full and frank exploration of the uses to which moving and still pictures both old and new are currently being put, with as much emphasis on what is happening in the media now, as on the glories, controversies and curiosities of the past.

There have been many changes in the media since FOCAL was created in 1985, and FOCAL has had an important and active role in keeping its members fully informed on all fronts – technical, legal, financial and contractual. The quarterly FOCAL Journal, *Archive Zones*, plays an important part in this as does the monthly *Newsletter* to members. FOCAL regularly holds workshops and seminars on a wide range of industry-related subjects ranging from new copyright laws and supplying content for the multimedia market to how to lace up a Steenbeck.

The organisation has also been represented at the major international fairs such as MIPCOM, MIPTV, NATPE, MILIA, Sunny Side of the Doc and the London Production Show and played a major part in the international newsfilm conferences *Story of the Century I* and *II* held at London's National Film Theatre in October 1996 and September 1998. In 1997 FOCAL established its own website on the Internet in order to extend further its primary role of disseminating information within and about the world of audio-visual libraries.

FOCAL has grown from a UK-based body into a truly international network and now has two overseas chapters in France and USA. Both these bodies, while benefiting from the administration and well-developed communications network which FOCAL has built up since its inception, have launched programmes of activities designed to carry out at a local level FOCAL's

primary purpose of promoting the use of library film and audiovisual material.

FOCAL believes very strongly that sharing information and expertise as widely as possible within the community that uses, provides and cares about archive library film is the best way of pursuing this aim. There is no sense of commercial rivalry within the organisation, though this undoubtedly and quite properly exists outside, and there is felt to be great advantage in including within its walls the professional researchers whose experience and expertise many libraries acknowledge to be enormously beneficial. Similarly, the membership of several of the leading facility houses in the UK is also recognised as being invaluable, not least because of the speed with which the technical developments of recent years have happened.

To mix metaphors, FOCAL is a broad church and its members are very proud of FOCAL's continuing role as marriage brokers within the media. Much of the work undertaken by the FOCAL administration involves putting potential users of footage in touch with sources and suppliers – free of charge – but the organisation also intends to continue to play an increasing role in keeping existing libraries and researchers informed about the constantly changing world in which they work and helping to train and encourage newcomers. FOCAL looks forward to carrying on with this work for many years to come.

THE INTERNATIONAL ASSOCIATION FOR MEDIA AND HISTORY (IAMHIST)

Web: http://www.iamhist.org
Contacts: Christine Whittaker (President)
christine@whittgc.demon.co.uk.
Dan Leab (Treasurer) dleab@snet.net.
Rainer Rother (Secretary General) rother@dhm.de

The International Association for Media and History is a family of professional film and television broadcasters, scholars, and others who are passionately concerned about film, radio, television and their relations to history. Some members study the development of broadcasting and film and its relation to history. Others make programmes dealing with historical personalities and events. IAMHIST encourages research into all aspects of the relations between history and the audio-visual media. Members need access to film archives and libraries for our work, and seek to make them as accessible as possible. IAMHIST believes that those who do not understand film can never fully understand the world in which we live. That is why the organisation 1) holds bi-annual conferences, to which members and non-members are cordially invited. Recent themes include: changing identities in film, television and the new media; the historian and television; the Cold War.

2) publishes a scholarly journal, *The Historical Journal of Film, Radio and Television*, at a special price to members. Recent issues include a special issue devoted to Irish media history. The journal actively encourages contributions from new scholars and offers a prize each year for the best contribution from a young scholar.

3) organises an e-mail forum that enables members to respond to articles and reviews.

4) runs a website with critically evaluated links to related websites and news relevant to the worlds of history and broadcasting.

5) issues a newsletter *Close-Ups* to keep members in touch with plans and with each other.

PUBLIC RECORD OFFICE

Records Management Department
Public Record Office
Kew, RICHMOND, Surrey
TW9 4DU
Tel: 020 8876 3444 Fax: 020 8878 8905
Web: http://www.pro.gov.uk

Contact: Catherine Harding

Who looks after Public Record Films in the UK? The answer is The National Film and Television Archive (NFTVA), which currently forms part of the Collections Department of the British Film Institute (BFI). The National Film Archive was founded in 1935 to acquire, preserve and make permanently available a national collection of moving images which have lasting value as examples of the art and history of cinema and television, or as a documentary record of the twentieth century. It now holds over 350,000 titles dating from 1895 to the present day. The collection comprises features and short films, animation, documentaries, newsreels, television programmes, amateur films and videos, and includes public record films which it holds on behalf of the Public Record Office (PRO).

The PRO at Kew in Surrey is the National Archives for England, Wales and the United Kingdom. It stores and makes available to the public the records of central government. The original PRO in Chancery Lane in central London, which was built in the middle of the last century, did not have facilities for either storing or providing access to films. In 1977 the new PRO building at Kew was completed, and in 1995 an additional building at Kew was opened and the Chancery Lane building was closed. Although the new building at Kew contains specialist

facilities for storing photographic records, there are no provisions for either storing or providing access to records in the form of moving images.

The PRO's authority is derived from the Public Records Act 1958, section 10(1) of which states '...*"Records"* include not only written records but records conveying information by any other means whatsoever'. Under section 2(4)(f) the Keeper of Public Records is given the authority to 'make arrangements for the separate housing of films and other records which have to be kept under special conditions', and it is under this provision that the BFI is appointed as an agent of the PRO.

In 1961, shortly after the Act came into force, the PRO entered into a contract with the BFI for the NFTVA to store and provide access to public records in film format. The contract was an acknowledgement of two things: firstly, that at that time the PRO was unable to store films; and secondly, and more importantly, that the NFTVA was a centre of expertise in the storage of films in the UK and could provide the PRO with the specialist guidance and advice which it required.

This is a working relationship which has continued to this day. In 1998 a new contract was signed with the BFI which means that PRO films will continue to be cared for at the NFTVA. In addition, new detailed procedures for the transfer, storage and cataloguing procedures have also been agreed, including new provisions to store sensitive material in a secure environment.

Until a decade ago the number of films selected for transfer to the PRO was tiny in relation to the number of paper files being accessioned. However, with the advance of modern technology and the increasing availability of equipment used to create films, the number is steadily rising. Current legislation states that records which have already been in the public domain must remain so on transfer to the BFI, and this applies to a high proportion of public record films. In recent years this has led to a considerable increase in the number of films coming into the PRO's collection, and this is further compounded by the realisation that film, in whatever format, can deteriorate very quickly. This has resulted in a decision by the PRO to review and transfer films to the Archive as soon as possible, regardless of when they will be made available to the public. The subject matter of public record films varies widely from public information films on health issues such as Aids, to pre-war training courses on how to use a telephone, to evidence given in murder trials.

Most public record films are stored at the BFI's J Paul Getty Conservation Centre in Hertfordshire, along with the majority of other non-public record film collections. As its name suggests, the centre also undertakes, on behalf of the PRO, any conservation work required to preserve the films for posterity. The public record films are then entered into the BFI's public catalogue, and can be ordered and viewed at its premises in Stephen Street in central London. Unlike the other collections held within the NFTVA, no charge is made for viewing public record films in line with the policy on public records created and held in other formats.

For information about the collections held by the BFI please contact the BFI Press Office at 21 Stephen Street, London W1P 2LN or visit its website at http://www.bfi.org.uk/. If you would like to know more about the Public Record Office please visit our website at http://www.pro.gov.uk/.

THE RADIO STUDIES NETWORK

Tel: 020-7955-6494 Fax: 020-7955-7405
E-mail:p.m.lewis@lse.ac.uk

Contact: Peter Lewis

The Radio Studies Network was founded in December 1998 by lecturers and researchers as an association whose aim is to encourage study and research in radio, and seek ways to improve its academic and cultural status. The Network grew out of an 18-month feasibility study called the Radio Research Project (RRP) which began in September 1997 and was carried out by Peter Lewis (then at Middlesex University). The RRP was funded by ten universities and the BBC, the Radio Academy, the Radio Advertising Bureau and the Community Media Association. The study concluded that there was a widely felt need for some kind of permanent institution or infrastructure to support radio study and research.

The Network is committed to a programme with seven aims or 'Actions':

Action 1: consolidation and expansion of the network of teachers and researchers in conjunction with industry professionals

Action 2: the encouragement of research

Action 3: building on the existing website (see under *Skills & Studies* at http://www.radioacademy.org to develop a centre for distribution of teaching and learning materials, as well as access to, and information about, the other Actions

Action 4: improving access to radio archives

Action 5: building European and international partnerships

Action 6: collaborating with other organisations in a programme of public events

Action 7: encouraging the development of Soundhouses – physical or electronic locations for performance, public enjoyment, and discussion of sound and radio.

Membership of the Network is open to any individual or organisation with an involvement or interest in studying, researching or teaching radio. The activities of the Network are co-ordinated by an annually elected Steering Group whose business is carried forward by four working groups: Network Development, Research, Teaching and Learning Development, Archives. The Network's Development Director, Peter Lewis, co-ordinates these activities as part of his Radio Research Project, funded as a Research Fellowship by the Economic and Social Research Council at the London School of Economics.

Visit http://www.jisc.ac.uk/lists/radio-studies/ to follow the Network's e-mail discussion group. For further information and to download an application form, visit http://www.radioacademy.org

The Radio Studies Network is co-hosting with the University of Sussex a major European conference, *2001: A Radiodyssey* at Brighton, 19-21 July 2001.

RESOURCE

The Council for Museums, Archives and Libraries,
16 Queen Anne's Gate,
LONDON
SW1H 9AA
Tel: 020 7273 1444 Fax: 020 7273 1404
E-mail: info@resource.gov.uk
Website: http://www.resource.gov.uk

Contact: Justin Frost, Archives Adviser

Resource is the new strategic agency launched in April 2000 to work with and for museums, archives and libraries within the UK, tapping the potential for collaboration between the sectors. *Resource* replaces the Museums & Galleries Commission and the Library and Information Commission and the new organisation also includes the archives sector. The organisation's *Manifesto*, with sections including Core Values, Objectives and Action Plan, has been published in several sections over a number of its web pages.

It currently maintains a database of Education & Access projects in UK museums for use as case studies in publications and reports. It is now proposing to extend the scope of this database to include case studies from the archive and library communities. Museum, library and archive professionals will be invited to submit details of projects in over 40 subject areas which include, for example, cultural diversity, freedom of information, intellectual access, local history, oral history, and theatre in education. The information supplied to the Case Studies Database is intended for publication by Resource in a variety of formats. A range of factsheets published by the Museums and Galleries Commission are available at http://www.resource.gov.uk/factsheets.html. These contain guidance on the appropriate handling, storage and packing of a wide range of museum objects and deal with, for example, museum conservation materials, archives, photographic materials, costumes, and books.

The organisation's mailing list Resourcenews at resourcenews@jiscmail.ac.uk gives the latest news and information about Resource.

Select Bibliography

Publications containing information on world-wide film and television collections

Arduini, Laura (ed.). *Guida agli Archivi Audiovisivi in Italia*. Roma: Archivio Audiovisivo del Movimento Operaio e Democratico, Presidenza del Consiglio dei Ministri, Dipartimento per l'Informazione e l'Editoria, 1995 (Descriptions of 214 Italian collections).

Barrera, Giulia; Martini, Alfredo; Mulè, Antonella (ed.). *Fonti Orali, Censimento degli Istituti di Conservazione*. Roma: Pubblicazione degli Archivi di Stato, Quaderni della Rassegna degli Archivi di Stato 71. Ministero per i Beni Culturali e Ambientali Ufficio Centrale per i Beni Archivistici, 1993 (Study of 164 Italian sound archives).

Ballantyne, James (ed.). *Researcher's Guide to British Newsreels*. Vols. I, II and III. London: British Universities Film & Video Council, 1983/1988/1993.

Beauclair, René (ed.), *International Directory of Film and TV Documentation Collections*, 4th edition, London: FIAF, 1993 (Entries on 125 documentation centres and libraries world-wide).

Ciarravano, Enzo; Mazzone, Giacomo. *Archivi Audiovisivi*. Roma: Videoplay, 1990 (Information on 18 Italian archives).

Cowie, Peter (ed.). *Variety International Film Guide*. London: Andre Deutsch. Annual (Film archives section lists and describes over 80 film archives world-wide).

Dyja, Eddie (ed.). *BFI Film and Television Handbook*. London: British Film Institute. Annual (Archives and Film Libraries section gives listing and brief descriptions of over 40 British sources).

FOCAL Members Guide. Harrow, Middlesex: Federation of Commercial Audiovisual Libraries Limited. Regularly updated (Details of a number of world-wide collections and information on film and television researchers world-wide. Available on disk and on FOCAL website www.focalint.org).

Gell, Rick (ed.). *Footage: the Worldwide Moving Image Sourcebook*. New York: Second Line Search, 1997 (Descriptions of 3,000 collections. Information at www.footagesources.com).

Guide des Collections Audiovisuelles en France. Institut National de l'Audiovisuel; Centre National de la Cinématographie. Bibliothèque Nationale de France. Paris: Les Editions du CFPJ; Diffusion La Découverte, Distribution Sodis, 1994 (Descriptions of over 400 French collections).

Guia dos Arquivos Audiovisuais em Portugal, Radiotelevisão Portuguesa, SA, Direcção de Arquivos Audiovisuais, Lisbon: RTP, 1996 (Descriptions of 151 Portuguese collections).

Guide to Audiovisual Archives. 6th edition, FIAT/IFTA, Helsinki: Yleisradio Finland, 1995 (Entries for over 90 FIAT members' collections and listings of 200 other organisations).

Hofmann, Paul (ed.) *Filmschätzen auf der Spur: Verzeichnis historischer Filmbestände in Nordrhein-Westfalen*, Düsseldorf: Nordrhein-Westfälisches Hauptstaatsarchiv, Staatliche Archive des Landes Nordrhein-Westfalen, Band 33, 1994 (Descriptions of 169 collections in North Rhine-Westfalia).

Holzbauer, Robert; Jagschitz, Gerhard; Malina, Peter (eds.). *Handbuch audiovisueller Medien in Österreich 1989*. Vienna: Audiovisuelle Medien, Arbeitsgemeinschaft Audiovisueller Archive Österreichs, 1989 (Lists Austrian media-related institutions, including film and television archives, with descriptions of their roles and activities. New edition was planned for 1997).

Houston, Penelope. *Keepers of the Frame: The Film Archives*. London: British Film Institute, 1994 (The appendix 'How Much has Been Saved?' provides a table of the success rate of world-wide film archives affiliated to FIAF in acquiring and preserving national productions).

Hutchinson, Sarah (ed.). *The White Book: International Production Directory*. Coventry: Inside Communications Ltd. Annual. (Film libraries and archives section gives listing of over 70 British sources).

International FilmArchive CD-ROM. Brussels: International Federation of Film Archives (FIAF). Twice a year. (Contains the *International Index to Film/TV Periodicals* and other databases, including the *Directory of Film/TV Documentation Collections* which gives details of 124 collections world-wide).

Kirchner, Daniela (ed.). *Film and Television Collections in Europe: The MAP-TV Guide*. London: Blueprint, Chapman & Hall, 1995 (Descriptions of 1,900 European collections).

Klaue, Wolfgang (ed.). *World Directory of Moving Image and Sound Archives*. Film – Television – Sound Archive Series Vol. 5 [FIAF/IASA/ICA/IFLA/IFTA]. Munich, New Providence, Paris, London: K. G. Saur, 1993 (Descriptions of 577 film and sound collections world-wide).

Lauwers, Mieke (ed.). *Gids voor Historisch Beeld- en Geluidsmateriaal*. 2nd edition. Amsterdam: Stichting Film en Wetenschap, 1994 (Descriptions of 393 Dutch collections).

Morgan, Jenny (ed.). *The Film Researcher's Handbook: A Guide to Sources in North America, South America, Asia, Australasia and Africa.* London: Blueprint, Routledge, 1996 (Descriptions of 266 collections in North America, South America, Asia, Australasia and Africa).

Roe, Marjorie; Dunlop, Pam; Cornelius, Bert. *Finding and Keeping: A Researcher's Guide to Audiovisual Resources in Australia.* Canberra: Australian Library and Information Association, Audiovisual Services Committee, 1989.

Slide, Anthony. *Nitrate Won't Wait: A History of Film Preservation in the United States.* Jefferson, NC, and London: McFarland & Company, 1992. (Chapters cover such topics as 'Newsreel Preservation and the National Archives', 'New Areas of Preservation', and 'Colourisation', and looks forward 'Into the Nineties'. Appendices include lists of FIAF members, major US commercial and non-commercial film archives, video libraries and stock footage libraries as well as a subject guide to US film preserved in US archives).

UK broadcasting guides

Mann, Robin (ed.) *The Blue Book of Broadcasting.* London, Tellex Monitors. Annual (Details of BBC national and local radio, local independent radio, with index to radio programmes. Also covers television across all platforms - terrestrial, satellite and cable).

UK documentation collection guides

Foster, Janet; Sheppard, Julia (eds.*) British Archives: A Guide to Archive Resources in the United Kingdom.* London: Macmillan Press, 3rd edition, 1995. (Descriptions of 1,109 British documentation collections).

Reynard, Keith W (ed.*) The Aslib Directory of Information Sources in the United Kingdom.* London: Aslib, the Association for Information Management, 11th edition, 2000. (Descriptions of over 11,600 British sources).

UK film and television archive catalogues

Baker, Simon (ed.) *Northern Ireland: 'The Troubles'.* London: British Film Institute. Regularly updated. (The holdings of the National Film and Television Archive).

Baker, Simon; Terris, Olwen (eds.). *A for Andromeda to Zoo Time.* London: British Film Institute: 1994 (The TV holdings of the National Film and Television Archive 1936-1979).

Baker, Simon; Terris, Olwen (eds.) *Aids.* London: British Film Institute, 1997. NFTVA Filmographies Series No. 6 (The holdings of the National Film and Television Archive).

British Universities Newsreel Project Database CD-ROM. London: British Universities Film & Video Council, 2000. (The first centralised record of British newsreel releases contains details of all traceable stories distributed by British newsreels and cinemagazines between 1910 and 1979. See also BUFVC website www.bufvc.ac.uk).

Burrows, Elaine; Moat, Janet; Sharp, David; Wood, Linda (eds.). *The British Cinema Source Book: BFI Archive Viewing Copies and Library Materials.* London: British Film Institute, 1995.

Burton, Alan (ed.). *The British Co-operative Movement Film Catalogue.* Trowbridge: Flicks Books, 1997.

Camden '97, The WTN Library's Database 1896-1997. CD-ROM catalogue. London: WTN, May 1997.

Cranston, Ros (ed.). *Ken Loach.* London: British Film Institute, 1997. NFTVA Filmographies Series No. 4 (The holdings of the National Film and Television Archive).

East Anglian Film Archive Catalogue, Vols I-IV. Norwich: East Anglian Film Archive.

The EMI-Pathé Film Library Card Catalogue to 75 Years of Newsreels (1896-1970). 68 reels of 16mm positive roll microfilm: London: World Microfilms Publications, 1990.

Finn, Eugene (ed.) *Irish History and the Troubles.* London: British Film Institute, 1998. NFTVA Filmographies Series No. 7 (Fiction film and TV holdings in the National Film and Television Archive).

Haig, Molly (ed.). *Women Film-Makers.* London: British Film Institute, 1996. NFTVA Filmographies Series No. 3 (The holdings of the National Film and Television Archive).

Hewitt, Marion (ed.) *North West Film Archive Film Catalogue.* Manchester: North West Film Archive, 1985.

McKernan, Luke (ed.) *The Boer War (1899-1902).* London: British Film Institute, 1996. NFTVA Filmographies Series No. 5. (The holdings of the National Film and Television Archive.)

McKernan, Luke (ed.) *The Spanish Civil War.* London: British Film Institute, 1996. NFTVA Filmographies Series No. 3 (The holdings of the National Film and Television Archive).

McKernan, Luke; Terris, Olwen (eds.). *Walking Shadows: Shakespeare in the National Film and Television Archive*. London: British Film Institute, 1994.

National Film Archive Catalogue, Part I, Silent News Film 1895-1933. London: The British Film Institute, 1951. 2nd edition, 1965.

National Film Archive Catalogue, Part II, Silent Non-Fiction Films 1895-1934. London: British Film Institute, 1960.

National Film Archive Catalogue, Part III, Silent Fiction Films 1895-1930. London: British Film Institute, 1966.

National Film Archive Catalogue, Volume 1, Non-Fiction Films, London: British Film Institute, 1980.

Peet, Verity (ed.) *NIFC Archive Survey 1999: Film and Television Archive Holdings Relevant to Northern Ireland in Northern Ireland, Great Britain [and] Republic of Ireland*. Belfast: Northern Ireland Film Commission, February 1999.

Scottish Film Archive Catalogue. Glasgow: Scottish Film Council, 1995.

Scottish Film Archive, A Companion to the Scottish Film Archive. Glasgow: Scottish Film Council, 1996.

Smither, Roger (ed.). *Imperial War Museum Film Catalogue, Volume 1: The First World War Archive*. Trowbridge: Flicks Books, 1994. Studies in War and Film, No. 1.

Staffordshire Film Archive Catalogue. Stafford: Staffordshire Film Archive, Staffordshire University, 1994

Terris, Olwen (ed.). *Dennis Potter*. London: British Film Institute, 1997. NFTVA Filmographies Series No. 1 (The holdings of the National Film and Television Archive).

Wales Film and Television Archive Catalogue, Vol. 1. Aberystwyth: Wales Film and Television Archive, August 1997.

Wessex Film & Sound Archive Catalogue and Index 1994. Winchester: Wessex Film & Sound Archive, Hampshire Record Office, 1994. 2 Vols.

UK film and television production guides

The Knowledge. Tonbridge, Miller Freeman. Annual. The Knowledge Online is at http://www.theknowledge online.com (Website for the film, television and video industries. Details of companies, freelance crew, researchers and location finders, etc.).

The Pact Directory of Independent Producers. London: Producers Alliance for Cinema and Television (PACT).

Annual. (Profiles of hundreds of key British independent production companies, including 300 based outside London).

The Production Guide. London, Emap Media. Annual. (Source of contact information, including URLs and e-mail addresses where applicable, published specifically for the UK production industry. Lists over 11,000 entries).

UK oral history guidelines

Oral History Guidelines. Lee, David. Winchester: Wessex Film & Sound Archive, 2000. (Practical information covering such topics as equipment, recording methodology, documentation and copyright, cataloguing, storage, etc., plus essential bibliography).

UK radio guides

London Radio Stations. Website: http://homepages. enterprise.net/paulbaker/london_radio/ (Helpful guide to all the Capital's radio stations).

Radio Authority Pocket Book. London, The Radio Authority. Annual (Contact details for all the independent radio services across the UK).

See also *The Blue Book of Broadcasting* under **UK broadcasting guides** above.

UK standards for managing television archives

Hanford, Anne (ed.). *Guidelines for Establishing and Maintaining Television Programme Archives*. London: Royal Television Society, History and Archives Specialist Group, April 1992. 5 pages (Offers professional advice on acquisition and retention, recording, storage, handling, documentation, access and service).

Scrase, Miranda (ed.). *Guidelines for Managing Television Written Archives*. London: Archivists in Independent Television (c/o The Library, Independent Television Commission), 1995, 137 pages (Offers professional and detailed advice on all aspects of managing television archives. Covers archives and records management, specialist broadcasting archives, documentation and organisation, and special collections).

Researcher's Guide to British Film & Television Collections – articles included in earlier editions

First edition, 1981
Film research: some starting points *by Seona Robertson*. Copyright in films *by Geoffrey Crabb*.

Postgraduate academic film research *by Timothy Hollins*.
An historian as film-maker *by Peter Stead*.
Researching for a television series *by Taylor Downing*.

Second edition, 1985
Reflections on film research *by James Barker*.
Copyright in films *by Geoffrey Crabb*.
Postgraduate academic film research *by Timothy Hollins*.
Researching for a television series *by Christine Whittaker*.

Third edition, 1989
What have you got on …?: Accommodating the needs of researchers: an archivist's view *by Janet McBain*.
Small film gauges *by David Cleveland*.
Researching for a television series: a reassessment *by Christine Whittaker*.
The new copyright legislation, 1988 *by Geoffrey Crabb*.

Fourth edition, 1993
The National Film Archive's BBC Television Dance Collection *by Steve Bryant*.
Amateur film and the archives *by Laraine Cookson*.
Broadcasting and other visual archives in Wales *by Jamie Medhurst*.
Researching in foreign archives *by Christine Whittaker and Elly Beintema*.
Film archive training at the University of East Anglia *by Jane Alvey*.

The copyright implications *by Geoffrey Crabb*.
Independent Television from ITV to Channel 3: franchises and programme Companies, 1955 to 1993 *by Barrie MacDonald*.
Video recording formats: a guide for archivists *by Peter Copeland*.
The technology, politics and promises of HDTV *by Ben Keen*.

Fifth edition, 1997
Unknown pioneer: Edward Foxen Cooper and the Imperial War Museum Film Archive, 1919–1934 *by Roger Smither and David Walsh*.
History and film and television archives *by Peter Catherall*.
Television history comes of age *by Taylor Downing*.
The camera never lies? *by Jerry Kuehl*.
Training for film researchers *by Jack Amos*.
Copyright and the European influence *by Heather Rosenblatt*.
Camcorder revolution *by Paul O'Connor*.
Digital technology and its application to conservation, preservation and accessing of film and video archive material *by Brian Jenkinson*.

Plus
Introduction:
The Researcher's Guide in historical perspective *by Lord Asa Briggs*.

Index to Directory by Subject

Please note that this is not a full listing of the subjects covered by all the collections. Many of the major collections, including national film archives, television companies and stock shot libraries will cover almost every subject.

Index to Directory by Collection

The main type of collection, for the purpose of this guide, is indicated by one of the following icons: ▥ Documentation   ▤ Moving Image   ▥ Radio

Many of the collections hold more than one type of material. This should be clear from the title or description of the individual collection.

Please photocopy and use if you want to send us details of a new collection or amend your existing RGO record.

AN ACCOUNT OF COLLECTIONS HELD BY

INSTITUTION

ADDRESS

CITY   COUNTY   POSTCODE

MAIN CONTACT

NAME

JOB TITLE

DEPARTMENT

TELEPHONE   FAX

E-MAIL

○ Mr
○ Ms
○ Mrs
○ Miss
○ Dr
○ Professor
○ _____

ENQUIRIES ABOUT THE COLLECTION

CONTACT

TELEPHONE   FAX

E-MAIL

WEB SITE

RIGHTS & ACCESS (please use a separate sheet if necessary)

Rights (specify any copyright held)

Viewing and listening facilities

Charges

Access restrictions (e.g. limited opening hours, prior permission).

Is the collection (or any part of it) open to researchers from outside your institution?

DESCRIPTION (please use a separate sheet)

Please provide a brief description of your collection (c.250 words), identifying its particular subject strengths. Please provide any additional information sheets or lists which further describe your collection.

CATALOGUES (please use a separate sheet if necessary)

Please specify type(s) of catalogue maintained.

Card catalogue

Printed catalogue

Library OPACs with major holdings on radio and moving image

Computerised databases

Catalogue(s) available offsite via the Internet

Websites relating to radio and moving images (including discographies and catalogues of overseas collections)

TYPES & SIZE OF COLLECTIONS (please use a separate sheet if necessary)

For radio and moving image material, please provide an estimate of the number of sound reels and/or audiocassettes, CDs, videocassettes, films (titles, or hours of video or cans of film), as applicable.

☐ **MASTERS** Master collections of sound and moving image material

☐ **VIDEO** Access libraries of moving image material (including off-air recordings)

☐ **MUSIC** Music collections, sound recordings and/or manuscripts relating to moving images

☐ **SOUND** Sound recordings and/or transcripts of material other than music.

For other media, please provide a rough breakdown of the types of material, numbers or volumes as applicable, including collections held on microform, or electronically (e.g. on disk, CD or online).

☐ **STILLS** Collections of still images and/or photographs relating to radio and moving images (including major picture libraries with incidental holdings)

☐ **BOOKS** Book collections relating to radio and moving images (including major libraries with large incidental holdings or which regularly purchase relevant overseas material)

☐ **MANUSCRIPTS** Manuscript (including personal) collections relating to radio and moving images

☐ **THESES** Theses (PhD, MPhil, MA) relating to radio and moving images

☐ **DATASETS** Databases of radio, film- and television-related material (e.g. SIFT).

☐ **JOURNALS** Journal collections relating to radio and moving images

☐ **NEWSPAPERS** Newspaper cuttings collections relating to radio and moving images

☐ **POSTERS** Poster collections relating to radio and moving images

☐ **EPHEMERA** Ephemera collections relating to radio and moving images

☐ **DESIGNS** Design collections relating to moving images

☐ **EQUIPMENT** Historical sound and moving image equipment (including incidental holdings)
Types and numbers held

DIGITISATION (please use a separate sheet if necessary)

Digitised collection:

PLEASE RETURN THE COMPLETED FORM TO

BRITISH UNIVERSITIES FILM & VIDEO COUNCIL (BUFVC) 77 WELLS STREET LONDON W1T 3QJ UK	TEL. FAX	(020) 7393 1500 (020) 7393 1555
	E-MAIL WEB	rgo@bufvc.ac.uk www.bufvc.ac.uk